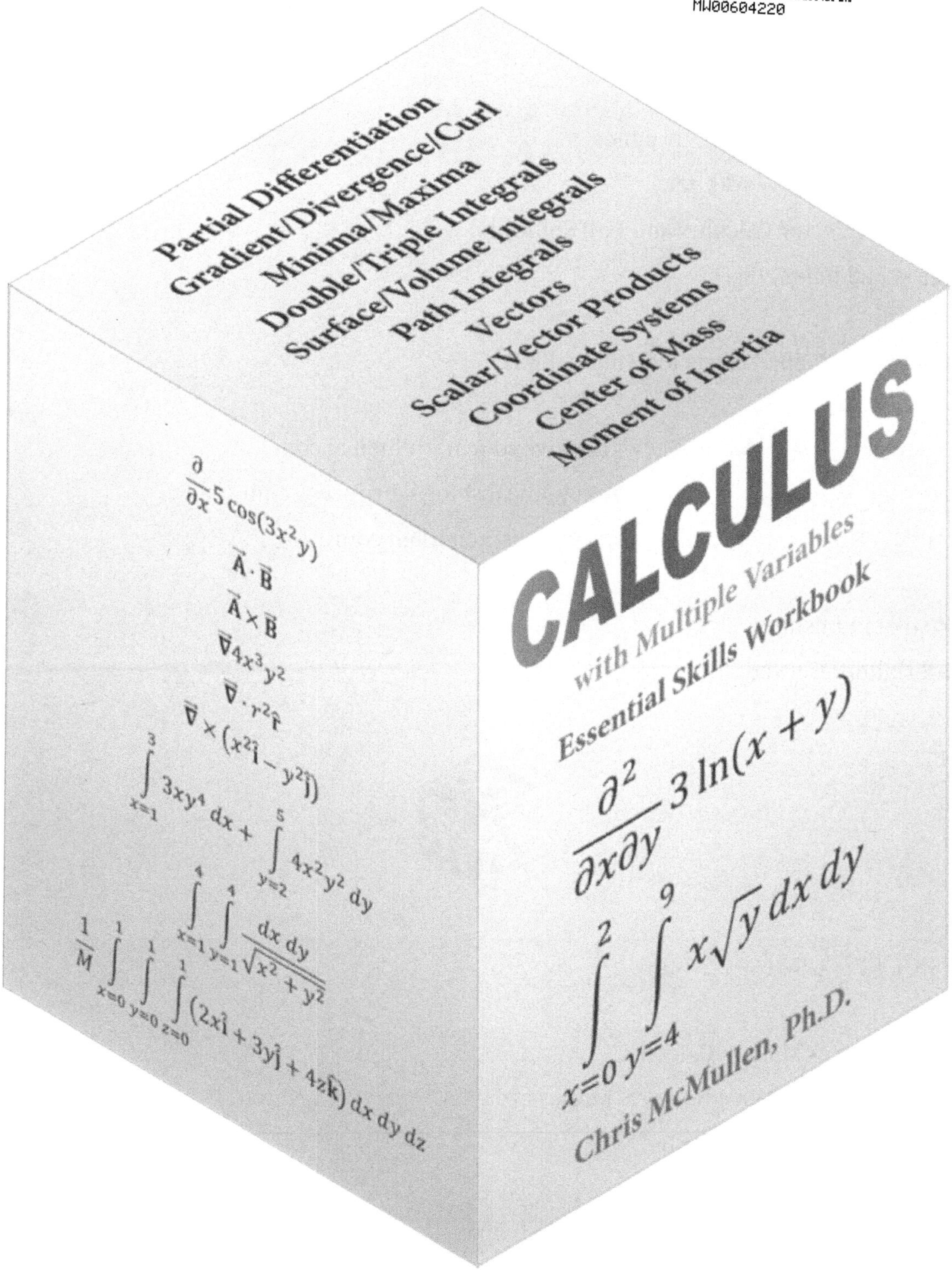
Partial Differentiation
Gradient/Divergence/Curl
Minima/Maxima
Double/Triple Integrals
Surface/Volume Integrals
Path Integrals
Vectors
Scalar/Vector Products
Coordinate Systems
Center of Mass
Moment of Inertia
CALCULUS
with Multiple Variables
Essential Skills Workbook
$\frac{\partial^2}{\partial x \partial y} 3 \ln(x + y)$
$\int_{x=0}^{2} \int_{y=4}^{9} x\sqrt{y}\, dx\, dy$
Chris McMullen, Ph.D.
$\frac{\partial}{\partial x} 5 \cos(3x^2 y)$
$\vec{A} \cdot \vec{B}$
$\vec{A} \times \vec{B}$
$\vec{\nabla} 4x^3 y^2$
$\vec{\nabla} \cdot r^2 \hat{r}$
$\vec{\nabla} \times (x^2 \hat{i} - y^2 \hat{j})$
$\int_{x=1}^{3} 3xy^4\, dx + \int_{y=2}^{5} 4x^2 y^2\, dy$
$\int_{x=1}^{4} \int_{y=1}^{4} \frac{dx\, dy}{\sqrt{x^2 + y^2}}$
$\frac{1}{M} \int_{x=0}^{1} \int_{y=0}^{1} \int_{z=0}^{1} (2x\hat{i} + 3y\hat{j} + 4z\hat{k})\, dx\, dy\, dz$

Calculus with Multiple Variables
Essential Skills Workbook
Includes Vector Calculus and Full Solutions
Chris McMullen, Ph.D.

www.improveyourmathfluency.com
www.monkeyphysicsblog.wordpress.com
www.chrismcmullen.com

Zishka Publishing

ISBN: 978-1-941691-37-3

Textbooks > Math > Calculus
Study Guides > Workbooks > Math
Education Math > Calculus

Contents

Introduction

This workbook is designed to help practice a variety of practical calculus skills that involve multiple variables, including vector calculus. Each chapter focuses on one main topic, like how to apply the gradient operator or how to perform a center of mass integral.

Prerequisites: The student should already be fluent in derivatives and integrals of polynomials, basic trig functions, exponentials, and logarithms.

Every chapter begins with a concise explanation of pertinent concepts, followed by a few examples. Every example is fully solved step-by-step with explanations. The examples should serve as a handy guide for how to solve the practice exercises. Every exercise is fully solved at the back of the book.

A variety of multivariable calculus skills are covered. This workbook begins with partial differentiation and finishes with various multivariable integrals. Students will learn:

- how to take a partial derivative.
- how to find the minimum and maximum values of a function of two variables.
- basic properties of vectors, including the scalar and vector product.
- essential properties of polar, spherical, and cylindrical coordinates.
- how to apply the gradient, divergence, and curl operators.
- how to integrate an expression over a path.
- how to perform double and triple integrals.
- how to perform surface and volume integrals.
- how to perform center of mass integrals.
- how to perform moment of inertia integrals.

May you (or your students) find this workbook useful and become more fluent with these essential multivariable calculus skills.

1 Partial Derivatives

When taking a **partial derivative** of a function with respect to one variable, treat the other independent variables as if they are constants. The symbol ∂ is used (instead of the letter d) to represent a partial derivative. For example, $\frac{\partial f}{\partial x}$ represents a partial derivative of the function f with respect to the variable x. (In contrast, $\frac{df}{dx}$ represents a total derivative. See Chapter 2.)

Example. Given $z = 4x^3y^2$, find $\frac{\partial z}{\partial x}$ and $\frac{\partial z}{\partial y}$.

When finding $\frac{\partial z}{\partial x}$, treat the independent variable y as if it were a constant.

$$\frac{\partial z}{\partial x} = \frac{\partial}{\partial x}4x^3y^2 = 4y^2\frac{\partial}{\partial x}x^3 = 4y^2(3x^2) = 12x^2y^2$$

Similarly, when finding $\frac{\partial z}{\partial y}$, treat the independent variable x as if it were a constant.

$$\frac{\partial z}{\partial y} = \frac{\partial}{\partial y}4x^3y^2 = 4x^3\frac{\partial}{\partial y}y^2 = 4x^3(2y) = 8x^3y$$

Example. Given $f = 3x \sin t$, find $\frac{\partial f}{\partial x}$ and $\frac{\partial f}{\partial t}$.

When finding $\frac{\partial f}{\partial x}$, treat the independent variable t as if it were a constant.

$$\frac{\partial f}{\partial x} = \frac{\partial}{\partial x}3x \sin t = 3 \sin t\frac{\partial}{\partial x}x = 3 \sin t\,(1) = 3 \sin t$$

Similarly, when finding $\frac{\partial f}{\partial t}$, treat the independent variable x as if it were a constant.

$$\frac{\partial f}{\partial t} = \frac{\partial}{\partial t}3x \sin t = 3x\frac{\partial}{\partial t}\sin t = 3x(\cos t) = 3x \cos t$$

To find a second partial derivative, take one partial derivative at a time. For example, $\frac{\partial^2 f}{\partial x^2}$ can be found as $\frac{\partial}{\partial x}\left(\frac{\partial f}{\partial x}\right)$. Note that a "mixed" partial derivative is possible, such as $\frac{\partial^2 f}{\partial x \partial y}$, which means $\frac{\partial}{\partial x}\left(\frac{\partial f}{\partial y}\right)$. For most common standard functions, $\frac{\partial^2 f}{\partial x \partial y}$ is equal to $\frac{\partial^2 f}{\partial y \partial x}$ except near discontinuities, in accordance with **Clairaut's theorem**.

Example. Given $z = 6x^4y^2$, find $\frac{\partial^2 z}{\partial x^2}$.

First find $\frac{\partial z}{\partial x}$, treating the independent variable y as if it were a constant.

$$\frac{\partial z}{\partial x} = \frac{\partial}{\partial x} 6x^4y^2 = 6y^2 \frac{\partial}{\partial x} x^4 = 6y^2(4x^3) = 24x^3y^2$$

Now find $\frac{\partial}{\partial x}\left(\frac{\partial z}{\partial x}\right)$, treating the independent variable y as if it were a constant.

$$\frac{\partial^2 z}{\partial x^2} = \frac{\partial}{\partial x}\left(\frac{\partial z}{\partial x}\right) = \frac{\partial}{\partial x} 24x^3y^2 = 24y^2 \frac{\partial}{\partial x} x^3 = 24y^2(3x^2) = 72x^2y^2$$

Example. Given $f = x^3y + x^2y^2$, find $\frac{\partial^2 f}{\partial y \partial x}$ and $\frac{\partial^2 f}{\partial x \partial y}$.

When finding $\frac{\partial f}{\partial x}$, treat the independent variable y as if it were a constant.

$$\frac{\partial f}{\partial x} = \frac{\partial}{\partial x}(x^3y + x^2y^2) = y\frac{\partial}{\partial x}x^3 + y^2\frac{\partial}{\partial x}x^2 = y(3x^2) + y^2(2x) = 3x^2y + 2xy^2$$

Similarly, when finding $\frac{\partial f}{\partial y}$, treat the independent variable x as if it were a constant.

$$\frac{\partial f}{\partial y} = \frac{\partial}{\partial y}(x^3y + x^2y^2) = x^3\frac{\partial}{\partial y}y + x^2\frac{\partial}{\partial y}y^2 = x^3(1) + x^2(2y) = x^3 + 2x^2y$$

Now find the mixed second derivatives.

$$\frac{\partial^2 f}{\partial y \partial x} = \frac{\partial}{\partial y}\left(\frac{\partial f}{\partial x}\right) = \frac{\partial}{\partial y}(3x^2y + 2xy^2) = 3x^2\frac{\partial}{\partial y}y + 2x\frac{\partial}{\partial y}y^2$$
$$= 3x^2(1) + 2x(2y) = 3x^2 + 4xy$$

$$\frac{\partial^2 f}{\partial x \partial y} = \frac{\partial}{\partial x}\left(\frac{\partial f}{\partial y}\right) = \frac{\partial}{\partial x}(x^3 + 2x^2y) = \frac{\partial}{\partial x}x^3 + 2y\frac{\partial}{\partial x}x^2$$
$$= 3x^2 + 2y(2x) = 3x^2 + 4xy$$

Interpretation of partial derivatives: The equation $z = f(x,y)$ represents a surface S. The point (a,b,c) lies on S if $c = f(a,b)$. The intersection of the vertical plane $x = a$ and the surface S is the curve C_1 (which is called the **trace** of S in the plane $x = a$) and the intersection of the vertical plane $y = b$ and the surface S is the curve C_2 (which is called the **trace** of S in the plane $y = b$). The **partial derivatives** $\frac{\partial f}{\partial x}$ and $\frac{\partial f}{\partial y}$ evaluated at (a,b) give the **slopes** of the **tangent lines** of the **traces** C_1 and C_2 at the point (a,b,c) in the planes $x = a$ and $y = b$.

Chapter 1 Exercises – Part A

Directions: Perform each partial derivative with respect to the indicated variable.

❶ Given $z = \frac{x^3 y^6}{3}$, find $\frac{\partial z}{\partial x}$ and $\frac{\partial z}{\partial y}$.

❷ Given $z = \frac{x}{y}$, find $\frac{\partial z}{\partial x}$ and $\frac{\partial z}{\partial y}$.

❸ Given $f = x\sqrt{y}$, find $\frac{\partial f}{\partial x}$ and $\frac{\partial f}{\partial y}$.

❹ Given $w = \sin t \cos u$, find $\frac{\partial w}{\partial t}$ and $\frac{\partial w}{\partial u}$.

❖ Check your answers at the back of the book.

Chapter 1 Exercises – Part B

Directions: Perform each partial derivative with respect to the indicated variable.

❺ Given $g = e^y \ln x$, find $\frac{\partial g}{\partial x}$ and $\frac{\partial g}{\partial y}$.

❻ Given $z = x^4 + 2x^2y^2$, find $\frac{\partial z}{\partial x}$ and $\frac{\partial z}{\partial y}$.

❼ Given $u = \sqrt{p^2 - q^2}$, find $\frac{\partial u}{\partial p}$ and $\frac{\partial u}{\partial q}$.

❽ Given $h = \ln(t^2 + tu)$, find $\frac{\partial h}{\partial t}$ and $\frac{\partial h}{\partial u}$.

❖ Check your answers at the back of the book.

Chapter 1 Exercises – Part C

Directions: Perform each partial derivative with respect to the indicated variable.

❾ Given $f = \frac{x^4}{y^2}$, find $\frac{\partial^2 f}{\partial x^2}$ and $\frac{\partial^2 f}{\partial y^2}$.

❿ Given $w = t^2 \sin u$, find $\frac{\partial^2 w}{\partial t^2}$ and $\frac{\partial^2 w}{\partial u^2}$.

❖ Check your answers at the back of the book.

Chapter 1 Exercises – Part D

Directions: Perform each partial derivative with respect to the indicated variables.

⓫ Given $z = \frac{x^8 y^4}{4}$, find $\frac{\partial^2 z}{\partial y \partial x}$ and $\frac{\partial^2 z}{\partial x \partial y}$.

⓬ Given $z = e^{xy}$, find $\frac{\partial^2 z}{\partial y \partial x}$ and $\frac{\partial^2 z}{\partial x \partial y}$.

❖ Check your answers at the back of the book.

2 The Chain Rule with Multiple Variables

First, recall the chain rule for a function of a single variable. If f is a function of u and if u is a function of t, then a derivative of f with respect to t may be found using the <u>**chain rule**</u> for a function of a <u>**single variable**</u>:

$$\frac{df}{dt} = \frac{df}{du}\frac{du}{dt}$$

For example, the chain rule may be applied to $\frac{d}{dt}\sin(3t^2)$ by identifying $u = 3t^2$ and $f = \sin(3t^2) = \sin u$. In this example, the chain rule gives:

$$\frac{d}{dt}\sin(3t^2) = \frac{df}{dt} = \left(\frac{d}{du}\sin u\right)\left(\frac{d}{dt}3t^2\right) = (\cos u)(6t) = 6t\cos(3t^2)$$

For a function of two variables, the chain rule is more involved. If f is a function of two independent variables, $f = f(x, y)$, and if these independent variables, x and y, are themselves functions of two other independent variables, $x = x(s, t)$ and $y = y(s, t)$, then partial derivatives of f with respect to s and t may be found using the <u>**chain rule**</u> for a function of <u>**two variables**</u>:

$$\frac{\partial f}{\partial s} = \frac{\partial f}{\partial x}\frac{\partial x}{\partial s} + \frac{\partial f}{\partial y}\frac{\partial y}{\partial s} \quad , \quad \frac{\partial f}{\partial t} = \frac{\partial f}{\partial x}\frac{\partial x}{\partial t} + \frac{\partial f}{\partial y}\frac{\partial y}{\partial t}$$

If there are three or more variables, the chain rule may be generalized by adding more terms. For example, the <u>**chain rule**</u> for a function of <u>**three variables**</u> is:

$$\frac{\partial f}{\partial s} = \frac{\partial f}{\partial x}\frac{\partial x}{\partial s} + \frac{\partial f}{\partial y}\frac{\partial y}{\partial s} + \frac{\partial f}{\partial z}\frac{\partial z}{\partial s} \quad , \quad \frac{\partial f}{\partial t} = \frac{\partial f}{\partial x}\frac{\partial x}{\partial t} + \frac{\partial f}{\partial y}\frac{\partial y}{\partial t} + \frac{\partial f}{\partial z}\frac{\partial z}{\partial t}$$

$$\frac{\partial f}{\partial u} = \frac{\partial f}{\partial x}\frac{\partial x}{\partial u} + \frac{\partial f}{\partial y}\frac{\partial y}{\partial u} + \frac{\partial f}{\partial z}\frac{\partial z}{\partial u}$$

Example. Given $z = x^3y^4$, $x = s\cos t$, and $y = s\sin t$, find $\frac{\partial z}{\partial s}$ and $\frac{\partial z}{\partial t}$.

Apply the chain rule:

$$\frac{\partial z}{\partial s} = \frac{\partial z}{\partial x}\frac{\partial x}{\partial s} + \frac{\partial z}{\partial y}\frac{\partial y}{\partial s} = \left(\frac{\partial}{\partial x}x^3y^4\right)\left(\frac{\partial}{\partial s}s\cos t\right) + \left(\frac{\partial}{\partial y}x^3y^4\right)\left(\frac{\partial}{\partial s}s\sin t\right)$$

$$\frac{\partial z}{\partial s} = (3x^2y^4)(\cos t) + (4x^3y^3)(\sin t) = 3x^2y^4\cos t + 4x^3y^3\sin t$$

Now plug in $x = s\cos t$ and $y = s\sin t$.

$$\frac{\partial z}{\partial s} = 3(s\cos t)^2(s\sin t)^4\cos t + 4(s\cos t)^3(s\sin t)^3\sin t$$

$$\frac{\partial z}{\partial s} = 3s^6\sin^4 t\cos^3 t + 4s^6\sin^4 t\cos^3 t = \boxed{7s^6\sin^4 t\cos^3 t}$$

Similarly, apply the chain rule for $\frac{\partial z}{\partial t}$:

$$\frac{\partial z}{\partial t} = \frac{\partial z}{\partial x}\frac{\partial x}{\partial t} + \frac{\partial z}{\partial y}\frac{\partial y}{\partial t} = \left(\frac{\partial}{\partial x}x^3y^4\right)\left(\frac{\partial}{\partial t}s\cos t\right) + \left(\frac{\partial}{\partial y}x^3y^4\right)\left(\frac{\partial}{\partial t}s\sin t\right)$$

$$\frac{\partial z}{\partial t} = (3x^2y^4)(-s\sin t) + (4x^3y^3)(s\cos t) = -3x^2y^4 s\sin t + 4x^3y^3 s\cos t$$

Now plug in $x = s\cos t$ and $y = s\sin t$.

$$\frac{\partial z}{\partial t} = -3(s\cos t)^2(s\sin t)^4 s\sin t + 4(s\cos t)^3(s\sin t)^3 s\cos t$$

$$\frac{\partial z}{\partial t} = \boxed{-3s^7\sin^5 t\cos^2 t + 4s^7\sin^3 t\cos^4 t}$$

We can check the answers by plugging $x = s\cos t$ and $y = s\sin t$ into $z = x^3y^4$ at the beginning and then taking each partial derivative directly.

$$z = x^3y^4 = (s\cos t)^3(s\sin t)^4 = s^3\cos^3 t\, s^4\sin^4 t = s^7\sin^4 t\cos^3 t$$

$$\frac{\partial z}{\partial s} = \frac{\partial}{\partial s}s^7\sin^4 t\cos^3 t = \sin^4 t\cos^3 t\frac{\partial}{\partial s}s^7 = \boxed{7s^6\sin^4 t\cos^3 t}$$

$$\frac{\partial z}{\partial t} = \frac{\partial}{\partial t}s^7\sin^4 t\cos^3 t = s^7\frac{\partial}{\partial t}\sin^4 t\cos^3 t = \boxed{-3s^7\sin^5 t\cos^2 t + 4s^7\sin^3 t\cos^4 t}$$

The last step used the product rule, $\frac{d}{dt}pq = p\frac{dq}{dt} + q\frac{dp}{dt}$, and single-variable chain rule.

The total derivative and total differential are based on the chain rule. For example, the **total derivative** and **total differential** for a function of two variables are:

$$\frac{df}{dt} = \frac{\partial f}{\partial x}\frac{dx}{dt} + \frac{\partial f}{\partial y}\frac{dy}{dt} \quad , \quad df = \frac{\partial f}{\partial x}dx + \frac{\partial f}{\partial y}dy$$

Example. Given $z = e^x\cos y$, $x = 3t + 2$, and $y = 4t^2$, find $\frac{dz}{dt}$.

Apply the formula for the total derivative. We are **not** finding $\frac{\partial z}{\partial t}$. We are finding $\frac{dz}{dt}$.

$$\frac{dz}{dt} = \frac{\partial z}{\partial x}\frac{dx}{dt} + \frac{\partial z}{\partial y}\frac{dy}{dt} = \left(\frac{\partial}{\partial x}e^x\cos y\right)\left[\frac{d}{dt}(3t+2)\right] + \left(\frac{\partial}{\partial y}e^x\cos y\right)\left(\frac{d}{dt}4t^2\right)$$

$$= e^x\cos y\,(3) - e^x\sin y\,(8t) = \boxed{3e^{3t+2}\cos(4t^2) - 8te^{3t+2}\sin(4t^2)}$$

Chapter 2 Exercises – Part A

Directions: Apply the multivariable chain rule to perform each partial derivative.

❶ Given $z = x^5\sqrt{y}$, $x = s^4 + t^2$, and $y = s^4 - t^4$, find $\frac{\partial z}{\partial s}$ and $\frac{\partial z}{\partial t}$.

❷ Given $f = \ln x \cos y$, $x = p^3q^2$, and $y = p^2q^3$, find $\frac{\partial f}{\partial p}$ and $\frac{\partial f}{\partial q}$.

❸ Given $w = xy^2z^3$, $x = s\cos t \sin u$, $y = s \sin t \sin u$, and $z = s\cos u$, find $\frac{\partial w}{\partial s}$, $\frac{\partial w}{\partial t}$, and $\frac{\partial w}{\partial u}$.

❖ Check your answers at the back of the book.

Chapter 2 Exercises – Part B

Directions: Perform the indicated total derivative.

❹ Given $z = \frac{x^3}{y}$, $x = \sin t$, and $y = \cos t$, find $\frac{dz}{dt}$.

❺ Given $z = \sec x \tan y$, $x = 1 + t^2$, and $y = 1 - t^2$, find $\frac{dz}{dt}$.

❻ Given $w = e^x e^{-y} \ln z$, $x = t^2 + 3t$, $y = t^3 + t^2$, and $z = 3t^2$, find $\frac{dw}{dt}$.

❖ Check your answers at the back of the book.

3 Extreme Values with Multiple Variables

To find the **relative extrema** for a function of two variables, $f(x, y)$, follow these steps (illustrated by the example that follows):

1. Take the first partial derivatives, $\frac{\partial f}{\partial x}$ and $\frac{\partial f}{\partial y}$.
2. Set both first partial derivatives equal to zero: $\frac{\partial f}{\partial x} = 0$ and $\frac{\partial f}{\partial y} = 0$. (Why? The slope of the tangent plane is zero at a relative minimum or relative maximum.)
3. Solve for the values of x and y that make the first partial derivatives zero. Call these x_c and y_c. These are the **critical points**. (Technically, points where first partial derivatives do not exist are also considered to be critical points.)
4. Take the second partial derivatives, $\frac{\partial^2 f}{\partial x^2}, \frac{\partial^2 f}{\partial y^2}, \frac{\partial^2 f}{\partial x \partial y}$, and $\frac{\partial^2 f}{\partial y \partial x}$.
5. Evaluate the second partial derivatives at each pair (x_c, y_c) from Step 3 (where the tangent plane is horizontal).
6. Evaluate $D = \frac{\partial^2 f}{\partial x^2}\frac{\partial^2 f}{\partial y^2} - \frac{\partial^2 f}{\partial x \partial y}\frac{\partial^2 f}{\partial y \partial x}$ at each pair (x_c, y_c) from Step 3. (Note that D is the determinant of the matrix formed by $\frac{\partial^2 f}{\partial x^2}, \frac{\partial^2 f}{\partial y \partial x}, \frac{\partial^2 f}{\partial x \partial y}$, and $\frac{\partial^2 f}{\partial y^2}$.)
7. Classify each critical point (x_c, y_c) based on the second derivative test:
   - If $D > 0$ and $\frac{\partial^2 f}{\partial x^2} > 0$ at (x_c, y_c), then $f(x_c, y_c)$ is a **local minimum**.
   - If $D > 0$ and $\frac{\partial^2 f}{\partial x^2} < 0$ at (x_c, y_c), then $f(x_c, y_c)$ is a **local maximum**.
   - If $D < 0$, then $f(x_c, y_c)$ is a **saddle point**.
   - If $D = 0$, the second derivative test alone is not enough to classify the critical point. It could be a local minimum, local maximum, or a saddle point. More information is needed to classify the critical point.
8. Evaluate the function at each critical point corresponding to a local minimum or local maximum. These are the **relative** (or **local**) **minima** and **maxima**.
9. To find the absolute extrema over a specified region, find the extreme values of the function on the boundary of the region. The **absolute extrema** include the largest and smallest values from Steps 8-9.

Example. (A) Find the relative extrema and saddle points of $z = x^2 - 6x - 8y + y^2$.
First set $\frac{\partial z}{\partial x}$ and $\frac{\partial z}{\partial y}$ each equal to zero.

$$\frac{\partial z}{\partial x} = \frac{\partial}{\partial x}(x^2 - 6x - 8y + y^2) = 2x - 6 = 0$$
$$\frac{\partial z}{\partial y} = \frac{\partial}{\partial y}(x^2 - 6x - 8y + y^2) = -8 + 2y = 0$$

The solutions to these equations are $x = 3$ and $y = 4$, respectively. The critical point is $(3,4)$. Now find the second partial derivatives.

$$\frac{\partial^2 z}{\partial x^2} = \frac{\partial}{\partial x}(2x - 6) = 2 \quad , \quad \frac{\partial^2 z}{\partial y \partial x} = \frac{\partial}{\partial y}(2x - 6) = 0$$
$$\frac{\partial^2 z}{\partial x \partial y} = \frac{\partial}{\partial x}(-8 + 2y) = 0 \quad , \quad \frac{\partial^2 z}{\partial y^2} = \frac{\partial}{\partial y}(-8 + 2y) = 2$$

Compute D (which is the determinant of the second partial derivative matrix).

$$D = \frac{\partial^2 f}{\partial x^2}\frac{\partial^2 f}{\partial y^2} - \frac{\partial^2 f}{\partial x \partial y}\frac{\partial^2 f}{\partial y \partial x} = (2)(2) - (0)(0) = 4 - 0 = 4$$

Evaluate D at each critical point. In this example, $D = 4$ is a constant; D equals 4 at every point (x, y), including the critical point $(3,4)$. Now apply the second derivative test. In this example, $D = 4 > 0$ and $\frac{\partial^2 z}{\partial x^2} = 2 > 0$. This shows that the critical point $(3,4)$ corresponds to a local minimum (or relative minimum). Plug $x = 3$ and $y = 4$ into the given function to find the value of the local minimum.

$$z_{min} = 3^2 - 6(3) - 8(4) + (4)^2 = 9 - 18 - 32 + 16 = -25$$

The function $z(x, y)$ has a **local minimum** of -25 at the point $(3,4,-25)$.
(B) Find the absolute extrema over the square $0 \leq x \leq 5$ and $0 \leq y \leq 5$.
Consider each edge of the square in addition to the critical point from Part (A).

- Bottom edge ($y = 0$): $z(x, 0) = x^2 - 6x$.
- Left edge ($x = 0$): $z(0, y) = -8y + y^2$.
- Top edge ($y = 5$): $z(x, 5) = x^2 - 6x - 8(5) + 5^2 = x^2 - 6x - 15$.
- Right edge ($x = 5$): $z(5, y) = 5^2 - 6(5) - 8y + y^2 = -5 - 8y + y^2$.

Find the extrema of each single-variable function above and compare to determine that, along these edges, the minimum is $z = -24$ at $(3,5)$ and the maximum is $z = 0$ at $(0,0)$. Compare these with the answer to Part (A). The **absolute minimum** is the local minimum of $z = -25$ at $(3,4,-25)$ and the **absolute maximum** is $z = 0$ at $(0,0,0)$.

Chapter 3 Exercises – Part A

Directions: For each function, find the relative extrema, saddle points, and absolute extrema over the indicated region.

❶ $z = x^2 + 2xy - y^2$ over the square $-1 \leq x \leq 1$ and $-1 \leq y \leq 1$.

❷ $z = e^{-x^2-y^2}$ over the disc $x^2 + y^2 \leq 1$.

❖ Check your answers at the back of the book.

Chapter 3 Exercises – Part B

Directions: For each function, find the relative extrema, saddle points, and absolute extrema over the indicated region.

❸ $z = x^3 - 6xy + y^3$ over the triangle with vertices at (0,0), (4,0), and (4,4).

❹ $z = \cos x \cos y$ over the square $\pi \leq x \leq 2\pi$ and $\pi \leq y \leq 2\pi$.

❖ Check your answers at the back of the book.

4 Vectors

A **vector** is a quantity that has both a magnitude and a direction. The **magnitude** of the vector indicates how much of the quantity there is, while the direction of the vector indicates which way it points. An example of a vector is force. If you exert a force, you can measure both how hard you push or pull (the magnitude of the force) and which way you push or pull (the direction of the force). Some other common vectors include velocity, acceleration, displacement, and electric field.

A **scalar** is a quantity that has only a magnitude. A scalar does not have a direction. An example of a scalar is mass. The amount of matter contained in an object does not have a direction; it only has a magnitude. Some other common scalars include energy and distance.

An arrow is used to represent a vector visually. The length of the arrow represents the magnitude of the vector and the orientation of the arrow indicates the direction of the vector. A vector is not fixed in position. Two arrows that have the same length and the same direction represent equivalent vectors, even if the arrows are drawn in different positions. If a vector is translated (which means to move it without rotating it or changing its length), it is the **same** vector.

Placing an arrow above a quantity, like $\vec{\mathbf{A}}$, indicates a vector. (In a textbook, boldface is often used instead of the arrow.) Placing double bars (or in some texts, single bars) around the vector, like $\|\vec{\mathbf{A}}\|$, indicates the magnitude of the vector. The magnitude of a vector is sometimes indicated by simply removing the arrow, such that A and $\|\vec{\mathbf{A}}\|$ are equivalent.

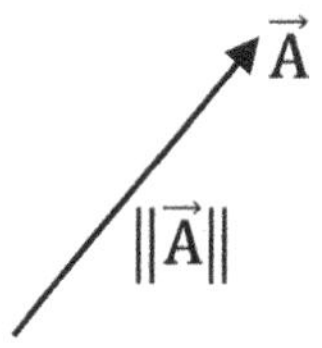

The **null vector** (or zero vector), $\vec{\mathbf{0}}$, is a vector with zero magnitude. The null vector does not have a specific direction.

A vector can be resolved into Cartesian **components** by projecting the vector onto the x-, y-, and z-axes. The subscripts on A_x, A_y, and A_z indicate that these are components of vector $\vec{\mathbf{A}}$. For a vector that lies in the xy plane,

$$A_x = A\cos\theta \quad , \quad A_y = A\sin\theta$$

where θ is the angle of the vector counterclockwise from the $+x$-axis. The magnitude and direction of a 2D vector can be found from its components by:

$$A = \|\vec{\mathbf{A}}\| = \sqrt{A_x^2 + A_y^2} \quad , \quad \theta = \tan^{-1}\left(\frac{A_y}{A_x}\right)$$

Look at the signs of A_x and A_y to put θ in the correct quadrant.

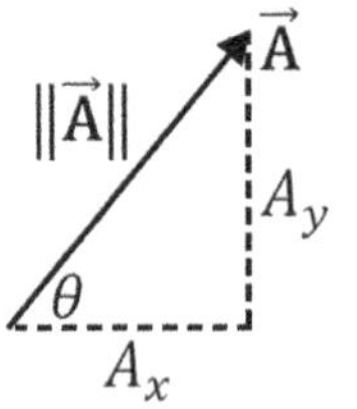

For a 3D vector, the magnitude of the vector is related to its components by:

$$A = \|\vec{\mathbf{A}}\| = \sqrt{A_x^2 + A_y^2 + A_z^2}$$

The direction of a 3D vector is specified using the two angles of spherical coordinates (Chapter 7). The above formula follows from the 3D **distance formula**:

$$d = \sqrt{(x_2 - x_1)^2 + (y_2 - y_1)^2 + (z_2 - z_1)^2}$$

A vector may be expressed in terms of its components as $\vec{\mathbf{A}} = \langle A_x, A_y \rangle$ if it lies in the xy plane or as $\vec{\mathbf{A}} = \langle A_x, A_y, A_z \rangle$ if it has three components. For example, the vector $\vec{\mathbf{A}} = \langle 7,2 \rangle$ has components $A_x = 7$ and $A_y = 2$. Alternatively, a vector may be expressed in terms of Cartesian unit vectors $\hat{\mathbf{i}}$, $\hat{\mathbf{j}}$, and $\hat{\mathbf{k}}$ as $\vec{\mathbf{A}} = A_x\hat{\mathbf{i}} + A_y\hat{\mathbf{j}} + A_z\hat{\mathbf{k}}$. A **unit vector** has a magnitude equal to one unit. The caret (^) above the vector indicates that it is a unit vector. The Cartesian unit vectors $\hat{\mathbf{i}}$, $\hat{\mathbf{j}}$, and $\hat{\mathbf{k}}$ point one unit along the x-, y-, and z-axes:

$$\hat{\mathbf{i}} = \langle 1,0,0 \rangle \quad , \quad \hat{\mathbf{j}} = \langle 0,1,0 \rangle \quad , \quad \hat{\mathbf{k}} = \langle 0,0,1 \rangle$$

Visually, **vector addition** joins vectors together tip-to-tail to form a **resultant** vector. For example, $\vec{\mathbf{A}} + \vec{\mathbf{B}} = \vec{\mathbf{R}}$ means that when $\vec{\mathbf{A}}$ and $\vec{\mathbf{B}}$ are joined tip-to-tail, the resultant vector $\vec{\mathbf{R}}$ extends from the tail of one vector to the tip of the other. According to the

parallelogram law, if $\vec{\mathbf{A}}$ and $\vec{\mathbf{B}}$ are placed on the sides of a parallelogram, $\vec{\mathbf{R}}$ lies along the diagonal.

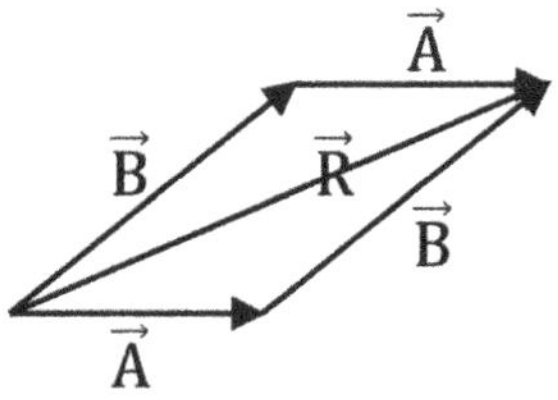

Given the magnitudes and directions of two or more vectors that lie in the xy plane, to find the magnitude and direction of the resultant vector, follow these steps:

1. First find the components of the given vectors.
$$A_x = A\cos\theta_A \quad , \quad B_x = B\cos\theta_B \quad , \quad \text{etc.}$$
$$A_y = A\sin\theta_A \quad , \quad B_y = B\sin\theta_B \quad , \quad \text{etc.}$$
2. Add the respective components together.
$$R_x = A_x + B_x + \cdots \quad , \quad R_y = A_y + B_y + \cdots$$
3. Find the magnitude and direction of the resultant from its components. Look at the signs of R_x and R_y to put θ_R in the correct quadrant.
$$R = \|\vec{\mathbf{R}}\| = \sqrt{R_x^2 + R_y^2} \quad , \quad \theta_R = \tan^{-1}\left(\frac{R_y}{R_x}\right)$$

In principle, the law of cosines could be used to add vectors. However, the method described above is more efficient when adding three or more vectors together. To add vectors in component form, simply add respective components together:
$$\langle A_x, A_y, A_z\rangle + \langle B_x, B_y, B_z\rangle = \langle A_x + B_x, A_y + B_y, A_z + B_z\rangle$$
Working with unit vectors is equivalent:
$$(A_x\hat{\mathbf{i}} + A_y\hat{\mathbf{j}} + A_z\hat{\mathbf{k}}) + (B_x\hat{\mathbf{i}} + B_y\hat{\mathbf{j}} + B_z\hat{\mathbf{k}}) = (A_x + B_x)\hat{\mathbf{i}} + (A_y + B_y)\hat{\mathbf{j}} + (A_z + B_z)\hat{\mathbf{k}}$$
The negative of a vector, $-\vec{\mathbf{A}}$, has the same magnitude and the opposite direction. To find the negative of a vector, simply negate each component: $-\vec{\mathbf{A}} = \langle -A_x, -A_y, -A_z\rangle$. To multiply a vector by a scalar, simply multiply each component by the scalar: $c\vec{\mathbf{A}} = \langle cA_x, cA_y, cA_z\rangle$. Vectors satisfy the following properties:
$$\vec{\mathbf{A}} + \vec{\mathbf{B}} = \vec{\mathbf{B}} + \vec{\mathbf{A}} \quad , \quad \vec{\mathbf{A}} + (\vec{\mathbf{B}} + \vec{\mathbf{C}}) = (\vec{\mathbf{A}} + \vec{\mathbf{B}}) + \vec{\mathbf{C}} = (\vec{\mathbf{A}} + \vec{\mathbf{C}}) + \vec{\mathbf{B}}$$
$$\vec{\mathbf{A}} + \vec{\mathbf{0}} = \vec{\mathbf{A}} \quad , \quad \vec{\mathbf{A}} + (-\vec{\mathbf{A}}) = \vec{\mathbf{0}} \quad , \quad 1\vec{\mathbf{A}} = \vec{\mathbf{A}} \quad , \quad (bc)\vec{\mathbf{A}} = b(c\vec{\mathbf{A}})$$
$$c(\vec{\mathbf{A}} + \vec{\mathbf{B}}) = c\vec{\mathbf{A}} + c\vec{\mathbf{B}} \quad , \quad (b + c)\vec{\mathbf{A}} = b\vec{\mathbf{A}} + c\vec{\mathbf{A}}$$

To find a unit vector in the same direction as a given vector, divide the vector by its magnitude: $\hat{\mathbf{A}} = \frac{\vec{\mathbf{A}}}{\|\vec{\mathbf{A}}\|}$. Recall that a unit vector has a magnitude of one unit: $\|\hat{\mathbf{A}}\| = 1$. A vector can be expressed as its magnitude times its unit vector: $\vec{\mathbf{A}} = \|\vec{\mathbf{A}}\|\hat{\mathbf{A}} = A\hat{\mathbf{A}}$ (since $A = \|\vec{\mathbf{A}}\|$). Look closely to distinguish between a vector $\vec{\mathbf{A}}$ and a unit vector $\hat{\mathbf{A}}$.

In general, a vector may be a **function**, meaning that its components may be functions of one or more variables. For example, $\vec{\mathbf{A}}(x,y) = \langle A_x(x,y), A_y(x,y), A_z(x,y)\rangle$ means that A_x, A_y, and A_z are each (different) functions of x and y. As another example, $\vec{\mathbf{B}}(t) = 4t^2\hat{\mathbf{i}} - 3t\hat{\mathbf{j}}$ has components $B_x(t) = 4t^2$ and $B_y(t) = -3t$. Vector **fields**, like electric field or magnetic field, are functions of the coordinates.

Calculus may be applied to vector functions as follows:

$$\frac{d}{dx}c\vec{\mathbf{A}}(x) = c\frac{d}{dx}\vec{\mathbf{A}}(x) \quad , \quad \frac{d}{dx}f(x)\vec{\mathbf{A}}(x) = \vec{\mathbf{A}}(x)\frac{d}{dx}f(x) + f(x)\frac{d}{dx}\vec{\mathbf{A}}(x)$$

$$\frac{d}{dx}\left[\vec{\mathbf{A}}(x) + \vec{\mathbf{B}}(x)\right] = \frac{d}{dx}\vec{\mathbf{A}}(x) + \frac{d}{dx}\vec{\mathbf{B}}(x) \quad , \quad \frac{d}{dx}\vec{\mathbf{A}}[f(x)] = \frac{d}{df}\vec{\mathbf{A}}[f(x)]\frac{d}{dx}f(x)$$

$$\int_i^f \vec{\mathbf{A}}\,dt = \hat{\mathbf{i}}\int_i^f A_x\,dt + \hat{\mathbf{j}}\int_i^f A_y\,dt + \hat{\mathbf{k}}\int_i^f A_z\,dt$$

The **position vector**, $\vec{\mathbf{r}}$, is a special vector function in that the components of the position vector are the Cartesian coordinates: $\vec{\mathbf{r}} = x\hat{\mathbf{i}} + y\hat{\mathbf{j}} + z\hat{\mathbf{k}}$. In general, the coordinates are time-dependent: $x = x(t), y = y(t)$, and $z = z(t)$. The **velocity** can be found by taking a derivative of the position vector with respect to time: $\vec{\mathbf{v}} = \frac{d\vec{\mathbf{r}}}{dt}$. The **acceleration** is a derivative of velocity with respect to time: $\vec{\mathbf{a}} = \frac{d\vec{\mathbf{v}}}{dt} = \frac{d^2\vec{\mathbf{r}}}{dt^2}$. Integrating acceleration over time results in the change in velocity:

$$\vec{\mathbf{v}} = \vec{\mathbf{v}}_0 + \int_{t=0}^{t} \vec{\mathbf{a}}\,dt$$

Similarly, integrating velocity over time results in **net displacement**, $\Delta\vec{\mathbf{r}}$ (which is the change in the position vector; it is a straight line from the initial point to the final point):

$$\Delta\vec{\mathbf{r}} = \vec{\mathbf{r}} - \vec{\mathbf{r}}_0 = \int_{t=0}^{t} \vec{\mathbf{v}}\,dt$$

Example. Given $\vec{\mathbf{A}} = \langle -3, \sqrt{3} \rangle$, find the magnitude and direction of $\vec{\mathbf{A}}$.
Use the equations that relate the magnitude and direction of a vector that lies in the xy plane to its components. Note that $A_x = -3$ and $A_y = \sqrt{3}$.

$$A = \|\vec{\mathbf{A}}\| = \sqrt{A_x^2 + A_y^2} = \sqrt{(-3)^2 + \left(\sqrt{3}\right)^2} = \sqrt{9+3} = \sqrt{12} = \sqrt{(4)(3)} = \sqrt{4}\sqrt{3} = \boxed{2\sqrt{3}}$$

$$\theta = \tan^{-1}\left(\frac{A_y}{A_x}\right) = \tan^{-1}\left(\frac{\sqrt{3}}{-3}\right) = \boxed{\frac{5\pi}{6}} = \boxed{150°}$$

Note that θ lies in Quadrant II because $A_x < 0$ and $A_y > 0$. We factored the perfect square 4 out of $\sqrt{12}$ to put the answer in standard form: $\sqrt{12} = 2\sqrt{3}$.

Example. $\vec{\mathbf{A}}$ has a magnitude of 4 and a direction of 60°, and $\vec{\mathbf{B}}$ has a magnitude of 8 and a direction of 300°. Find the magnitude and direction of $\vec{\mathbf{R}}$, where $\vec{\mathbf{R}} = \vec{\mathbf{A}} + \vec{\mathbf{B}}$.
Apply the formulas for vector addition where the vectors lie in the xy plane.

$$A_x = A\cos\theta_A = 4\cos 60° = 4\left(\frac{1}{2}\right) = 2$$

$$B_x = B\cos\theta_B = 8\cos 300° = 8\left(\frac{1}{2}\right) = 4$$

$$A_y = A\sin\theta_A = 4\sin 60° = 4\left(\frac{\sqrt{3}}{2}\right) = 2\sqrt{3}$$

$$B_y = B\sin\theta_B = 8\sin 300° = 8\left(-\frac{\sqrt{3}}{2}\right) = -4\sqrt{3}$$

$$R_x = A_x + B_x = 2 + 4 = 6$$

$$R_y = A_y + B_y = 2\sqrt{3} - 4\sqrt{3} = -2\sqrt{3}$$

$$R = \|\vec{\mathbf{R}}\| = \sqrt{R_x^2 + R_y^2} = \sqrt{6^2 + \left(-2\sqrt{3}\right)^2} = \sqrt{36 + (4)(3)} = \sqrt{48} = \sqrt{(16)(3)} = \boxed{4\sqrt{3}}$$

$$\theta_R = \tan^{-1}\left(\frac{R_y}{R_x}\right) = \tan^{-1}\left(\frac{-2\sqrt{3}}{6}\right) = \tan^{-1}\left(\frac{\sqrt{3}}{-3}\right) = \boxed{-\frac{\pi}{6}} = \boxed{-30°}$$

Note that θ_R lies in Quadrant IV because $R_x > 0$ and $R_y < 0$. It is instructive to compare the inverse tangents in this and the previous example. We factored the perfect square 16 out of $\sqrt{48}$ to put the answer in standard form: $\sqrt{48} = 4\sqrt{3}$.

Example. Given $\vec{\mathbf{A}} = 5\hat{\mathbf{i}} + 2\hat{\mathbf{j}} + \hat{\mathbf{k}}$ and $\vec{\mathbf{B}} = 3\hat{\mathbf{i}} - 4\hat{\mathbf{j}} + 6\hat{\mathbf{k}}$, find $3\vec{\mathbf{A}} - 2\vec{\mathbf{B}}$.

Multiply each component of $\vec{\mathbf{A}}$ by 3 and each component of $\vec{\mathbf{B}}$ by 2, and then subtract respective components.

$$3\vec{\mathbf{A}} - 2\vec{\mathbf{B}} = 3(5\hat{\mathbf{i}} + 2\hat{\mathbf{j}} + \hat{\mathbf{k}}) - 2(3\hat{\mathbf{i}} - 4\hat{\mathbf{j}} + 6\hat{\mathbf{k}})$$
$$3\vec{\mathbf{A}} - 2\vec{\mathbf{B}} = 15\hat{\mathbf{i}} + 6\hat{\mathbf{j}} + 3\hat{\mathbf{k}} - (6\hat{\mathbf{i}} - 8\hat{\mathbf{j}} + 12\hat{\mathbf{k}})$$
$$3\vec{\mathbf{A}} - 2\vec{\mathbf{B}} = (15 - 6)\hat{\mathbf{i}} + [6 - (-8)]\hat{\mathbf{j}} + (3 - 12)\hat{\mathbf{k}}$$
$$3\vec{\mathbf{A}} - 2\vec{\mathbf{B}} = \boxed{9\hat{\mathbf{i}} + 14\hat{\mathbf{j}} - 9\hat{\mathbf{k}}}$$

Example. Find the magnitude of $\vec{\mathbf{A}} = 3\hat{\mathbf{i}} - 12\hat{\mathbf{j}} + 4\hat{\mathbf{k}}$. Also find a unit vector parallel to $\vec{\mathbf{A}}$.

Use the 3D distance formula. For the unit vector, divide $\vec{\mathbf{A}}$ by its magnitude.

$$A = \|\vec{\mathbf{A}}\| = \sqrt{A_x^2 + A_y^2 + A_z^2} = \sqrt{3^2 + (-12)^2 + 4^2} = \sqrt{9 + 144 + 16} = \sqrt{169} = \boxed{13}$$

$$\hat{\mathbf{A}} = \frac{\vec{\mathbf{A}}}{\|\vec{\mathbf{A}}\|} = \frac{3\hat{\mathbf{i}} - 12\hat{\mathbf{j}} + 4\hat{\mathbf{k}}}{13} = \boxed{\frac{3}{13}\hat{\mathbf{i}} - \frac{12}{13}\hat{\mathbf{j}} + \frac{4}{13}\hat{\mathbf{k}}}$$

Example. The velocity of an object is given by $\vec{\mathbf{v}} = t^2\hat{\mathbf{i}} - 6\hat{\mathbf{j}}$. Find the acceleration at $t = 3$ and the net displacement from $t = 0$ to $t = 2$.

Take a derivative with respect to time to find acceleration.

$$\vec{\mathbf{a}}(t) = \frac{d\vec{\mathbf{v}}}{dt} = \frac{d}{dt}(t^2\hat{\mathbf{i}} - 6\hat{\mathbf{j}}) = \hat{\mathbf{i}}\frac{d}{dt}t^2 - \hat{\mathbf{j}}\frac{d}{dt}6 = 2t\hat{\mathbf{i}} - 0\hat{\mathbf{j}} = 2t\hat{\mathbf{i}}$$
$$\vec{\mathbf{a}}(3) = 2(3)\hat{\mathbf{i}} = \boxed{6\hat{\mathbf{i}}}$$

Integrate velocity to find net displacement.

$$\Delta\vec{\mathbf{r}} = \int_{t=0}^{t} \vec{\mathbf{v}}\,dt = \int_{t=0}^{2} (t^2\hat{\mathbf{i}} - 6\hat{\mathbf{j}})\,dt = \hat{\mathbf{i}}\int_{t=0}^{2} t^2\,dt - 6\hat{\mathbf{j}}\int_{t=0}^{2} dt$$
$$\Delta\vec{\mathbf{r}} = \hat{\mathbf{i}}\left[\frac{t^3}{3}\right]_{t=0}^{2} - 6\hat{\mathbf{j}}[t]_{t=0}^{2} = \hat{\mathbf{i}}\left(\frac{2^3}{3} - \frac{0^3}{3}\right) - 6\hat{\mathbf{j}}(2 - 0) = \boxed{\frac{8}{3}\hat{\mathbf{i}} - 12\hat{\mathbf{j}}}$$

Chapter 4 Exercises – Part A

Directions: Determine the indicated quantities.

❶ Find the magnitude and direction of $\vec{\mathbf{A}}$.

$$\vec{\mathrm{A}} = \langle -\sqrt{2}, -\sqrt{2} \rangle$$

❷ Find the magnitude and direction of $\vec{\mathbf{B}}$.

$$\vec{\mathrm{B}} = -\hat{\imath} + \hat{\jmath}\sqrt{3}$$

❸ $\vec{\mathbf{C}}$ has a magnitude of 6 and direction of 210°. Find the x- and y-components of $\vec{\mathbf{C}}$.

❖ Check your answers at the back of the book.

Chapter 4 Exercises – Part B

Directions: Determine the indicated quantities.

❹ Find the magnitude of $\vec{\mathbf{D}}$. Also find a unit vector parallel to $\vec{\mathbf{D}}$.

$$\vec{\mathbf{D}} = 2\hat{\mathbf{i}} + \hat{\mathbf{j}}\sqrt{5} - 4\hat{\mathbf{k}}$$

❺ Express the resultant of $\vec{\mathbf{E}}$ and $\vec{\mathbf{F}}$ in component form.

$$\vec{\mathbf{E}} = \langle 7, -4, 6 \rangle \quad , \quad \vec{\mathbf{F}} = \langle 5, 9, -8 \rangle$$

❻ Express $2\vec{\mathbf{G}} - 5\vec{\mathbf{H}}$ in terms of Cartesian unit vectors.

$$\vec{\mathbf{G}} = 4\hat{\mathbf{i}} + 2\hat{\mathbf{j}} - 3\hat{\mathbf{k}} \quad , \quad \vec{\mathbf{H}} = 3\hat{\mathbf{i}} - \hat{\mathbf{k}}$$

❖ Check your answers at the back of the book.

Chapter 4 Exercises – Part C

Directions: Determine the indicated quantities.

❼ $\vec{A}$ has a magnitude of 6 and a direction of 150°, and $\vec{B}$ has a magnitude of 12 and a direction of 270°. Find the magnitude and direction of $\vec{R}$, where $\vec{R} = \vec{A} + \vec{B}$.

❽ $\vec{C}$ has a magnitude of 4 and a direction of 210°, and $\vec{D}$ has a magnitude of $4\sqrt{3}$ and a direction of 180°. Find the magnitude and direction of $\vec{S}$, where $\vec{S} = \vec{D} - \vec{C}$.

❖ Check your answers at the back of the book.

Chapter 4 Exercises – Part D

Directions: Determine the indicated quantities.

❾ The position vector for an object is $\vec{\mathbf{r}} = \hat{\mathbf{i}}\sqrt{t} - 2\hat{\mathbf{j}}$. Find the velocity and acceleration of the object at $t = 4$.

❿ The acceleration of an object is given by $\vec{\mathbf{a}} = 6t\hat{\mathbf{j}}$. The initial velocity at $t = 0$ is $4\hat{\mathbf{i}}$. Find the velocity at $t = 2$ and the net displacement from $t = 0$ to $t = 2$.

⓫ The velocity of an object is given by $\vec{\mathbf{v}} = 8\hat{\mathbf{i}}\sin(2t) - 4\hat{\mathbf{j}}$. Find the acceleration at $t = \frac{\pi}{6}$ and the net displacement from $t = 0$ to $t = \frac{\pi}{6}$.

❖ Check your answers at the back of the book.

5 Scalar and Vector Products

The **scalar product** (also called the **dot product**) between two vectors is:

$$\vec{\mathbf{A}} \cdot \vec{\mathbf{B}} = A_x B_x + A_y B_y + A_z B_z = \|\vec{\mathbf{A}}\| \|\vec{\mathbf{B}}\| \cos\theta = AB\cos\theta$$

where θ is the (smallest) angle between the two vectors. The notation $\|\vec{\mathbf{A}}\| \|\vec{\mathbf{B}}\| \cos\theta$ emphasizes that $\|\vec{\mathbf{A}}\|$ and $\|\vec{\mathbf{B}}\|$ are the magnitudes of the vectors, while $AB\cos\theta$ means the exact same thing. The answer to the scalar product is always a **scalar** (which is a number that does not have any direction). If two vectors are perpendicular, the scalar product is zero. Note that $0 \le \theta \le \pi$.

The **vector product** (also called the **cross product**) between two vectors is:

$$\vec{\mathbf{A}} \times \vec{\mathbf{B}} = \begin{vmatrix} \hat{\mathbf{i}} & \hat{\mathbf{j}} & \hat{\mathbf{k}} \\ A_x & A_y & A_z \\ B_x & B_y & B_z \end{vmatrix} = \hat{\mathbf{i}} \begin{vmatrix} A_y & A_z \\ B_y & B_z \end{vmatrix} - \hat{\mathbf{j}} \begin{vmatrix} A_x & A_z \\ B_x & B_z \end{vmatrix} + \hat{\mathbf{k}} \begin{vmatrix} A_x & A_y \\ B_x & B_y \end{vmatrix}$$

$$\vec{\mathbf{A}} \times \vec{\mathbf{B}} = (A_y B_z - A_z B_y)\hat{\mathbf{i}} - (A_x B_z - A_z B_x)\hat{\mathbf{j}} + (A_x B_y - A_y B_x)\hat{\mathbf{k}}$$

$$\vec{\mathbf{A}} \times \vec{\mathbf{B}} = (A_y B_z - A_z B_y)\hat{\mathbf{i}} + (A_z B_x - A_x B_z)\hat{\mathbf{j}} + (A_x B_y - A_y B_x)\hat{\mathbf{k}}$$

$$\vec{\mathbf{A}} \times \vec{\mathbf{B}} = \langle A_y B_z - A_z B_y, A_z B_x - A_x B_z, A_x B_y - A_y B_x \rangle$$

The answer to the vector product is always a **vector** with components (equivalent to a magnitude and a direction). The vector product of any vector with itself equals zero: $\vec{\mathbf{A}} \times \vec{\mathbf{A}} = 0$. If two vectors are parallel (or antiparallel), the vector product is zero. The magnitude of the vector product is:

$$\|\vec{\mathbf{A}} \times \vec{\mathbf{B}}\| = \|\vec{\mathbf{A}}\| \|\vec{\mathbf{B}}\| \sin\theta = AB\sin\theta$$

where θ is the (smallest) angle between the two vectors. Note that $0 \le \theta \le \pi$.

The scalar product between two unit vectors equals one if they are parallel and zero if they are perpendicular.

$$\hat{\mathbf{i}} \cdot \hat{\mathbf{i}} = \hat{\mathbf{j}} \cdot \hat{\mathbf{j}} = \hat{\mathbf{k}} \cdot \hat{\mathbf{k}} = 1$$

$$\hat{\mathbf{i}} \cdot \hat{\mathbf{j}} = \hat{\mathbf{j}} \cdot \hat{\mathbf{i}} = \hat{\mathbf{k}} \cdot \hat{\mathbf{i}} = \hat{\mathbf{i}} \cdot \hat{\mathbf{k}} = \hat{\mathbf{j}} \cdot \hat{\mathbf{k}} = \hat{\mathbf{k}} \cdot \hat{\mathbf{j}} = 0$$

To find the vector product between two unit vectors, note that $\hat{\mathbf{i}} = \langle 1,0,0 \rangle$, $\hat{\mathbf{j}} = \langle 0,1,0 \rangle$, and $\hat{\mathbf{k}} = \langle 0,0,1 \rangle$.

$$\hat{\mathbf{i}} \times \hat{\mathbf{j}} = \hat{\mathbf{k}} \quad , \quad \hat{\mathbf{k}} \times \hat{\mathbf{i}} = \hat{\mathbf{j}} \quad , \quad \hat{\mathbf{j}} \times \hat{\mathbf{k}} = \hat{\mathbf{i}}$$

$$\hat{\mathbf{j}} \times \hat{\mathbf{i}} = -\hat{\mathbf{k}} \quad , \quad \hat{\mathbf{i}} \times \hat{\mathbf{k}} = -\hat{\mathbf{j}} \quad , \quad \hat{\mathbf{k}} \times \hat{\mathbf{j}} = -\hat{\mathbf{i}}$$

$$\hat{\mathbf{i}} \times \hat{\mathbf{i}} = \hat{\mathbf{j}} \times \hat{\mathbf{j}} = \hat{\mathbf{k}} \times \hat{\mathbf{k}} = 0$$

Properties of scalar and vector products include:

$$\vec{\mathbf{A}} \cdot \vec{\mathbf{A}} = \left\|\vec{\mathbf{A}}\right\|^2 = A^2 \quad , \quad \vec{\mathbf{A}} \cdot \vec{\mathbf{B}} = \vec{\mathbf{B}} \cdot \vec{\mathbf{A}} \quad , \quad \vec{\mathbf{0}} \cdot \vec{\mathbf{A}} = 0$$

$$\vec{\mathbf{A}} \cdot \left(\vec{\mathbf{B}} + \vec{\mathbf{C}}\right) = \vec{\mathbf{A}} \cdot \vec{\mathbf{B}} + \vec{\mathbf{A}} \cdot \vec{\mathbf{C}} \quad , \quad \left(c\vec{\mathbf{A}}\right) \cdot \vec{\mathbf{B}} = c\left(\vec{\mathbf{A}} \cdot \vec{\mathbf{B}}\right)$$

$$\vec{\mathbf{A}} \times \vec{\mathbf{A}} = 0 \quad , \quad \vec{\mathbf{A}} \times \vec{\mathbf{B}} = -\vec{\mathbf{B}} \times \vec{\mathbf{A}} \quad , \quad \left(c\vec{\mathbf{A}}\right) \times \vec{\mathbf{B}} = c\left(\vec{\mathbf{A}} \times \vec{\mathbf{B}}\right)$$

$$\vec{\mathbf{A}} \times \left(\vec{\mathbf{B}} + \vec{\mathbf{C}}\right) = \vec{\mathbf{A}} \times \vec{\mathbf{B}} + \vec{\mathbf{A}} \times \vec{\mathbf{C}} \quad , \quad \left(\vec{\mathbf{A}} + \vec{\mathbf{B}}\right) \times \vec{\mathbf{C}} = \vec{\mathbf{A}} \times \vec{\mathbf{C}} + \vec{\mathbf{B}} \times \vec{\mathbf{C}}$$

$$\vec{\mathbf{A}} \cdot \left(\vec{\mathbf{B}} \times \vec{\mathbf{C}}\right) = \left(\vec{\mathbf{A}} \times \vec{\mathbf{B}}\right) \cdot \vec{\mathbf{C}} \quad , \quad \vec{\mathbf{A}} \times \left(\vec{\mathbf{B}} \times \vec{\mathbf{C}}\right) = \left(\vec{\mathbf{A}} \cdot \vec{\mathbf{C}}\right)\vec{\mathbf{B}} - \left(\vec{\mathbf{A}} \cdot \vec{\mathbf{B}}\right)\vec{\mathbf{C}}$$

The **triple scalar product**, $\vec{\mathbf{A}} \cdot \left(\vec{\mathbf{B}} \times \vec{\mathbf{C}}\right)$, represents the volume of a parallelepiped with $\vec{\mathbf{A}}$, $\vec{\mathbf{B}}$, and $\vec{\mathbf{C}}$ along its edges.

The direction of $\vec{\mathbf{A}} \times \vec{\mathbf{B}}$ is perpendicular to the plane that contains both $\vec{\mathbf{A}}$ and $\vec{\mathbf{B}}$. The direction of $\vec{\mathbf{A}} \times \vec{\mathbf{B}}$ is determined by a **right-hand rule**:

- Point the extended fingers of your right hand along $\vec{\mathbf{A}}$.
- Rotate your right forearm until you can naturally curl your fingers toward $\vec{\mathbf{B}}$.
- When your right hand is simultaneously doing both of the first two points (so that your uncurled fingers point toward $\vec{\mathbf{A}}$, but when you curl your fingers they point toward $\vec{\mathbf{B}}$), the thumb of your right hand points toward $\vec{\mathbf{A}} \times \vec{\mathbf{B}}$.

Example. Given $\vec{\mathbf{A}} = 2\hat{\mathbf{i}} - \hat{\mathbf{j}} + 3\hat{\mathbf{k}}$ and $\vec{\mathbf{B}} = 3\hat{\mathbf{i}} + 2\hat{\mathbf{j}} - 4\hat{\mathbf{k}}$, find $\vec{\mathbf{A}} \cdot \vec{\mathbf{B}}$ and $\vec{\mathbf{A}} \times \vec{\mathbf{B}}$.

$$\vec{\mathbf{A}} \cdot \vec{\mathbf{B}} = A_x B_x + A_y B_y + A_z B_z$$

$$\vec{\mathbf{A}} \cdot \vec{\mathbf{B}} = (2)(3) + (-1)(2) + (3)(-4) = 6 - 2 - 12 = \boxed{-8}$$

$$\vec{\mathbf{A}} \times \vec{\mathbf{B}} = \left(A_y B_z - A_z B_y\right)\hat{\mathbf{i}} + \left(A_z B_x - A_x B_z\right)\hat{\mathbf{j}} + \left(A_x B_y - A_y B_x\right)\hat{\mathbf{k}}$$

$$\vec{\mathbf{A}} \times \vec{\mathbf{B}} = [(-1)(-4) - (3)(2)]\hat{\mathbf{i}} + [(3)(3) - (2)(-4)]\hat{\mathbf{j}} + [(2)(2) - (-1)(3)]\hat{\mathbf{k}}$$

$$\vec{\mathbf{A}} \times \vec{\mathbf{B}} = (4 - 6)\hat{\mathbf{i}} + (9 + 8)\hat{\mathbf{j}} + (4 + 3)\hat{\mathbf{k}} = \boxed{-2\hat{\mathbf{i}} + 17\hat{\mathbf{j}} + 7\hat{\mathbf{k}}}$$

Example. Find the angle between $\vec{\mathbf{A}} = \langle 2,0,-2 \rangle$ and $\vec{\mathbf{B}} = \langle 0,3,-3 \rangle$.

First find the scalar product.

$$\vec{\mathbf{A}} \cdot \vec{\mathbf{B}} = A_x B_x + A_y B_y + A_z B_z$$

$$\vec{\mathbf{A}} \cdot \vec{\mathbf{B}} = (2)(0) + (0)(3) + (-2)(-3) = 0 + 0 + 6 = 6$$

Now find the magnitude of each given vector.

$$\|\vec{\mathbf{A}}\| = \sqrt{A_x^2 + A_y^2 + A_z^2} = \sqrt{2^2 + 0^2 + (-2)^2} = \sqrt{4+0+4} = \sqrt{8} = \sqrt{(4)(2)} = 2\sqrt{2}$$

$$\|\vec{\mathbf{B}}\| = \sqrt{B_x^2 + B_y^2 + B_z^2} = \sqrt{0^2 + 3^2 + (-3)^2} = \sqrt{0+9+9} = \sqrt{18} = \sqrt{(9)(2)} = 3\sqrt{2}$$

Finally, use the alternative formula for the scalar product.

$$\vec{\mathbf{A}} \cdot \vec{\mathbf{B}} = \|\vec{\mathbf{A}}\| \|\vec{\mathbf{B}}\| \cos\theta$$

$$6 = \left(2\sqrt{2}\right)\left(3\sqrt{2}\right)\cos\theta$$

$$6 = 6(2)\cos\theta$$

$$\frac{1}{2} = \cos\theta$$

$$\theta = \cos^{-1}\left(\frac{1}{2}\right) = \boxed{\frac{\pi}{3}} = \boxed{60°}$$

Example. Given $\vec{\mathbf{A}} = 3\hat{\mathbf{i}} + \hat{\mathbf{j}} + 4\hat{\mathbf{k}}$, $\vec{\mathbf{B}} = 2\hat{\mathbf{i}} - \hat{\mathbf{k}}$, and $\vec{\mathbf{C}} = 5\hat{\mathbf{i}} - \hat{\mathbf{j}} + 2\hat{\mathbf{k}}$, find $\vec{\mathbf{A}} \times \left(\vec{\mathbf{B}} \times \vec{\mathbf{C}}\right)$.

One way to perform this calculation is to apply one of the identities.

$$\vec{\mathbf{A}} \times \left(\vec{\mathbf{B}} \times \vec{\mathbf{C}}\right) = \left(\vec{\mathbf{A}} \cdot \vec{\mathbf{C}}\right)\vec{\mathbf{B}} - \left(\vec{\mathbf{A}} \cdot \vec{\mathbf{B}}\right)\vec{\mathbf{C}}$$

$$\vec{\mathbf{A}} \times \left(\vec{\mathbf{B}} \times \vec{\mathbf{C}}\right) = \left[\left(3\hat{\mathbf{i}} + \hat{\mathbf{j}} + 4\hat{\mathbf{k}}\right) \cdot \left(5\hat{\mathbf{i}} - \hat{\mathbf{j}} + 2\hat{\mathbf{k}}\right)\right]\left(2\hat{\mathbf{i}} - \hat{\mathbf{k}}\right) - \left[\left(3\hat{\mathbf{i}} + \hat{\mathbf{j}} + 4\hat{\mathbf{k}}\right) \cdot \left(2\hat{\mathbf{i}} - \hat{\mathbf{k}}\right)\right]\left(5\hat{\mathbf{i}} - \hat{\mathbf{j}} + 2\hat{\mathbf{k}}\right)$$

$$\vec{\mathbf{A}} \times \left(\vec{\mathbf{B}} \times \vec{\mathbf{C}}\right) = [(3)(5) + (1)(-1) + (4)(2)]\left(2\hat{\mathbf{i}} - \hat{\mathbf{k}}\right) - [(3)(2) + (1)(0) + (4)(-1)]\left(5\hat{\mathbf{i}} - \hat{\mathbf{j}} + 2\hat{\mathbf{k}}\right)$$

$$\vec{\mathbf{A}} \times \left(\vec{\mathbf{B}} \times \vec{\mathbf{C}}\right) = (15 - 1 + 8)\left(2\hat{\mathbf{i}} - \hat{\mathbf{k}}\right) - (6 + 0 - 4)\left(5\hat{\mathbf{i}} - \hat{\mathbf{j}} + 2\hat{\mathbf{k}}\right)$$

$$\vec{\mathbf{A}} \times \left(\vec{\mathbf{B}} \times \vec{\mathbf{C}}\right) = 22\left(2\hat{\mathbf{i}} - \hat{\mathbf{k}}\right) - 2\left(5\hat{\mathbf{i}} - \hat{\mathbf{j}} + 2\hat{\mathbf{k}}\right)$$

$$\vec{\mathbf{A}} \times \left(\vec{\mathbf{B}} \times \vec{\mathbf{C}}\right) = 44\hat{\mathbf{i}} - 22\hat{\mathbf{k}} - \left(10\hat{\mathbf{i}} - 2\hat{\mathbf{j}} + 4\hat{\mathbf{k}}\right)$$

$$\vec{\mathbf{A}} \times \left(\vec{\mathbf{B}} \times \vec{\mathbf{C}}\right) = 44\hat{\mathbf{i}} - 22\hat{\mathbf{k}} - 10\hat{\mathbf{i}} + 2\hat{\mathbf{j}} - 4\hat{\mathbf{k}} = \boxed{34\hat{\mathbf{i}} + 2\hat{\mathbf{j}} - 26\hat{\mathbf{k}}}$$

Chapter 5 Exercises – Part A

Directions: For each pair of vectors, find both the scalar product and vector product.

❶ $\vec{A} = 5\hat{i} + 2\hat{j} - 4\hat{k}$ and $\vec{B} = 6\hat{i} - 3\hat{j} - \hat{k}$.

❷ $\vec{C} = 8\hat{i} - 3\hat{j} + 6\hat{k}$ and $\vec{D} = 9\hat{i} - 7\hat{k}$.

❸ $\vec{E} = \langle 4,1,-2 \rangle$ and $\vec{F} = \langle -3,5,-2 \rangle$.

❖ Check your answers at the back of the book.

Chapter 5 Exercises – Part B

Directions: Find the indicated quantities.

❹ $\vec{\mathbf{A}}$ has a magnitude of 6, $\vec{\mathbf{B}}$ has a magnitude of 12, and the (smallest) angle between $\vec{\mathbf{A}}$ and $\vec{\mathbf{B}}$ equals 150°. Find $\vec{\mathbf{A}} \cdot \vec{\mathbf{B}}$ and $\|\vec{\mathbf{A}} \times \vec{\mathbf{B}}\|$.

❺ Find the angle between $\vec{\mathbf{C}} = \hat{\mathbf{i}}\sqrt{3} + \hat{\mathbf{j}} - 2\hat{\mathbf{k}}$ and $\vec{\mathbf{D}} = \hat{\mathbf{i}} - \hat{\mathbf{j}}\sqrt{3} + 2\hat{\mathbf{k}}$.

❖ Check your answers at the back of the book.

Chapter 5 Exercises – Part C

Directions: For each set of three vectors, find $\vec{\mathbf{A}} \cdot (\vec{\mathbf{B}} \times \vec{\mathbf{C}})$ and $\vec{\mathbf{A}} \times (\vec{\mathbf{B}} \times \vec{\mathbf{C}})$.

❻ $\vec{\mathbf{A}} = 4\hat{\mathbf{i}} - 2\hat{\mathbf{j}} + 3\hat{\mathbf{k}}$, $\vec{\mathbf{B}} = 2\hat{\mathbf{i}} - 3\hat{\mathbf{j}} - \hat{\mathbf{k}}$, and $\vec{\mathbf{C}} = -3\hat{\mathbf{i}} + 4\hat{\mathbf{k}}$.

❼ $\vec{\mathbf{A}} = \langle 6,2,-4 \rangle$, $\vec{\mathbf{B}} = \langle 4,0,-4 \rangle$, and $\vec{\mathbf{C}} = \langle 8,-4,2 \rangle$.

❖ Check your answers at the back of the book.

6 Polar Coordinates

Any point P in the plane can be expressed using 2D **polar coordinates** (r, θ) as follows:

- r is the distance from the origin to point P.
- θ is the angle counterclockwise from the $+x$-axis to r.

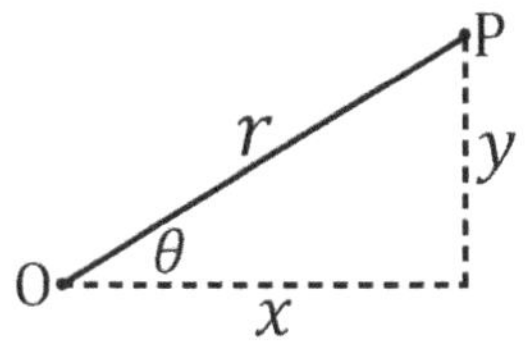

Given 2D polar coordinates, Cartesian coordinates (x, y) can be found by:

$$x = r\cos\theta \quad , \quad y = r\sin\theta$$

Given Cartesian coordinates, 2D polar coordinates can be found by:

$$r = \sqrt{x^2 + y^2} \quad , \quad \theta = \tan^{-1}\left(\frac{y}{x}\right)$$

Some notable cases of 2D polar coordinates include:

- $r = 0$ corresponds to the point at the origin for any value of θ.
- $r = a$ is the equation for a **circle** with radius a centered about the origin.
- $\theta = a$ is a semi-infinite ray (for $r \geq 0$) or an infinite line if r is unrestricted.
- $r = a\cos\theta$ is the equation for a **circle** with radius $\frac{a}{2}$ centered about $\left(\frac{a}{2}, 0\right)$.
- $r = a\cos(k\theta)$, where k is an integer, is the equation for a **rose** with k petals if k is odd or $2k$ petals if k is even.
- $r = 1 + \sin\theta$ or $r = 1 + \cos\theta$ is the equation for a (heart-shaped) **cardioid**.
- $r = a\theta$ is a simple Archimedean **spiral**.
- $r = \frac{\ell}{1 - e\cos\theta}$ is the equation for a **conic section**, where e is the **eccentricity** and ℓ is the **semi-latus** rectum (which is the perpendicular distance from the major axis): $e > 1$ is a hyperbola, $e = 1$ is a parabola, $0 < e < 1$ is an ellipse, and $e = 0$ is a circle with radius ℓ.

The 2D polar unit vectors are $\hat{\mathbf{r}}$ and $\hat{\boldsymbol{\theta}}$. At point P, if a circle centered about the origin is drawn through P, the radial unit vector $\hat{\mathbf{r}}$ points one unit outward away from the origin and $\hat{\boldsymbol{\theta}}$ points one unit tangent to the circle in a counterclockwise sense.

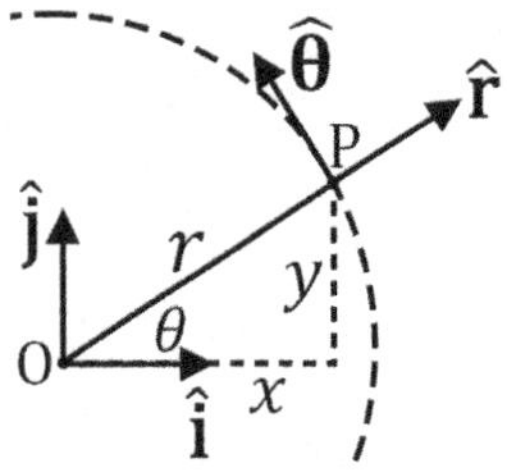

The 2D polar **unit vectors** are related to the Cartesian unit vectors by:

$$\hat{\mathbf{r}} = \hat{\mathbf{i}}\cos\theta + \hat{\mathbf{j}}\sin\theta$$

$$\widehat{\boldsymbol{\theta}} = -\hat{\mathbf{i}}\sin\theta + \hat{\mathbf{j}}\cos\theta$$

The top equation follows from the fact that the **position vector** (Chapter 4), which is $\vec{\mathbf{r}} = x\hat{\mathbf{i}} + y\hat{\mathbf{j}}$ in Cartesian coordinates, is simply $\vec{\mathbf{r}} = r\hat{\mathbf{r}}$ in 2D polar coordinates. Set these equal to get $r\hat{\mathbf{r}} = x\hat{\mathbf{i}} + y\hat{\mathbf{j}}$, divide by r to get $\hat{\mathbf{r}} = \frac{x}{r}\hat{\mathbf{i}} + \frac{y}{r}\hat{\mathbf{j}}$, and then use $x = r\cos\theta$ and $y = r\sin\theta$. The second equation is easy to obtain by remembering that $\widehat{\boldsymbol{\theta}} = \frac{\partial}{\partial\theta}\hat{\mathbf{r}}$.

A 2D **vector function** (Chapter 4) that has the form $\vec{\mathbf{A}}(x,y) = A_x(x,y)\hat{\mathbf{i}} + A_y(x,y)\hat{\mathbf{j}}$ in Cartesian coordinates can be expressed in the form $\vec{\mathbf{A}}(r,\theta) = A_r(r,\theta)\hat{\mathbf{r}} + A_\theta(r,\theta)\widehat{\boldsymbol{\theta}}$ in 2D polar coordinates, where the polar components and Cartesian components of the vector function are related by:

$$A_x = A_r\cos\theta - A_\theta\sin\theta \quad , \quad A_y = A_r\sin\theta + A_\theta\cos\theta$$

For a function of 2D polar coordinates $f(r,\theta)$, when taking a partial derivative with respect to r, hold θ constant, and when taking a partial derivative with respect to θ, hold r constant. To find a partial derivative of $f(r,\theta)$ with respect to x or y, or to take a partial derivative of $g(x,y)$ with respect to r or θ, apply the multivariable chain rule (Chapter 2). Since $x = r\cos\theta$ and $y = r\sin\theta$, it follows that:

$$\frac{\partial x}{\partial r} = \frac{\partial}{\partial r} r\cos\theta = \cos\theta\frac{\partial}{\partial r}r = \cos\theta\,(1) = \cos\theta$$

$$\frac{\partial y}{\partial r} = \frac{\partial}{\partial r} r\sin\theta = \sin\theta\frac{\partial}{\partial r}r = \sin\theta\,(1) = \sin\theta$$

$$\frac{\partial x}{\partial\theta} = \frac{\partial}{\partial\theta} r\cos\theta = r\frac{\partial}{\partial\theta}\cos\theta = r(-\sin\theta) = -r\sin\theta$$

$$\frac{\partial y}{\partial\theta} = \frac{\partial}{\partial\theta} r\sin\theta = r\frac{\partial}{\partial\theta}\sin\theta = r\cos\theta$$

Example. Convert the point $\left(6, \frac{\pi}{3}\right)$ from polar coordinates to Cartesian coordinates.

Use the formulas for x and y. Note that $r = 6$ and $\theta = \frac{\pi}{3}$ rad.

$$x = r\cos\theta = 6\cos\frac{\pi}{3} = 6\left(\frac{1}{2}\right) = \boxed{3}$$

$$y = r\sin\theta = 6\sin\frac{\pi}{3} = 6\left(\frac{\sqrt{3}}{2}\right) = \boxed{3\sqrt{3}}$$

Example. Convert the point $(-5, -5)$ from Cartesian coordinates to polar coordinates.

Use the formulas for r and θ. Note that $x = y = -5$.

$$r = \sqrt{x^2 + y^2} = \sqrt{(-5)^2 + (-5)^2} = \sqrt{25 + 25} = \sqrt{50} = \sqrt{(25)(2)} = \boxed{5\sqrt{2}}$$

$$\theta = \tan^{-1}\left(\frac{y}{x}\right) = \tan^{-1}\left(\frac{-5}{-5}\right) = \tan^{-1}(1) = \boxed{\frac{5\pi}{4}} = \boxed{225°}$$

Note that θ lies in Quadrant III because $x < 0$ and $y < 0$.

Example. Express the 2D polar equation $r = \csc(2\theta)$ in Cartesian coordinates.

Apply the trig identities $\csc\theta = \frac{1}{\sin\theta}$ and $\sin(2\theta) = 2\sin\theta\cos\theta$.

$$r = \frac{1}{\sin(2\theta)} = \frac{1}{2\sin\theta\cos\theta}$$

Since $x = r\cos\theta$, it follows that $\cos\theta = \frac{x}{r}$ and $\frac{1}{\cos\theta} = \frac{r}{x}$. Similarly, $\frac{1}{\sin\theta} = \frac{r}{y}$.

$$r = \frac{1}{2}\left(\frac{r}{y}\right)\left(\frac{r}{x}\right) = \frac{r^2}{2xy}$$

Divide both sides by r and multiply both sides by $2xy$.

$$2xy = r$$

Use the equation $r = \sqrt{x^2 + y^2}$.

$$2xy = \sqrt{x^2 + y^2}$$

Square both sides.

$$\boxed{4x^2y^2 = x^2 + y^2}$$

Example. Express the equation $x^2 + y^2 = 9$ in polar coordinates. Describe the curve.

Use the equations $x = r\cos\theta$ and $y = r\sin\theta$.

$$r^2\cos^2\theta + r^2\sin^2\theta = 9$$

$$r^2(\cos^2\theta + \sin^2\theta) = 9$$

Apply the trig identity $\cos^2\theta + \sin^2\theta = 1$.

$$r^2 = 9$$

Square root both sides. Take the positive root.

$$r = \boxed{3}$$

The equation $r = 3$ represents a circle with a radius of 3 centered about the origin.

Example. Express the 2D polar vector $\vec{\mathbf{A}} = r\hat{\mathbf{r}} - r\hat{\boldsymbol{\theta}}$ in Cartesian coordinates.

First use $\hat{\mathbf{r}} = \hat{\mathbf{i}}\cos\theta + \hat{\mathbf{j}}\sin\theta$ and $\hat{\boldsymbol{\theta}} = -\hat{\mathbf{i}}\sin\theta + \hat{\mathbf{j}}\cos\theta$.

$$\vec{\mathbf{A}} = r(\hat{\mathbf{i}}\cos\theta + \hat{\mathbf{j}}\sin\theta) - r(-\hat{\mathbf{i}}\sin\theta + \hat{\mathbf{j}}\cos\theta)$$

$$\vec{\mathbf{A}} = \hat{\mathbf{i}}\,r\cos\theta + \hat{\mathbf{j}}\,r\sin\theta + \hat{\mathbf{i}}\,r\sin\theta - \hat{\mathbf{j}}\,r\cos\theta$$

Now use $x = r\cos\theta$ and $y = r\sin\theta$.

$$\vec{\mathbf{A}} = x\hat{\mathbf{i}} + y\hat{\mathbf{j}} + y\hat{\mathbf{i}} - x\hat{\mathbf{j}} = \boxed{(x+y)\hat{\mathbf{i}} + (-x+y)\hat{\mathbf{j}}}$$

Alternatively, use the equations to transform a vector function from polar to Cartesian coordinates. Compare the given equation $\vec{\mathbf{A}} = r\hat{\mathbf{r}} - r\hat{\boldsymbol{\theta}}$ with the general formula $\vec{\mathbf{A}} = A_r\hat{\mathbf{r}} - A_\theta\hat{\boldsymbol{\theta}}$ to see that $A_r = r$ and $A_\theta = -r$.

$$A_x = A_r\cos\theta - A_\theta\sin\theta = r\cos\theta - (-r)\sin\theta = x + y$$

$$A_y = A_r\sin\theta + A_\theta\cos\theta = r\sin\theta + (-r)\cos\theta = y - x$$

$$\vec{\mathbf{A}} = A_x\hat{\mathbf{i}} + A_y\hat{\mathbf{j}} = \boxed{(x+y)\hat{\mathbf{i}} + (-x+y)\hat{\mathbf{j}}}$$

Chapter 6 Exercises – Part A

Directions: Convert each point from polar coordinates to Cartesian coordinates.

❶ $\left(1, \frac{5\pi}{6}\right)$

❷ $\left(8, \frac{4\pi}{3}\right)$

Directions: Convert each point from Cartesian coordinates to polar coordinates.

❸ $(\sqrt{3}, -1)$

❹ $(0, -3)$

Directions: Express each equation in Cartesian coordinates. Describe or sketch the curve.

❺ $r = \cos(2\theta)$

❻ $r = 1 + \sin\theta$

❼ $r = 1 + r\cos\theta$

❽ $r = \tan\theta\sec\theta$

❖ Check your answers at the back of the book.

Chapter 6 Exercises – Part B

Directions: Express each equation in polar coordinates. Describe or sketch the curve.

❾ $y = \frac{1}{x}$

❿ $y = x^2$

⓫ $y = \frac{x}{2}$

⓬ $y^2 + \frac{x^2}{4} = 1$

Directions: Express each 2D polar vector function in Cartesian coordinates.

⓭ $\vec{\mathbf{A}} = r^2\hat{\mathbf{r}}\sin\theta + r^2\hat{\boldsymbol{\theta}}\cos\theta$

⓮ $\vec{\mathbf{B}} = \hat{\mathbf{r}}\sec\theta - \hat{\boldsymbol{\theta}}\csc\theta$

❖ Check your answers at the back of the book.

7 Spherical Coordinates

Any point P can be expressed using **spherical coordinates** (r, θ, φ) as follows:

- r is the distance from the origin to point P.
- θ is the **azimuthal** angle counterclockwise from $+x$ to the projection of r onto the xy plane, basically the same way that θ is defined in 2D polar coordinates.
- φ is the **polar** (or **zenith**) angle between r and $+z$. **Note:** $0 \le \varphi \le \pi$ and $0 \le \theta \le 2\pi$.

Notation: Most **math** textbooks and instructors use θ and φ backwards to most **physics** textbooks and instructors. Since this is a math workbook, this workbook is using the common math notation. If you take a physics course, θ and φ will probably be used opposite to the way they are being used in this book and in most math textbooks. Most students who take advanced math and physics courses simultaneously experience this inconvenience. Also, the **order of the angles can differ** and some texts use ρ instead of r.

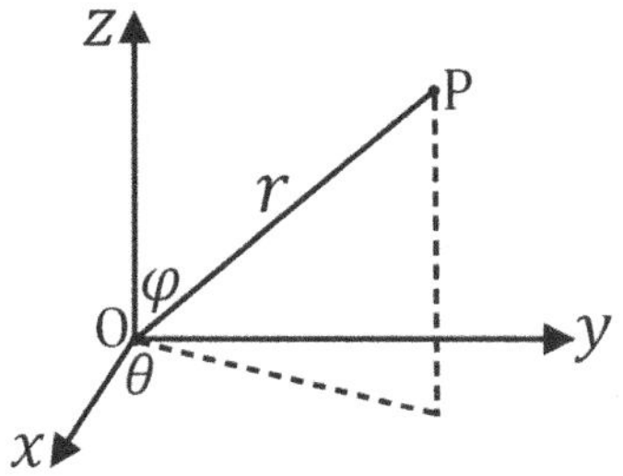

Given spherical coordinates, Cartesian coordinates (x, y, z) can be found by:

$$x = r\cos\theta\sin\varphi \quad , \quad y = r\sin\theta\sin\varphi \quad , \quad z = r\cos\varphi$$

Given Cartesian coordinates, spherical coordinates can be found by:

$$r = \sqrt{x^2 + y^2 + z^2} \quad , \quad \theta = \tan^{-1}\left(\frac{y}{x}\right) \quad , \quad \varphi = \cos^{-1}\left(\frac{z}{r}\right)$$

A few special cases of spherical coordinates include:

- $r = a$ is the equation for a **sphere** with radius a centered about the origin.
- $\theta = a$ is a semi-infinite plane containing the z-axis.
- $\varphi = c$ is the equation for a semi-infinite **cone** with its apex at the origin.

The spherical unit vectors are $\hat{\mathbf{r}}$, $\hat{\boldsymbol{\theta}}$, and $\hat{\boldsymbol{\varphi}}$. The radial unit vector $\hat{\mathbf{r}}$ points one unit outward away from the origin, $\hat{\boldsymbol{\theta}}$ is tangent to a circle parallel to the xy plane and centered about the z-axis in a counterclockwise sense (just as in 2D polar coordinates), and $\hat{\boldsymbol{\varphi}}$ is tangent to a circle centered about the origin with a diameter on the z-axis.

The spherical **unit vectors** are related to the Cartesian unit vectors by:

$$\hat{\mathbf{r}} = \hat{\mathbf{i}}\cos\theta\sin\varphi + \hat{\mathbf{j}}\sin\theta\sin\varphi + \hat{\mathbf{k}}\cos\varphi$$

$$\widehat{\boldsymbol{\theta}} = -\hat{\mathbf{i}}\sin\theta + \hat{\mathbf{j}}\cos\theta$$

$$\widehat{\boldsymbol{\varphi}} = \hat{\mathbf{i}}\cos\theta\cos\varphi + \hat{\mathbf{j}}\sin\theta\cos\varphi - \hat{\mathbf{k}}\sin\varphi$$

The top equation follows from the fact that the **position vector** (Chapter 4), which is $\vec{\mathbf{r}} = x\hat{\mathbf{i}} + y\hat{\mathbf{j}} + z\hat{\mathbf{k}}$ in Cartesian coordinates, is simply $\vec{\mathbf{r}} = r\hat{\mathbf{r}}$ in spherical coordinates. Set these equal to get $r\hat{\mathbf{r}} = x\hat{\mathbf{i}} + y\hat{\mathbf{j}} + z\hat{\mathbf{k}}$, divide by r to get $\hat{\mathbf{r}} = \frac{x}{r}\hat{\mathbf{i}} + \frac{y}{r}\hat{\mathbf{j}} + \frac{z}{r}\hat{\mathbf{k}}$, and then use $x = r\cos\theta\sin\varphi$, $y = r\sin\theta\sin\varphi$, and $z = r\cos\varphi$. The other equations are easy to obtain by remembering that $\widehat{\boldsymbol{\theta}} = \frac{\partial}{\partial\theta}\hat{\mathbf{r}}$ (with $\varphi = \frac{\pi}{2}$ since we project down onto the xy plane in order to define θ) and $\widehat{\boldsymbol{\varphi}} = \frac{\partial}{\partial\varphi}\hat{\mathbf{r}}$. Remember, in this book, φ is the polar angle.

A **vector function** (Chapter 4) that has the form $\vec{\mathbf{A}} = A_x\hat{\mathbf{i}} + A_y\hat{\mathbf{j}} + A_z\hat{\mathbf{k}}$ in Cartesian coordinates, where A_x, A_y, and A_z are each functions of x, y, and z, can be expressed in the form $\vec{\mathbf{A}} = A_r\hat{\mathbf{r}} + A_\theta\widehat{\boldsymbol{\theta}} + A_\varphi\widehat{\boldsymbol{\varphi}}$ in spherical coordinates, where:

$$A_x = A_r\cos\theta\sin\varphi - A_\theta\sin\theta + A_\varphi\cos\theta\cos\varphi$$

$$A_y = A_r\sin\theta\sin\varphi + A_\theta\cos\theta + A_\varphi\sin\theta\cos\varphi$$

$$A_z = A_r\cos\varphi - A_\varphi\sin\varphi$$

For a function of spherical coordinates $f(r,\theta,\varphi)$, when taking a partial derivative with respect to one of these three variables (r, θ, or φ), hold the other two constant. To find a partial derivative of $f(r,\theta,\varphi)$ with respect to x, y, or z, or to take a partial derivative of $g(x,y,z)$ with respect to r, θ, or φ, apply the multivariable chain rule (Chapter 2). Since $x = r\cos\theta\sin\varphi$, $y = r\sin\theta\sin\varphi$, and $z = r\cos\varphi$, it follows that:

$$\frac{\partial x}{\partial r} = \frac{\partial}{\partial r} r\cos\theta\sin\varphi = \cos\theta\sin\varphi \quad , \quad \frac{\partial y}{\partial r} = \frac{\partial}{\partial r} r\sin\theta\sin\varphi = \sin\theta\sin\varphi$$

$$\frac{\partial z}{\partial r} = \frac{\partial}{\partial r} r\cos\varphi = \cos\varphi \quad , \quad \frac{\partial x}{\partial\theta} = \frac{\partial}{\partial\theta} r\cos\theta\sin\varphi = -r\sin\theta\sin\varphi$$

$$\frac{\partial y}{\partial\theta} = \frac{\partial}{\partial\theta} r\sin\theta\sin\varphi = r\cos\theta\sin\varphi \quad , \quad \frac{\partial z}{\partial\theta} = \frac{\partial}{\partial\theta} r\cos\varphi = 0$$

$$\frac{\partial x}{\partial\varphi} = \frac{\partial}{\partial\varphi} r\cos\theta\sin\varphi = r\cos\theta\cos\varphi \quad , \quad \frac{\partial y}{\partial\varphi} = \frac{\partial}{\partial\varphi} r\sin\theta\sin\varphi = r\sin\theta\cos\varphi$$

$$\frac{\partial z}{\partial\varphi} = \frac{\partial}{\partial\varphi} r\cos\varphi = -r\sin\varphi$$

In 3D space, the direction of a **vector** can be specified using the two angles of spherical coordinates. For example, the vector $\langle A_x, A_y, A_z \rangle$ has a magnitude of $\sqrt{A_x^2 + A_y^2 + A_z^2}$ and a direction specified by $\theta = \tan^{-1}\left(\frac{A_y}{A_x}\right)$ and $\varphi = \cos^{-1}\left(\frac{A_z}{\|\vec{A}\|}\right)$.

Example. Convert the point $\left(4, \frac{\pi}{6}, \frac{\pi}{3}\right)$ from spherical to Cartesian coordinates. **Note**: In this book, the first angle (θ) is **azimuthal** and the second angle (φ) is **polar**.

Use the formulas for x, y, and z. Note that $r = 4$, $\theta = \frac{\pi}{6}$ rad, and $\varphi = \frac{\pi}{3}$ rad.

$$x = r\cos\theta\sin\varphi = 4\cos\frac{\pi}{6}\sin\frac{\pi}{3} = 4\left(\frac{\sqrt{3}}{2}\right)\left(\frac{\sqrt{3}}{2}\right) = \boxed{3}$$

$$y = r\sin\theta\sin\varphi = 4\sin\frac{\pi}{6}\sin\frac{\pi}{3} = 4\left(\frac{1}{2}\right)\left(\frac{\sqrt{3}}{2}\right) = \boxed{\sqrt{3}}$$

$$z = r\cos\varphi = 4\cos\frac{\pi}{3} = 4\left(\frac{1}{2}\right) = \boxed{2}$$

Example. Convert the point $(-1, 0, \sqrt{3})$ from Cartesian to spherical coordinates.

Use the formulas for r, θ, and φ. Note that $x = -1$, $y = 0$, and $z = \sqrt{3}$.

$$r = \sqrt{x^2 + y^2 + z^2} = \sqrt{(-1)^2 + 0^2 + \left(\sqrt{3}\right)^2} = \sqrt{1 + 0 + 3} = \sqrt{4} = \boxed{2}$$

$$\theta = \tan^{-1}\left(\frac{y}{x}\right) = \tan^{-1}\left(\frac{0}{-5}\right) = \tan^{-1}(0) = \boxed{\pi} = \boxed{180°}$$

$$\varphi = \cos^{-1}\left(\frac{z}{r}\right) = \cos^{-1}\left(\frac{\sqrt{3}}{2}\right) = \boxed{\frac{\pi}{6}} = \boxed{30°}$$

Note that $\theta = 180°$ because $x < 0$ and $y = 0$.

Example. Express the spherical equation $r = \tan\theta\sec\varphi$ in Cartesian coordinates.

Note that $\frac{y}{x} = \tan\theta$ and $\frac{r}{z} = \frac{1}{\cos\varphi} = \sec\varphi$.

$$r = \tan\theta\sec\varphi = \frac{y}{x}\frac{r}{z} = \frac{yr}{xz}$$

Divide both sides of $r = \frac{yr}{xz}$ by r and multiply both sides by z.

$$\boxed{z = \frac{y}{x}}$$

Example. Express the equation $x^2 + y^2 = z^2$ in spherical coordinates.

Since $r^2 = x^2 + y^2 + z^2$, it is helpful to add z^2 to both sides to get $x^2 + y^2 + z^2 = 2z^2$, which becomes $r^2 = 2z^2$. Divide by r^2 on both sides to get $1 = 2\frac{z^2}{r^2}$. Since $z = r\cos\varphi$, it follows that $\frac{z}{r} = \cos\varphi$, such that the equation $1 = 2\frac{z^2}{r^2}$ becomes $1 = 2\cos^2\varphi$.

$$\boxed{\cos^2\varphi = \frac{1}{2}}$$

Example. Express the spherical vector $\vec{\mathbf{A}} = r\hat{\mathbf{r}} + r\hat{\boldsymbol{\theta}}\sin\varphi$ in Cartesian coordinates.

Use $\hat{\mathbf{r}} = \hat{\mathbf{i}}\cos\theta\sin\varphi + \hat{\mathbf{j}}\sin\theta\sin\varphi + \hat{\mathbf{k}}\cos\varphi$ and $\hat{\boldsymbol{\theta}} = -\hat{\mathbf{i}}\sin\theta + \hat{\mathbf{j}}\cos\theta$.

$$\vec{\mathbf{A}} = r(\hat{\mathbf{i}}\cos\theta\sin\varphi + \hat{\mathbf{j}}\sin\theta\sin\varphi + \hat{\mathbf{k}}\cos\varphi) + r\sin\varphi\,(-\hat{\mathbf{i}}\sin\theta + \hat{\mathbf{j}}\cos\theta)$$

$$\vec{\mathbf{A}} = \hat{\mathbf{i}}\,r\cos\theta\sin\varphi + \hat{\mathbf{j}}\,r\sin\theta\sin\varphi + \hat{\mathbf{k}}\,r\cos\varphi - \hat{\mathbf{i}}\,r\sin\theta\sin\varphi + \hat{\mathbf{j}}\,r\cos\theta\sin\varphi$$

Now use $x = r\cos\theta\sin\varphi$, $y = r\sin\theta\sin\varphi$, and $z = r\cos\varphi$.

$$\vec{\mathbf{A}} = x\hat{\mathbf{i}} + y\hat{\mathbf{j}} + z\hat{\mathbf{k}} - y\hat{\mathbf{i}} + x\hat{\mathbf{j}} = \boxed{(x-y)\hat{\mathbf{i}} + (x+y)\hat{\mathbf{j}} + z\hat{\mathbf{k}}}$$

Alternatively, use the equations to transform a vector function from polar to Cartesian coordinates. Compare the given equation $\vec{\mathbf{A}} = r\hat{\mathbf{r}} + r\hat{\boldsymbol{\theta}}\sin\varphi$ with the general formula $\vec{\mathbf{A}} = A_r\hat{\mathbf{r}} + A_\theta\hat{\boldsymbol{\theta}} + A_\varphi\hat{\boldsymbol{\varphi}}$ to see that $A_r = r$, $A_\theta = r\sin\varphi$, and $A_\varphi = 0$.

$$A_x = A_r\cos\theta\sin\varphi - A_\theta\sin\theta + A_\varphi\cos\theta\cos\varphi = r\cos\theta\sin\varphi - r\sin\varphi\sin\theta + 0$$

$$A_x = r\cos\theta\sin\varphi - r\sin\theta\sin\varphi = x - y$$

$$A_y = A_r\sin\theta\sin\varphi + A_\theta\cos\theta + A_\varphi\sin\theta\cos\varphi = r\sin\theta\sin\varphi + r\sin\varphi\cos\theta + 0$$

$$A_y = r\sin\theta\sin\varphi + r\cos\theta\sin\varphi = x + y$$

$$A_z = A_r\cos\varphi - A_\varphi\sin\varphi = r\cos\varphi - 0$$

$$A_z = r\cos\varphi = z$$

$$\vec{\mathbf{A}} = A_x\hat{\mathbf{i}} + A_y\hat{\mathbf{j}} + A_z\hat{\mathbf{k}} = \boxed{(x-y)\hat{\mathbf{i}} + (x+y)\hat{\mathbf{j}} + z\hat{\mathbf{k}}}$$

Chapter 7 Exercises – Part A

Directions: Convert each point from spherical coordinates to Cartesian coordinates.
Note: In this book, the first angle (θ) is **azimuthal** and the second angle (φ) is **polar**. In physics texts, these angles may be swapped and/or the order may be different.

❶ $(r, \theta, \varphi) = \left(8, \frac{2\pi}{3}, \frac{\pi}{4}\right)$

❷ $(r, \theta, \varphi) = \left(\frac{1}{2}, \frac{3\pi}{2}, \frac{5\pi}{6}\right)$

Directions: Convert each point from Cartesian coordinates to spherical coordinates.

❸ $(\sqrt{3}, -3, -2)$

❹ $\left(-\frac{3}{2}, \frac{3}{2}, \frac{\sqrt{6}}{2}\right)$

Directions: Express each spherical equation in Cartesian coordinates.

❺ $\tan\theta = \sec\varphi$

❻ $\frac{1}{r^2} = \cos^2\theta\sin^2\varphi + \cos^2\varphi$

❖ Check your answers at the back of the book.

Chapter 7 Exercises – Part B

Directions: Express each equation in spherical coordinates.

❼ $x^2 + y^2 = z^2$

❽ $x^2 + z^2 = 25$

❾ $z = x^2$

❿ $y = \frac{x}{z}$

Directions: Express the spherical vector function in Cartesian coordinates.
Note: In this book, θ is the **azimuthal** angle and φ is the **polar** angle (or **zenith** angle).

⓫ $\vec{\mathbf{A}} = r^2\hat{\mathbf{r}}\cos\theta\sin\varphi + r^2\hat{\boldsymbol{\theta}}\sin\theta\sin^2\varphi + \hat{\boldsymbol{\varphi}}r^2\sin\varphi$

❖ Check your answers at the back of the book.

8 Cylindrical Coordinates

Any point P can be expressed using **cylindrical coordinates** (r_c, θ, z) as follows:

- r_c is the distance from the z-axis to point P. Note that the cylindrical coordinate r_c is different from the spherical coordinate r in that r_c is measured from the z-axis (**not** the origin).
- θ is the angle counterclockwise from the $+x$-axis, basically the same way that θ is defined in 2D polar coordinates.
- z is the same in cylindrical coordinates as it is in Cartesian coordinates.

Notation: Textbooks and instructors are not consistent with the notation for spherical and cylindrical coordinates. Some use ρ for spherical and r for cylindrical, others use r for spherical and ρ for cylindrical. Occasionally, the same symbol r is used for both. If you use more than one book, instructor, or article, pay close attention to the notation.

Given cylindrical coordinates, Cartesian coordinates (x, y, z) can be found by:

$$x = r_c \cos\theta \quad , \quad y = r_c \sin\theta \quad , \quad z = z$$

Given Cartesian coordinates, cylindrical coordinates can be found by:

$$r_c = \sqrt{x^2 + y^2} \quad , \quad \theta = \tan^{-1}\left(\frac{y}{x}\right) \quad , \quad z = z$$

A few special cases of cylindrical coordinates include:

- $r = a$ is the equation for an infinite right-circular **cylinder** with radius a coaxial with the z-axis.
- $\theta = a$ is a semi-infinite plane containing the z-axis.
- $z = ar_c$ is the equation for a semi-infinite **cone** with its apex at the origin.

Cylindrical unit vectors are $\hat{\mathbf{r}}_c$ and $\hat{\boldsymbol{\theta}}$. At point P, if a circle centered about the z-axis is drawn through P, the radial unit vector $\hat{\mathbf{r}}_c$ points one unit outward away from the z-axis, $\hat{\boldsymbol{\theta}}$ points one unit tangent to the circle in a counterclockwise sense, and $\hat{\mathbf{k}}$ points one unit along the $+z$-axis (which is the same as it does in Cartesian coordinates). The cylindrical **unit vectors** are related to the Cartesian unit vectors by:

$$\hat{\mathbf{r}}_c = \hat{\mathbf{i}}\cos\theta + \hat{\mathbf{j}}\sin\theta$$
$$\hat{\boldsymbol{\theta}} = -\hat{\mathbf{i}}\sin\theta + \hat{\mathbf{j}}\cos\theta$$
$$\hat{\mathbf{k}} = \hat{\mathbf{k}}$$

The top equation follows from the fact that the **position vector** (Chapter 4), which is $\vec{\mathbf{r}} = x\hat{\mathbf{i}} + y\hat{\mathbf{j}} + z\hat{\mathbf{k}}$ in Cartesian coordinates, is $\vec{\mathbf{r}} = r_c\hat{\mathbf{r}}_\mathbf{c} + z\hat{\mathbf{k}}$ in cylindrical coordinates. Set these equal to get $r_c\hat{\mathbf{r}}_\mathbf{c} = x\hat{\mathbf{i}} + y\hat{\mathbf{j}}$, divide by r_c to get $\hat{\mathbf{r}}_\mathbf{c} = \frac{x}{r_c}\hat{\mathbf{i}} + \frac{y}{r_c}\hat{\mathbf{j}}$, and then use $x = r_c \cos\theta$ and $y = r_c \sin\theta$. The second equation is easy to obtain by remembering that $\hat{\boldsymbol{\theta}} = \frac{\partial}{\partial\theta}\hat{\mathbf{r}}_\mathbf{c}$.

A **vector function** (Chapter 4) that has the form $\vec{\mathbf{A}} = A_x\hat{\mathbf{i}} + A_y\hat{\mathbf{j}} + A_z\hat{\mathbf{k}}$ in Cartesian coordinates, where A_x, A_y, and A_z are each functions of x, y, and z, can be expressed in the form $\vec{\mathbf{A}} = A_{r_c}\hat{\mathbf{r}}_\mathbf{c} + A_\theta\hat{\boldsymbol{\theta}} + A_z\hat{\mathbf{k}}$ in cylindrical coordinates, where:

$$A_x = A_{r_c}\cos\theta - A_\theta \sin\theta$$

$$A_y = A_{r_c}\sin\theta + A_\theta \cos\theta$$

$$A_z = A_z$$

For a function of cylindrical coordinates $f(r_c, \theta, z)$, when taking a partial derivative with respect to one of these three variables (r_c, θ, or z), hold the other two constant. To find a partial derivative of $f(r_c, \theta, z)$ with respect to x or y, or to take a partial derivative of $g(x, y, z)$ with respect to r_c or θ, apply the multivariable chain rule (Chapter 2). Since $x = r_c \cos\theta$ and $y = r_c \sin\theta$, it follows that:

$$\frac{\partial x}{\partial r_c} = \frac{\partial}{\partial r_c} r_c \cos\theta = \cos\theta \frac{\partial}{\partial r_c} r_c = \cos\theta\,(1) = \cos\theta$$

$$\frac{\partial y}{\partial r_c} = \frac{\partial}{\partial r_c} r_c \sin\theta = \sin\theta \frac{\partial}{\partial r_c} r_c = \sin\theta\,(1) = \sin\theta$$

$$\frac{\partial z}{\partial r_c} = 0$$

$$\frac{\partial x}{\partial \theta} = \frac{\partial}{\partial \theta} r_c \cos\theta = r_c \frac{\partial}{\partial \theta}\cos\theta = r_c(-\sin\theta) = -r_c \sin\theta$$

$$\frac{\partial y}{\partial \theta} = \frac{\partial}{\partial \theta} r_c \sin\theta = r_c \frac{\partial}{\partial \theta}\sin\theta = r_c \cos\theta$$

$$\frac{\partial z}{\partial \theta} = 0$$

Example. Convert the point $\left(2, \frac{\pi}{6}, 3\right)$ from cylindrical to Cartesian coordinates.

Use the formulas for x, y, and z. Note that $r_c = 2$, $\theta = \frac{\pi}{6}$ rad, and $z = 3$.

$$x = r_c \cos\theta = 2\cos\frac{\pi}{6} = 2\left(\frac{\sqrt{3}}{2}\right) = \boxed{\sqrt{3}}$$

$$y = r_c \sin\theta = 2\sin\frac{\pi}{6} = 2\left(\frac{1}{2}\right) = \boxed{1}$$

$$z = \boxed{3}$$

Example. Convert the point $\left(1, -1, \sqrt{5}\right)$ from Cartesian to cylindrical coordinates.

Use the formulas for r_c, θ, and z. Note that $x = 1$, $y = -1$, and $z = \sqrt{5}$.

$$r_c = \sqrt{x^2 + y^2} = \sqrt{1^2 + (-1)^2} = \sqrt{1+1} = \boxed{\sqrt{2}}$$

$$\theta = \tan^{-1}\left(\frac{y}{x}\right) = \tan^{-1}\left(\frac{-1}{1}\right) = \tan^{-1}(-1) = \boxed{-\frac{\pi}{4}} = \boxed{-45°}$$

$$z = \boxed{\sqrt{5}}$$

Note that θ lies in Quadrant IV because $x > 0$ and $y < 0$. The answer could alternatively be expressed as $\frac{7\pi}{4}$ or $315°$.

Example. Express the cylindrical equation $r_c = z\tan\theta$ in Cartesian coordinates.

Note that $\frac{y}{x} = \tan\theta$ and $r_c = \sqrt{x^2 + y^2}$.

$$\sqrt{x^2 + y^2} = z\left(\frac{y}{x}\right)$$

Square both sides: $x^2 + y^2 = \frac{y^2 z^2}{x^2}$. Multiply by x^2 on both sides: $\boxed{x^4 + x^2 y^2 = y^2 z^2}$.

Example. Express the equation $x^2 + y^2 = 4z^2$ in cylindrical coordinates.

Since $r_c^2 = x^2 + y^2$, this is $r_c^2 = 4z^2$. Square root both sides: $\boxed{r_c = 2|z|}$. This is the equation for an infinite double cone.

Example. Express the cylindrical vector $\vec{\mathbf{A}} = r_c\hat{\boldsymbol{\theta}} + z\hat{\mathbf{k}}$ in Cartesian coordinates.

First use $\hat{\boldsymbol{\theta}} = -\hat{\mathbf{i}}\sin\theta + \hat{\mathbf{j}}\cos\theta$.

$$\vec{\mathbf{A}} = r_c(-\hat{\mathbf{i}}\sin\theta + \hat{\mathbf{j}}\cos\theta) + z\hat{\mathbf{k}}$$

$$\vec{\mathbf{A}} = -\hat{\mathbf{i}}\, r_c\sin\theta + \hat{\mathbf{j}}\, r_c\cos\theta + z\hat{\mathbf{k}}$$

Now use $x = r\cos\theta$ and $y = r\sin\theta$.

$$\vec{\mathbf{A}} = \boxed{-y\hat{\mathbf{i}} + x\hat{\mathbf{j}} + z\hat{\mathbf{k}}}$$

Alternatively, use the equations to transform a vector function from polar to Cartesian coordinates. Compare the given equation $\vec{\mathbf{A}} = r_c\hat{\boldsymbol{\theta}} + z\hat{\mathbf{k}}$ with the general formula $\vec{\mathbf{A}} = A_{r_c}\hat{\mathbf{r}}_c + A_\theta\hat{\boldsymbol{\theta}} + A_z\hat{\mathbf{k}}$ to see that $A_{r_c} = 0$, $A_\theta = r_c$, and $A_z = z$.

$$A_x = A_{r_c}\cos\theta - A_\theta\sin\theta = 0\cos\theta - r_c\sin\theta = -y$$

$$A_y = A_{r_c}\sin\theta + A_\theta\cos\theta = 0\sin\theta + r_c\cos\theta = x$$

$$A_z = z$$

$$\vec{\mathbf{A}} = A_x\hat{\mathbf{i}} + A_y\hat{\mathbf{j}} + z\hat{\mathbf{k}} = \boxed{-y\hat{\mathbf{i}} + x\hat{\mathbf{j}} + z\hat{\mathbf{k}}}$$

Chapter 8 Exercises – Part A

Directions: Convert each point from cylindrical coordinates to Cartesian coordinates.

❶ $\left(4, -\frac{\pi}{6}, 6\right)$

❷ $\left(\frac{2}{3}, \frac{2\pi}{3}, -\frac{1}{3}\right)$

Directions: Convert each point from Cartesian coordinates to cylindrical coordinates.

❸ $(-2,0,2)$

❹ $(-\sqrt{6}, \sqrt{2}, \sqrt{3})$

Directions: Express each cylindrical equation in Cartesian coordinates.

❺ $z = r_c^2$

❻ $z \tan\theta = 1$

❖ Check your answers at the back of the book.

Chapter 8 Exercises – Part B

Directions: Express each equation in cylindrical coordinates.

❼ $x^2 + y^2 + z^2 = 9$

❽ $\sqrt{x^2 + y^2} = 2z$

❾ $z = 2xy$

❿ $x^2y^2 + y^4 = x^2z^2$

Directions: Express the cylindrical vector function in Cartesian coordinates.

⓫ $\vec{\mathbf{A}} = r_c^2 \hat{\mathbf{r}}_\mathbf{c} \cos\theta - r_c^2 \hat{\boldsymbol{\theta}} \sin\theta + z^2 \hat{\mathbf{k}}$

❖ Check your answers at the back of the book.

9 The Gradient

The gradient operator, $\vec{\nabla}$, is a vector that has partial derivatives as components:

$$\vec{\nabla} = \hat{\mathbf{i}}\frac{\partial}{\partial x} + \hat{\mathbf{j}}\frac{\partial}{\partial y} + \hat{\mathbf{k}}\frac{\partial}{\partial z}$$

The gradient operator acts on a multivariable function to make the **gradient vector**:

$$\vec{\nabla} f = \hat{\mathbf{i}}\frac{\partial f}{\partial x} + \hat{\mathbf{j}}\frac{\partial f}{\partial y} + \hat{\mathbf{k}}\frac{\partial f}{\partial z}$$

In spherical coordinates, the gradient vector is (where φ is polar and θ is azimuthal):

$$\vec{\nabla} f = \hat{\mathbf{r}}\frac{\partial f}{\partial r} + \hat{\boldsymbol{\theta}}\frac{1}{r\sin\varphi}\frac{\partial f}{\partial \theta} + \hat{\boldsymbol{\varphi}}\frac{1}{r}\frac{\partial f}{\partial \varphi}$$

Note: Recall that θ and φ are often backwards in math compared to physics.

In cylindrical coordinates, the gradient vector is:

$$\vec{\nabla} f = \hat{\mathbf{r}}_c\frac{\partial f}{\partial r_c} + \hat{\boldsymbol{\theta}}\frac{1}{r_c}\frac{\partial f}{\partial \theta} + \hat{\mathbf{k}}\frac{\partial f}{\partial z}$$

The different forms of the gradient vector in different coordinate systems are related by transformations of coordinates, unit vectors, and partial derivatives. For example, $\hat{\mathbf{r}} = \hat{\mathbf{i}}\cos\theta\sin\varphi + \hat{\mathbf{j}}\sin\theta\sin\varphi + \hat{\mathbf{k}}\cos\varphi$ relates the spherical unit vector $\hat{\mathbf{r}}$ to Cartesian unit vectors. To transform the partial derivatives, use the multivariable chain rule (Chapter 2). For example, $\frac{\partial f}{\partial r} = \frac{\partial f}{\partial x}\frac{\partial x}{\partial r} + \frac{\partial f}{\partial y}\frac{\partial y}{\partial r} + \frac{\partial f}{\partial z}\frac{\partial z}{\partial r}$ (see Chapter 7).

One way to remember the gradient in each coordinate system is to note that the arc lengths in spherical coordinates are dr (radially outward), $r\sin\varphi\, d\theta$ (a horizontal circle made by projecting r down onto the xy plane), and $rd\varphi$ (a vertical circle), and that the arc lengths in cylindrical coordinates are dr_c (away from the z-axis), $rd\theta$ (a horizontal circle), and dz (vertical). In any coordinate system, $\vec{\nabla} f = \frac{\hat{\mathbf{e}}_1}{h_1}\frac{\partial f}{\partial u_1} + \frac{\hat{\mathbf{e}}_2}{h_2}\frac{\partial f}{\partial u_2} + \frac{\hat{\mathbf{e}}_3}{h_3}\frac{\partial f}{\partial u_3}$, where u_1, u_2, and u_3 are the coordinates, $\hat{\mathbf{e}}_1$, $\hat{\mathbf{e}}_2$, and $\hat{\mathbf{e}}_3$ are the unit vectors, and $h_1 = \left|\frac{\partial \vec{\mathbf{r}}}{\partial u_1}\right|$, $h_2 = \left|\frac{\partial \vec{\mathbf{r}}}{\partial u_2}\right|$, and $h_3 = \left|\frac{\partial \vec{\mathbf{r}}}{\partial u_3}\right|$ are the arc length factors, where $\vec{\mathbf{r}}$ is the position vector. For example, $\vec{\mathbf{r}} = r\hat{\mathbf{r}}$ in spherical and $\vec{\mathbf{r}} = r_c\hat{\mathbf{r}}_c + z\hat{\mathbf{k}}$ in cylindrical.

Interpretation of the gradient vector: The significance of the gradient vector, $\vec{\nabla} f$, is that it gives both the rate and the direction of the **fastest increase** of the function f. The direction of $\vec{\nabla} f$ at a point (x_0, y_0, z_0) is **perpendicular** to the **level surface** (where f equals a constant) of f at (x_0, y_0, z_0). This property of the gradient vector will be utilized in Chapter 12 (see page 71).

A **directional derivative**, $D_{\vec{A}} f$, is the scalar product of the gradient and a unit vector in the direction of $\vec{\mathbf{A}}$. Recall from Chapter 4 that $\hat{\mathbf{A}} = \frac{\vec{\mathbf{A}}}{\|\vec{\mathbf{A}}\|}$. Make sure that you use the unit vector, $\hat{\mathbf{A}}$, and not the vector itself, $\vec{\mathbf{A}}$, in the formula below.

$$D_{\vec{A}} f = \vec{\nabla} f \cdot \hat{\mathbf{A}}$$

Example. Find the gradient of $f(x,y,z) = z^2 - xy$.
Use the formula for the gradient vector in Cartesian coordinates.

$$\vec{\nabla} f = \hat{\mathbf{i}}\frac{\partial f}{\partial x} + \hat{\mathbf{j}}\frac{\partial f}{\partial y} + \hat{\mathbf{k}}\frac{\partial f}{\partial z} = \hat{\mathbf{i}}\frac{\partial}{\partial x}(z^2 - xy) + \hat{\mathbf{j}}\frac{\partial}{\partial y}(z^2 - xy) + \hat{\mathbf{k}}\frac{\partial}{\partial z}(z^2 - xy)$$

$$\vec{\nabla} f = \boxed{-y\hat{\mathbf{i}} - x\hat{\mathbf{j}} + 2z\hat{\mathbf{k}}}$$

Example. Find the gradient of $g(r,\theta,\varphi) = r^2 \sin\theta$.
Use the formula for the gradient vector in spherical coordinates.

$$\vec{\nabla} g = \hat{\mathbf{r}}\frac{\partial g}{\partial r} + \hat{\boldsymbol{\theta}}\frac{1}{r\sin\varphi}\frac{\partial g}{\partial \theta} + \hat{\boldsymbol{\varphi}}\frac{1}{r}\frac{\partial g}{\partial \varphi} = \hat{\mathbf{r}}\frac{\partial}{\partial r}r^2\sin\theta + \hat{\boldsymbol{\theta}}\frac{1}{r\sin\varphi}\frac{\partial}{\partial\theta}r^2\sin\theta + \hat{\boldsymbol{\varphi}}\frac{1}{r}\frac{\partial}{\partial\varphi}r^2\sin\theta$$

$$\vec{\nabla} g = 2r\hat{\mathbf{r}}\sin\theta + \frac{r^2\cos\theta}{r\sin\varphi}\hat{\boldsymbol{\theta}} + \frac{r^2\sin\theta}{r}\hat{\boldsymbol{\varphi}}(0) = \boxed{2r\hat{\mathbf{r}}\sin\theta + \frac{r\cos\theta}{\sin\varphi}\hat{\boldsymbol{\theta}}}$$

Example. Find the directional derivative of $h = x^2yz$ in the direction of $3\hat{\mathbf{i}} - 4\hat{\mathbf{j}}$.
The magnitude of $\vec{\mathbf{A}} = 3\hat{\mathbf{i}} - 4\hat{\mathbf{j}}$ is $\|\vec{\mathbf{A}}\| = \sqrt{A_x^2 + A_y^2 + A_z^2} = \sqrt{3^2 + 4^2 + 0^2} = \sqrt{9+16}$ $= \sqrt{25} = 5$, such that a unit vector along $\vec{\mathbf{A}}$ is $\hat{\mathbf{A}} = \frac{\vec{\mathbf{A}}}{\|\vec{\mathbf{A}}\|} = \frac{3\hat{\mathbf{i}} - 4\hat{\mathbf{j}}}{5} = \frac{3}{5}\hat{\mathbf{i}} - \frac{4}{5}\hat{\mathbf{j}}$.

$$D_{\vec{A}} h = \vec{\nabla} h \cdot \hat{\mathbf{A}} = \left(\hat{\mathbf{i}}\frac{\partial h}{\partial x} + \hat{\mathbf{j}}\frac{\partial h}{\partial y} + \hat{\mathbf{k}}\frac{\partial h}{\partial z}\right) \cdot \left(\frac{3}{5}\hat{\mathbf{i}} - \frac{4}{5}\hat{\mathbf{j}}\right) = \frac{3}{5}\frac{\partial h}{\partial x} - \frac{4}{5}\frac{\partial h}{\partial y}$$

$$D_{\vec{A}} h = \frac{3}{5}\frac{\partial}{\partial x}x^2yz - \frac{4}{5}\frac{\partial}{\partial y}x^2yz + 0 = \boxed{\frac{6}{5}xyz - \frac{4}{5}x^2z} = \boxed{\frac{2xz}{5}(3y - 2x)}$$

Chapter 9 Exercises – Part A

Directions: Determine the indicated quantity for each function.

Note: In this book, in spherical coordinates, θ is **azimuthal** and φ is **polar**.

❶ Given $f = x^5y^3$, find $\vec{\nabla}f$.

❷ Given $f = \frac{x^3y^2}{z}$, find $\vec{\nabla}f$.

❸ Given $f = y\sqrt{x}$, find $\vec{\nabla}f$.

❹ Given $f = r^3 \cos^2 \varphi$, find $\vec{\nabla}f$.

❺ Given $f = r^2 \cos\theta \sin\varphi$, find $\vec{\nabla}f$.

❻ Given $f = r_c^2 - r_c z \cos\theta + z^2$, find $\vec{\nabla}f$.

❼ Given $f = x^2 - y^2$, find the directional derivative in the direction of $\hat{\mathbf{i}} + \hat{\mathbf{j}}$.

❖ Check your answers at the back of the book.

Chapter 9 Exercises – Part B

Directions: Evaluate the indicated quantity at the specified point for each function. **Note**: In this book, the first angle (θ) is **azimuthal** and the second angle (φ) is **polar**. In physics texts, these angles may be swapped and/or the order of the angles may differ.

❽ Given $f = \frac{x}{y}$, evaluate $\vec{\nabla} f$ at $(2,4)$.

❾ Given $f = x^2 y^2 z^4$, evaluate $\vec{\nabla} f$ at $(3,3,2)$.

❿ Given $f = r \tan\theta$, evaluate $\vec{\nabla} f$ at $\left(2, \frac{\pi}{3}, \frac{\pi}{2}\right)$.

⓫ Given $f = \frac{\sqrt{z}}{xy}$, evaluate $\vec{\nabla} f$ at $(-2,-2,9)$.

⓬ Given $f = r_c^2 z^3$, evaluate $\vec{\nabla} f$ at $\left(3, \frac{\pi}{4}, 4\right)$.

⓭ Given $f = \frac{\sin\varphi}{r\cos\theta}$, evaluate $\vec{\nabla} f$ at $\left(4, \frac{4\pi}{3}, \frac{3\pi}{4}\right)$.

⓮ Given $f = x^3 + xyz + z^3$, evaluate the directional derivative in the direction of $10\hat{\mathbf{i}} - 5\hat{\mathbf{j}} + 10\hat{\mathbf{k}}$ at $(2,-1,2)$.

❖ Check your answers at the back of the book.

10 The Divergence

The **divergence** of a vector function is the scalar product (Chapter 5) of the gradient operator and the vector function: $\vec{\nabla} \cdot \vec{\mathbf{A}}$. The divergence operates on a vector function and results in a scalar function (whereas the gradient operates on a scalar function and results in a vector function).

$$\vec{\nabla} \cdot \vec{\mathbf{A}} = \left(\hat{\mathbf{i}}\frac{\partial}{\partial x} + \hat{\mathbf{j}}\frac{\partial}{\partial y} + \hat{\mathbf{k}}\frac{\partial}{\partial z}\right) \cdot \left(A_x\hat{\mathbf{i}} + A_y\hat{\mathbf{j}} + A_z\hat{\mathbf{k}}\right) = \frac{\partial A_x}{\partial x} + \frac{\partial A_y}{\partial y} + \frac{\partial A_z}{\partial z}$$

In spherical and cylindrical coordinates, the divergence is:

$$\vec{\nabla} \cdot \vec{\mathbf{A}} = \frac{1}{r^2}\frac{\partial}{\partial r}(r^2 A_r) + \frac{1}{r\sin\varphi}\frac{\partial A_\theta}{\partial \theta} + \frac{1}{r\sin\varphi}\frac{\partial}{\partial \varphi}(A_\varphi \sin\varphi)$$

$$\vec{\nabla} \cdot \vec{\mathbf{A}} = \frac{1}{r_c}\frac{\partial}{\partial r_c}\left(r_c A_{r_c}\right) + \frac{1}{r_c}\frac{\partial A_\theta}{\partial \theta} + \frac{\partial A_z}{\partial z}$$

Note: Recall that θ and φ are often backwards in math compared to physics. In this book (which uses math notation), in spherical coordinates φ is polar (measured from $+z$) and θ is azimuthal. The important point is that $\frac{1}{r\sin\varphi}\frac{\partial}{\partial\varphi}(A_\varphi \sin\varphi)$ has a partial derivative with respect to the polar angle (φ), while $\frac{1}{r\sin\varphi}\frac{\partial A_\theta}{\partial\theta}$ has a partial derivative with respect to the azimuthal angle (θ).

Note: The product rule, $\frac{d}{dx}pq = p\frac{dq}{dx} + q\frac{dp}{dx}$, is involved in $\frac{\partial}{\partial r}(r^2 A_r)$ and in $\frac{\partial}{\partial\varphi}(A_\varphi \sin\varphi)$.

The general form of the divergence is $\vec{\nabla} \cdot \vec{\mathbf{A}} = \frac{1}{h_1 h_2 h_3}\left[\frac{\partial}{\partial u_1}(h_2 h_3 A_1) + \frac{\partial}{\partial u_2}(h_3 h_1 A_2) + \frac{\partial}{\partial u_3}(h_1 h_2 A_3)\right]$, where u_1, u_2, and u_3 are the coordinates and $h_1 = \left|\frac{\partial \vec{\mathbf{r}}}{\partial u_1}\right|$, $h_2 = \left|\frac{\partial \vec{\mathbf{r}}}{\partial u_2}\right|$, and $h_3 = \left|\frac{\partial \vec{\mathbf{r}}}{\partial u_3}\right|$ are the arc length factors, where $\vec{\mathbf{r}}$ is the position vector (see Chapter 9).

Interpretation of the divergence: The significance of the divergence, $\vec{\nabla} \cdot \vec{\mathbf{A}}$, is that it provides a measure of the net flux of field lines radiating outward from a point, which indicates how much of the source of the field is contained at the point. The divergence is positive if there is a net outward flux, negative if there is a net inward flux, and zero if the net flux is zero (or balanced). For example, in physics a positive charge is a source of electric field, creating electric field lines that radiate outward from it. As another example, in fluid flow there is a negative divergence of field lines at a sink, where the fluid radiates inward. If $\vec{\nabla} \cdot \vec{A} = 0$, then $\vec{A}$ is **incompressible**.

The **Laplacian**, ∇^2, is the divergence of the gradient: $\nabla^2 = \vec{\nabla} \cdot \vec{\nabla}$. The Laplacian operator may be applied to a scalar function $f(x, y, z)$ or a vector function $\vec{A}(x, y, z)$.

$$\nabla^2 f = \vec{\nabla} \cdot \vec{\nabla} f = \left(\hat{\mathbf{i}}\frac{\partial}{\partial x} + \hat{\mathbf{j}}\frac{\partial}{\partial y} + \hat{\mathbf{k}}\frac{\partial}{\partial z}\right) \cdot \left(\hat{\mathbf{i}}\frac{\partial f}{\partial x} + \hat{\mathbf{j}}\frac{\partial f}{\partial y} + \hat{\mathbf{k}}\frac{\partial f}{\partial z}\right) = \frac{\partial^2 f}{\partial x^2} + \frac{\partial^2 f}{\partial y^2} + \frac{\partial^2 f}{\partial z^2}$$

$$\nabla^2 \vec{A} = \nabla^2 A_x \hat{\mathbf{i}} + \nabla^2 A_y \hat{\mathbf{j}} + \nabla^2 A_z \hat{\mathbf{k}}$$

In spherical or cylindrical coordinates, the Laplacian of a scalar function is:

$$\nabla^2 f = \frac{1}{r^2}\frac{\partial}{\partial r}\left(r^2 \frac{\partial f}{\partial r}\right) + \frac{1}{r^2 \sin^2 \varphi}\frac{\partial^2 f}{\partial \theta^2} + \frac{1}{r^2 \sin \varphi}\frac{\partial}{\partial \varphi}\left(\sin \varphi \frac{\partial f}{\partial \varphi}\right)$$

$$\nabla^2 f = \frac{1}{r_c}\frac{\partial}{\partial r_c}\left(r_c \frac{\partial f}{\partial r_c}\right) + \frac{1}{r_c^2}\frac{\partial^2 f}{\partial \theta^2} + \frac{\partial^2 f}{\partial z^2}$$

Note: Again, φ is the polar angle and θ is the azimuthal angle in common math notation. For common physics notation, swap φ and θ in spherical coordinates.

Example. Find the divergence of $\vec{A} = x^2 y \hat{\mathbf{i}} + xy^2 \hat{\mathbf{j}} + xyz \hat{\mathbf{k}}$.
Use the formula for the divergence in Cartesian coordinates.

$$\vec{\nabla} \cdot \vec{A} = \frac{\partial A_x}{\partial x} + \frac{\partial A_y}{\partial y} + \frac{\partial A_z}{\partial z} = \frac{\partial}{\partial x} x^2 y + \frac{\partial}{\partial y} xy^2 + \frac{\partial}{\partial z} xyz$$

$$\vec{\nabla} \cdot \vec{A} = 2xy + 2xy + xy = \boxed{5xy}$$

Example. Find the divergence of $\vec{B} = r^2 \hat{\mathbf{r}} + r^2 \sin\theta \sin\varphi \, \hat{\boldsymbol{\theta}} + r^2 \cos\theta \, \hat{\boldsymbol{\varphi}}$.
Use the formula for the divergence in spherical coordinates.

$$\vec{\nabla} \cdot \vec{B} = \frac{1}{r^2}\frac{\partial}{\partial r}(r^2 B_r) + \frac{1}{r \sin\varphi}\frac{\partial B_\theta}{\partial \theta} + \frac{1}{r \sin\varphi}\frac{\partial}{\partial \varphi}(B_\varphi \sin\varphi)$$

$$\vec{\nabla} \cdot \vec{B} = \frac{1}{r^2}\frac{\partial}{\partial r}(r^2 r^2) + \frac{1}{r \sin\varphi}\frac{\partial}{\partial \theta}(r^2 \sin\theta \sin\varphi) + \frac{1}{r \sin\varphi}\frac{\partial}{\partial \varphi}(r^2 \cos\theta \sin\varphi)$$

$$\vec{\nabla} \cdot \vec{B} = \frac{1}{r^2}\frac{\partial}{\partial r} r^4 + \frac{r^2 \sin\varphi}{r \sin\varphi}\frac{\partial}{\partial \theta}\sin\theta + \frac{r^2 \cos\theta}{r \sin\varphi}\frac{\partial}{\partial \varphi}\sin\varphi$$

$$\vec{\nabla} \cdot \vec{\mathbf{B}} = \frac{1}{r^2} 4r^3 + r\cos\theta + \frac{r\cos\theta}{\sin\varphi}\cos\varphi$$

$$\vec{\nabla} \cdot \vec{\mathbf{B}} = \boxed{4r + r\cos\theta + r\cos\theta\cot\varphi}$$

Example. Find the Laplacian of $f(x, y, z) = x^2y^3z^2$.

Use the formula for the Laplacian in Cartesian coordinates.

$$\nabla^2 f = \frac{\partial^2 f}{\partial x^2} + \frac{\partial^2 f}{\partial y^2} + \frac{\partial^2 f}{\partial z^2} = \frac{\partial^2}{\partial x^2} x^2y^3z^2 + \frac{\partial^2}{\partial y^2} x^2y^3z^2 + \frac{\partial^2}{\partial z^2} x^2y^3z^2$$

$$\nabla^2 f = \frac{\partial}{\partial x}\left(\frac{\partial}{\partial x} x^2y^3z^2\right) + \frac{\partial}{\partial y}\left(\frac{\partial}{\partial y} x^2y^3z^2\right) + \frac{\partial}{\partial z}\left(\frac{\partial}{\partial z} x^2y^3z^2\right)$$

$$\nabla^2 f = \frac{\partial}{\partial x}(2xy^3z^2) + \frac{\partial}{\partial y}(3x^2y^2z^2) + \frac{\partial}{\partial z}(2x^2y^3z)$$

$$\nabla^2 f = \boxed{2y^3z^2 + 6x^2yz^2 + 2x^2y^3}$$

Example. Find the Laplacian of $g(r_c, \theta, z) = r_c^2 \cos\theta$.

Use the formula for the Laplacian in cylindrical coordinates.

$$\nabla^2 g = \frac{1}{r_c}\frac{\partial}{\partial r_c}\left(r_c \frac{\partial g}{\partial r_c}\right) + \frac{1}{r_c^2}\frac{\partial^2 g}{\partial \theta^2} + \frac{\partial^2 g}{\partial z^2}$$

$$\nabla^2 g = \frac{1}{r_c}\frac{\partial}{\partial r_c}\left(r_c \frac{\partial}{\partial r_c} r_c^2 \cos\theta\right) + \frac{1}{r_c^2}\frac{\partial}{\partial \theta}\left(\frac{\partial}{\partial \theta} r_c^2 \cos\theta\right) + \frac{\partial}{\partial z}\left(\frac{\partial}{\partial z} r_c^2 \cos\theta\right)$$

$$\nabla^2 g = \frac{1}{r_c}\frac{\partial}{\partial r_c}(r_c 2r_c \cos\theta) + \frac{1}{r_c^2}\frac{\partial}{\partial \theta}(-r_c^2 \sin\theta) + \frac{\partial}{\partial z}(0)$$

$$\nabla^2 g = \frac{\cos\theta}{r_c}\frac{\partial}{\partial r_c}(2r_c^2) - \frac{r_c^2}{r_c^2}\frac{\partial}{\partial \theta}(\sin\theta) + 0$$

$$\nabla^2 g = \frac{\cos\theta}{r_c} 4r_c - \cos\theta = 4\cos\theta - \cos\theta = \boxed{3\cos\theta}$$

Chapter 10 Exercises – Part A

Directions: Find the divergence of each vector function.

Note: In this book, in spherical coordinates, θ is **azimuthal** and φ is **polar**.

❶ $\vec{\mathbf{A}} = x^3\hat{\mathbf{i}} + x^2y\hat{\mathbf{j}} + xy^2\hat{\mathbf{k}}$

❷ $\vec{\mathbf{B}} = x^4y^3\hat{\mathbf{i}} - x^3y^4\hat{\mathbf{j}} + x^2y^2z^3\hat{\mathbf{k}}$

❸ $\vec{\mathbf{C}} = \hat{\mathbf{i}}e^{xy} + \hat{\mathbf{j}}e^{xy} - xz\hat{\mathbf{k}}e^{xy}$

❹ $\vec{\mathbf{D}} = \langle y \ln x, \frac{y^2}{x}, \frac{\ln y}{x} \rangle$

❺ $\vec{\mathbf{E}} = \langle x^2 + yz, xy - z^2, y^2 + xz \rangle$

❻ $\vec{\mathbf{F}} = r_c^2 \hat{\mathbf{r}}_c \cos\theta + r_c^2 \hat{\boldsymbol{\theta}} \sin\theta$

❼ $\vec{\mathbf{G}} = r\hat{\mathbf{r}} + r\tan\theta\,\hat{\boldsymbol{\theta}} + r\cos\theta\cot\varphi\,\hat{\boldsymbol{\varphi}}$

❽ $\vec{\mathbf{H}} = r^3\hat{\mathbf{r}} + r^3\cos\theta\cos\varphi\,\hat{\boldsymbol{\theta}} + r^3\sin\theta\,\hat{\boldsymbol{\varphi}}$

❖ Check your answers at the back of the book.

Chapter 10 Exercises – Part B

Directions: Find the Laplacian of each scalar function.

Note: In this book, in spherical coordinates, θ is **azimuthal** and φ is **polar**.

❾ $f(x, y, z) = x^5 y^3 z$

❿ $g(x, y, z) = \frac{z^2}{xy}$

⓫ $h(x, y, z) = x^2 + y^2 + z^2$

⓬ $p(r_c, \theta, z) = r_c^2 z^2 \sin\theta$

⓭ $q(r, \theta, \varphi) = r^2 \cos\theta \sin\varphi$

⓮ $w(r, \theta, \varphi) = r^4 \tan\theta \cot\varphi$

❖ Check your answers at the back of the book.

Chapter 10 Exercises – Part C

Directions: In the problems below, $\vec{\mathbf{r}} = x\hat{\mathbf{i}} + y\hat{\mathbf{j}} + z\hat{\mathbf{k}} = r\hat{\mathbf{r}}$ is the position vector (see Chapters 4 and 7). First find the indicated quantity by working exclusively in spherical coordinates and then find the indicated quantity by working exclusively in Cartesian coordinates. Note that $r = \|\vec{\mathbf{r}}\|$. Two of the exercises involve the gradient (Chapter 9).

⓯ $\vec{\nabla} r$

⓰ $\vec{\nabla} \cdot \vec{\mathbf{r}}$

⓱ $\nabla^2 r^2$

⓲ $\vec{\nabla} \cdot (r\vec{\mathbf{r}})$

⓳ $\nabla^2 r^3$

⓴ $\vec{\nabla}\left(\frac{1}{r}\right)$

❖ Check your answers at the back of the book.

11 The Curl

The <u>curl</u> of a vector function is the vector product (Chapter 5) of the gradient operator and the vector function: $\vec{\nabla} \times \vec{\mathbf{A}}$. The curl operates on a vector function and results in a vector function (whereas the divergence results in a scalar function).

$$\vec{\nabla} \times \vec{\mathbf{A}} = \begin{vmatrix} \hat{\mathbf{i}} & \hat{\mathbf{j}} & \hat{\mathbf{k}} \\ \frac{\partial}{\partial x} & \frac{\partial}{\partial y} & \frac{\partial}{\partial z} \\ A_x & A_y & A_z \end{vmatrix} = \hat{\mathbf{i}} \begin{vmatrix} \frac{\partial}{\partial y} & \frac{\partial}{\partial z} \\ A_y & A_z \end{vmatrix} - \hat{\mathbf{j}} \begin{vmatrix} \frac{\partial}{\partial x} & \frac{\partial}{\partial z} \\ A_x & A_z \end{vmatrix} + \hat{\mathbf{k}} \begin{vmatrix} \frac{\partial}{\partial x} & \frac{\partial}{\partial y} \\ A_x & A_y \end{vmatrix}$$

$$\vec{\nabla} \times \vec{\mathbf{A}} = \left(\frac{\partial A_z}{\partial y} - \frac{\partial A_y}{\partial z}\right)\hat{\mathbf{i}} - \left(\frac{\partial A_z}{\partial x} - \frac{\partial A_x}{\partial z}\right)\hat{\mathbf{j}} + \left(\frac{\partial A_y}{\partial x} - \frac{\partial A_x}{\partial y}\right)\hat{\mathbf{k}}$$

$$\vec{\nabla} \times \vec{\mathbf{A}} = \left(\frac{\partial A_z}{\partial y} - \frac{\partial A_y}{\partial z}\right)\hat{\mathbf{i}} + \left(\frac{\partial A_x}{\partial z} - \frac{\partial A_z}{\partial x}\right)\hat{\mathbf{j}} + \left(\frac{\partial A_y}{\partial x} - \frac{\partial A_x}{\partial y}\right)\hat{\mathbf{k}}$$

In spherical and cylindrical coordinates, the curl is:

$$\vec{\nabla} \times \vec{\mathbf{A}} = \frac{1}{r^2 \sin\varphi} \begin{vmatrix} \hat{\mathbf{r}} & r\hat{\boldsymbol{\varphi}} & r\hat{\boldsymbol{\theta}} \sin\varphi \\ \frac{\partial}{\partial r} & \frac{\partial}{\partial \varphi} & \frac{\partial}{\partial \theta} \\ A_r & rA_\varphi & rA_\theta \sin\varphi \end{vmatrix} = \begin{vmatrix} \frac{\hat{\mathbf{r}}}{r^2 \sin\varphi} & \frac{\hat{\boldsymbol{\varphi}}}{r \sin\varphi} & \frac{\hat{\boldsymbol{\theta}}}{r} \\ \frac{\partial}{\partial r} & \frac{\partial}{\partial \varphi} & \frac{\partial}{\partial \theta} \\ A_r & rA_\varphi & rA_\theta \sin\varphi \end{vmatrix}$$

$$\vec{\nabla} \times \vec{\mathbf{A}} = \frac{1}{r \sin\varphi}\left(\frac{\partial}{\partial \varphi} A_\theta \sin\varphi - \frac{\partial}{\partial \theta} A_\varphi\right)\hat{\mathbf{r}} + \frac{1}{r}\left(\frac{1}{\sin\varphi}\frac{\partial A_r}{\partial \theta} - \frac{\partial}{\partial r} rA_\theta\right)\hat{\boldsymbol{\varphi}} + \frac{1}{r}\left(\frac{\partial}{\partial r} rA_\varphi - \frac{\partial A_r}{\partial \varphi}\right)\hat{\boldsymbol{\theta}}$$

$$\vec{\nabla} \times \vec{\mathbf{A}} = \frac{1}{r_c} \begin{vmatrix} \hat{\mathbf{r}}_c & r_c\hat{\boldsymbol{\theta}} & \hat{\mathbf{k}} \\ \frac{\partial}{\partial r_c} & \frac{\partial}{\partial \theta} & \frac{\partial}{\partial z} \\ A_{r_c} & r_c A_\theta & A_z \end{vmatrix} = \begin{vmatrix} \frac{\hat{\mathbf{r}}_c}{r_c} & \hat{\boldsymbol{\theta}} & \frac{\hat{\mathbf{k}}}{r_c} \\ \frac{\partial}{\partial r_c} & \frac{\partial}{\partial \theta} & \frac{\partial}{\partial z} \\ A_{r_c} & r_c A_\theta & A_z \end{vmatrix}$$

$$\vec{\nabla} \times \vec{\mathbf{A}} = \left(\frac{1}{r_c}\frac{\partial A_z}{\partial \theta} - \frac{\partial}{\partial z} A_\theta\right)\hat{\mathbf{r}}_c + \left(\frac{\partial A_{r_c}}{\partial z} - \frac{\partial A_z}{\partial r_c}\right)\hat{\boldsymbol{\theta}} + \frac{1}{r_c}\left(\frac{\partial}{\partial r_c} r_c A_\theta - \frac{\partial A_{r_c}}{\partial \theta}\right)\hat{\mathbf{k}}$$

Note: Recall that φ is the polar angle and θ is the azimuthal angle in common math notation. For common physics notation, swap φ and θ in spherical coordinates.

Note: The product rule, $\frac{d}{dx} pq = p\frac{dq}{dx} + q\frac{dp}{dx}$, is involved in $\frac{\partial}{\partial \varphi} A_\theta \sin\varphi$, for example.

The general form of the curl is $\vec{\nabla} \times \vec{\mathbf{A}} = \frac{1}{h_1 h_2 h_3} \begin{vmatrix} h_1 \hat{\mathbf{e}}_1 & h_2 \hat{\mathbf{e}}_2 & h_3 \hat{\mathbf{e}}_3 \\ \frac{\partial}{\partial u_1} & \frac{\partial}{\partial u_2} & \frac{\partial}{\partial u_3} \\ h_1 A_1 & h_2 A_2 & h_3 A_3 \end{vmatrix}$, where the symbols are defined according to Chapters 10-11.

Interpretation of the curl: The significance of the curl, $\vec{\nabla} \times \vec{\mathbf{A}}$, is that it provides a measure of the net circulation of field lines at a point. An example of circulating field lines occurs in magnetism, where a long straight current-carrying conductor creates magnetic field lines that circulate around the wire. If $\vec{\nabla} \times \vec{\mathbf{A}} = 0$, then $\vec{\mathbf{A}}$ is **irrotational**.

The curl of the gradient of a scalar function is zero, $\vec{\nabla} \times (\vec{\nabla} f) = 0$, and the divergence of the curl of a vector function is zero, $\vec{\nabla} \cdot (\vec{\nabla} \times \vec{\mathbf{A}}) = 0$, provided that the second-order partial derivatives are continuous (so that f satisfies Clairaut's theorem, which means that $\frac{\partial^2 f}{\partial x \partial y} = \frac{\partial^2 f}{\partial y \partial x}, \frac{\partial^2 f}{\partial x \partial z} = \frac{\partial^2 f}{\partial z \partial x}$, and $\frac{\partial^2 f}{\partial x \partial z} = \frac{\partial^2 f}{\partial z \partial x}$).

Example. Find the curl of $\vec{\mathbf{A}} = x^2 y \hat{\mathbf{i}} - x y^2 \hat{\mathbf{j}} + xyz \hat{\mathbf{k}}$.
Use the formula for the curl in Cartesian coordinates.

$$\vec{\nabla} \times \vec{\mathbf{A}} = \left(\frac{\partial A_z}{\partial y} - \frac{\partial A_y}{\partial z} \right) \hat{\mathbf{i}} + \left(\frac{\partial A_x}{\partial z} - \frac{\partial A_z}{\partial x} \right) \hat{\mathbf{j}} + \left(\frac{\partial A_y}{\partial x} - \frac{\partial A_x}{\partial y} \right) \hat{\mathbf{k}}$$

$$\vec{\nabla} \times \vec{\mathbf{A}} = \left[\frac{\partial}{\partial y} xyz - \frac{\partial}{\partial z} (-xy^2) \right] \hat{\mathbf{i}} + \left(\frac{\partial}{\partial z} x^2 y - \frac{\partial}{\partial x} xyz \right) \hat{\mathbf{j}} + \left[\frac{\partial}{\partial x} (-xy^2) - \frac{\partial}{\partial y} x^2 y \right] \hat{\mathbf{k}}$$

$$\vec{\nabla} \times \vec{\mathbf{A}} = (xz + 0)\hat{\mathbf{i}} + (0 - yz)\hat{\mathbf{j}} + (-y^2 - x^2)\hat{\mathbf{k}} = \boxed{xz\hat{\mathbf{i}} - yz\hat{\mathbf{j}} - (x^2 + y^2)\hat{\mathbf{k}}}$$

Example. Find the curl of $\vec{\mathbf{B}} = r^2 \cos\theta \, \hat{\boldsymbol{\varphi}}$.
Use the formula for the curl in spherical coordinates.

$$\vec{\nabla} \times \vec{\mathbf{B}} = \frac{1}{r \sin\varphi} \left(\frac{\partial}{\partial \varphi} B_\theta \sin\varphi - \frac{\partial}{\partial \theta} B_\varphi \right) \hat{\mathbf{r}} + \frac{1}{r} \left(\frac{1}{\sin\varphi} \frac{\partial B_r}{\partial \theta} - \frac{\partial}{\partial r} r B_\theta \right) \hat{\boldsymbol{\varphi}} + \frac{1}{r} \left(\frac{\partial}{\partial r} r B_\varphi - \frac{\partial B_r}{\partial \varphi} \right) \hat{\boldsymbol{\theta}}$$

$$\vec{\nabla} \times \vec{\mathbf{B}} = \frac{1}{r \sin\varphi} \left[\frac{\partial}{\partial \varphi} (0) \sin\varphi - \frac{\partial}{\partial \theta} r^2 \cos\theta \right] \hat{\mathbf{r}} + \frac{1}{r} \left[\frac{1}{\sin\varphi} \frac{\partial}{\partial \theta} (0) - \frac{\partial}{\partial r} r(0) \right] \hat{\boldsymbol{\varphi}} + \frac{1}{r} \left[\frac{\partial}{\partial r} r r^2 \cos\theta - \frac{\partial}{\partial \varphi} (0) \right] \hat{\boldsymbol{\theta}}$$

$$\vec{\nabla} \times \vec{\mathbf{B}} = \frac{1}{r \sin\varphi} \left(-\frac{\partial}{\partial \theta} r^2 \cos\theta \right) \hat{\mathbf{r}} + \frac{1}{r} \left(\frac{\partial}{\partial r} r^3 \cos\theta \right) \hat{\boldsymbol{\theta}} = \frac{1}{r \sin\varphi} (r^2 \sin\theta) \hat{\mathbf{r}} + \frac{1}{r} (3r^2 \cos\theta) \hat{\boldsymbol{\theta}}$$

$$\vec{\nabla} \times \vec{\mathbf{B}} = \boxed{\frac{r \sin\theta}{\sin\varphi} \hat{\mathbf{r}} + 3r \hat{\boldsymbol{\theta}} \cos\theta}$$

Chapter 11 Exercises – Part A

Directions: Find the curl of each vector function.

Note: In this book, in spherical coordinates, θ is **azimuthal** and φ is **polar** (or zenith).

❶ $\vec{\mathrm{A}} = yz\hat{\mathbf{i}} + xz\hat{\mathbf{j}} + xy\hat{\mathbf{k}}$

❷ $\vec{\mathrm{B}} = x^3y^2\hat{\mathbf{i}} - x^2y^3\hat{\mathbf{j}}$

❸ $\vec{\mathrm{C}} = (y^2 - z^2)\hat{\mathbf{i}} + (z^2 - x^2)\hat{\mathbf{j}} + (x^2 - y^2)\hat{\mathbf{k}}$

❹ $\vec{\mathrm{D}} = r \sin\theta \sin\varphi\, \hat{\boldsymbol{\theta}}$

❖ Check your answers at the back of the book.

Chapter 11 Exercises – Part B

Directions: Find the curl of each vector function.

❺ $\vec{\mathrm{A}} = xy^2\hat{\mathbf{i}} + yz^2\hat{\mathbf{j}} + zx^2\hat{\mathbf{k}}$

❻ $\vec{\mathrm{B}} = x^3y^2z^2\hat{\mathbf{i}} + x^2y^3z^2\hat{\mathbf{j}} + x^2y^2z^3\hat{\mathbf{k}}$

❼ $\vec{\mathrm{C}} = r_c\hat{\mathbf{r}}_c \cos\theta + r_c\hat{\boldsymbol{\theta}} \sin\theta$

❽ $\vec{\mathrm{D}} = r\hat{\mathbf{r}}$

❖ Check your answers at the back of the book.

12 Normal and Tangent Vectors

Orthogonal vectors are perpendicular to one another. The angle between orthogonal vectors is 90°. A **normal** vector is orthogonal to a plane. The symbol $\vec{\mathbf{n}}$ represents a normal vector, while the symbol $\hat{\mathbf{n}}$ represents a **unit normal** (which is a unit vector in the direction of $\vec{\mathbf{n}}$). A **tangent** vector is tangent to a curve or surface at a particular point. The symbol $\vec{\mathbf{T}}$ represents a tangent vector, while the symbol $\hat{\mathbf{T}}$ represents a **unit tangent** (which is a unit vector in the direction of $\vec{\mathbf{T}}$). The unit normal and unit tangent are related to the corresponding vectors by $\hat{\mathbf{n}} = \frac{\vec{\mathbf{n}}}{\|\vec{\mathbf{n}}\|}$ and $\hat{\mathbf{T}} = \frac{\vec{\mathbf{T}}}{\|\vec{\mathbf{T}}\|}$ (Chapter 4).

The scalar product and vector product (Chapter 5) relate to normal vectors as follows:

- Since $\vec{\mathbf{A}} \cdot \vec{\mathbf{B}} = \|\vec{\mathbf{A}}\|\|\vec{\mathbf{B}}\| \cos\theta$, if two vectors are orthogonal, their scalar product is zero: $\vec{\mathbf{A}} \cdot \vec{\mathbf{B}} = 0$.
- The vector product $\vec{\mathbf{A}} \times \vec{\mathbf{B}}$ is orthogonal to both $\vec{\mathbf{A}}$ and $\vec{\mathbf{B}}$, (but $\vec{\mathbf{A}}$ and $\vec{\mathbf{B}}$ are not necessarily orthogonal). Given two vectors, one way to find a third vector that is orthogonal to both vectors is to find the vector product.

Two **lines** lying in the xy plane are orthogonal if their slopes are related by $m_1 m_2 = -1$. For example, $y = -\frac{x}{2} + 5$ is orthogonal to $y = 2x + 3$ because $\left(-\frac{1}{2}\right)(2) = -1$. In 3D space, the symmetric equations $\frac{x - x_0}{a} = \frac{y - y_0}{b} = \frac{z - z_0}{c}$ represent a line along the vector $\langle a, b, c\rangle$, where a, b, and c are the **direction numbers** of the line. Two lines along vectors $\langle a, b, c\rangle$ and $\langle d, e, f\rangle$ are orthogonal if $\langle a, b, c\rangle \cdot \langle d, e, f\rangle = 0$.

The vector $\langle a, b, c\rangle$ is normal to the **plane** with linear equation $ax + by + cz + d = 0$. If $\vec{\mathbf{r}}$ and $\vec{\mathbf{r}}_0$ represent two position vectors lying in the plane, then $\vec{\mathbf{n}} \cdot (\vec{\mathbf{r}} - \vec{\mathbf{r}}_0) = 0$, where $\vec{\mathbf{n}} = \langle a, b, c\rangle$. This may also be expressed as $\vec{\mathbf{n}} \cdot \vec{\mathbf{r}} = \vec{\mathbf{n}} \cdot \vec{\mathbf{r}}_0$. If $\langle d, e, f\rangle$ and $\langle p, q, r\rangle$ lie in the plane, then $\vec{\mathbf{n}} = \langle d, e, f\rangle \times \langle p, q, r\rangle$ is orthogonal to the plane. The angle between two planes equals the (acute) angle between their normal vectors. Specifically, $|\vec{\mathbf{n}}_1 \cdot \vec{\mathbf{n}}_2| = \|\vec{\mathbf{n}}_1\|\|\vec{\mathbf{n}}_2\| \cos\theta$, where θ is the angle between the planes. If the normal vectors for two planes are parallel, meaning that $\theta = 0°$, then the planes are parallel.

If two **planes intersect**, the vector product of their normal vectors, $\vec{\mathbf{n}}_1 \times \vec{\mathbf{n}}_2$, is a vector parallel to the line of intersection. The **distance from a point to a plane** is:

$$\frac{|ax_0 + by_0 + cz_0 + d|}{\sqrt{a^2 + b^2 + c^2}}$$

where (x_0, y_0, z_0) are the coordinates of the point and $ax + by + cz + d = 0$ is the equation for the plane. The **distance between two parallel planes** equals the distance from one plane to any point in the other plane.

If $\vec{\mathbf{r}}(t)$ is a **vector function** of the parameter t, its derivative $\frac{d}{dt}\vec{\mathbf{r}}(t)$ is tangent to the curve traced out by $\vec{\mathbf{r}}(t)$. Note that $\frac{d}{dt}\vec{\mathbf{r}}(t)$ is not tangent to the vector $\vec{\mathbf{r}}$ at time t, but is tangent to the curve that is formed by $\vec{\mathbf{r}}$'s tip as t increases. The unit tangent is $\hat{\mathbf{T}} = \frac{\frac{d}{dt}\vec{\mathbf{r}}(t)}{\left\|\frac{d}{dt}\vec{\mathbf{r}}(t)\right\|}$. The curvature of the curve $\vec{\mathbf{r}}(t)$ is $\kappa = \left\|\frac{d\hat{\mathbf{T}}}{ds}\right\|$. Since $\frac{ds}{dt} = \left\|\frac{d}{dt}\vec{\mathbf{r}}(t)\right\|$, the curvature may be expressed as $\kappa = \frac{\left\|\frac{d\hat{\mathbf{T}}}{dt}\right\|}{\left\|\frac{ds}{st}\right\|} = \frac{\left\|\frac{d\hat{\mathbf{T}}}{dt}\right\|}{\left\|\frac{d\vec{\mathbf{r}}}{dt}\right\|}$. (For the case where $\vec{\mathbf{r}}$ represents the position vector and the parameter t is time, the equation $\frac{ds}{dt} = \left\|\frac{d}{dt}\vec{\mathbf{r}}(t)\right\|$ states that the speed of an object equals the magnitude of its velocity.) The curvature may also be expressed as $\kappa = \frac{\left\|\frac{d\vec{\mathbf{r}}}{dt}\times\frac{d^2\vec{\mathbf{r}}}{dt^2}\right\|}{\left\|\frac{d\vec{\mathbf{r}}}{dt}\right\|^3}$. For example, if an object travels in a counterclockwise circle in the xy plane centered at the origin with constant speed (this is called uniform circular motion) starting on the $+x$-axis at $t = 0$, the position of the object as a function of time is $\vec{\mathbf{r}}(t) = R_0\hat{\mathbf{i}}\cos(\omega t) + R_0\hat{\mathbf{j}}\sin(\omega t)$, where R_0 is the radius and ω is the angular speed in radians per second. The velocity is $\vec{\mathbf{v}}(t) = \frac{d}{dt}\vec{\mathbf{r}}(t) = -R_0\omega\hat{\mathbf{i}}\sin(\omega t) + R_0\omega\hat{\mathbf{j}}\cos(\omega t)$, the speed is $\|\vec{\mathbf{v}}(t)\| = \left\|\frac{d}{dt}\vec{\mathbf{r}}(t)\right\| = \sqrt{[-R_0\omega\sin(\omega t)]^2 + [R_0\omega\cos(\omega t)]^2} = R_0\omega$ (using the identity $\sin^2\theta + \cos^2\theta = 1$), the acceleration is $\vec{\mathbf{a}}(t) = \frac{d}{dt}\vec{\mathbf{v}}(t) = -R_0\omega^2\hat{\mathbf{i}}\cos(\omega t) - R_0\omega^2\hat{\mathbf{j}}\sin(\omega t)$, the magnitude of the acceleration is $\|\vec{\mathbf{a}}(t)\| = R_0\omega^2 = \frac{\|\vec{\mathbf{v}}(t)\|^2}{R_0}$ (this is called centripetal acceleration, and applies when velocity changes direction), a unit tangent is $\hat{\mathbf{T}} = \frac{\frac{d}{dt}\vec{\mathbf{r}}(t)}{\left\|\frac{d}{dt}\vec{\mathbf{r}}(t)\right\|} = \frac{\vec{\mathbf{v}}(t)}{\|\vec{\mathbf{v}}(t)\|} = \frac{-R_0\omega\hat{\mathbf{i}}\sin(\omega t)+R_0\omega\hat{\mathbf{j}}\cos(\omega t)}{R_0\omega} = -\hat{\mathbf{i}}\sin(\omega t) + \hat{\mathbf{j}}\cos(\omega t)$, and the curvature is: $\kappa = \frac{\left\|\frac{d\hat{T}}{dt}\right\|}{\left\|\frac{d\vec{r}}{dt}\right\|} = \frac{\left\|\frac{d}{dt}[-\hat{\imath}\sin(\omega t)+\hat{\jmath}\cos(\omega t)]\right\|}{\|\vec{v}(t)\|} = \frac{\|-\omega\hat{\imath}\cos(\omega t)-\omega\hat{\jmath}\sin(\omega t)\|}{R_0\omega} = \frac{\omega}{R_0\omega} = \frac{1}{R_0}$.

The greater the curvature at a particular point on a curve, the more rapidly the curve changes direction at that point. For a **circle**, the curvature equals the reciprocal of the radius: $\kappa = \frac{1}{R_0}$. A circle with a smaller radius has a larger value of curvature, while a circle with a larger radius has a smaller value of curvature. For a straight line, the curvature is exactly zero.

For the special case where the **magnitude** of the vector function $\vec{r}(t)$ happens to be **constant**, the scalar product $\vec{r} \cdot \frac{d\vec{r}}{dt}$ is zero, showing that the vector $\vec{r}$ and its derivative $\frac{d\vec{r}}{dt}$ are orthogonal if $\vec{r}(t)$ is constant. Here, $\vec{r}(t)$ is a vector function (not necessarily the position vector). As mentioned previously, $\frac{d\vec{r}}{dt}$ is tangent to the path that the tip of $\vec{r}$ sweeps out as the parameter t increases (but $\frac{d\vec{r}}{dt}$ is not necessarily tangent to the vector $\vec{r}$ itself). In the special case that $\|\vec{r}(t)\|$ happens to be constant, $\frac{d\vec{r}}{dt}$ is orthogonal to the vector $\vec{r}$. When the vector function is a unit vector, its magnitude equals one (and is therefore constant) for all values of t, which means that the derivative of a unit vector with respect to t is orthogonal to the unit vector. For example, the unit tangent $\hat{T}$ is always orthogonal to its derivative, $\frac{d\hat{T}}{dt}$, meaning that $\hat{T} \cdot \frac{d\hat{T}}{dt} = 0$. Beware that although $\hat{T}$ is a unit vector, $\frac{d\hat{T}}{dt}$ is not necessarily a unit vector. Since $\hat{T}$ and $\frac{d\hat{T}}{dt}$ are orthogonal and since $\hat{T}$ is tangent to the path swept out by $\vec{r}$'s tip as t increases, it follows that $\vec{N} = \frac{d\hat{T}}{dt}$ is a normal vector (it is called the **principal normal vector**). The principal normal unit vector is $\hat{N} = \frac{\vec{N}}{\|\vec{N}\|} = \frac{d\hat{T}/dt}{\|d\hat{T}/dt\|}$. Since $\hat{T} \times \hat{N}$ is orthogonal to both $\hat{T}$ and $\hat{N}$, the vector $\hat{B} = \hat{T} \times \hat{N}$ (called the **binormal unit vector**) is orthogonal to both $\hat{T}$ and $\hat{N}$. The unit vectors $\hat{N}$ and $\hat{B}$ are both normal unit vectors. (There are actually an infinite number of unit vectors perpendicular to the path swept out by the tip of $\vec{r}$, since an infinite number of vectors are perpendicular to a curve at any point on the curve. The normal vectors $\hat{N}$ and $\hat{B}$ are two special normal unit vectors that are easy to find.) The vectors $\hat{N}$ and

$\hat{\mathbf{B}}$ define the **normal plane** for a point along the curve swept out by the tip of $\vec{\mathbf{r}}$, while the vectors $\hat{\mathbf{T}}$ and $\hat{\mathbf{N}}$ define the **osculating plane**. The **osculating circle** lies within the osculating plane, is tangent to the curve, lies on the concave side of the curve (as indicated by the principal normal unit vector $\hat{\mathbf{N}}$), and has radius $\frac{1}{\kappa}$. For a **plane curve** $y = y(x)$, the curvature is $\kappa = \frac{\left|\frac{d^2y}{dx^2}\right|}{\left[1+\left(\frac{dy}{dx}\right)^2\right]^{3/2}}$ and the osculating plane is the xy plane.

For the case where $\vec{\mathbf{r}}(t)$ is the **position vector** and t represents time, the first derivative is the velocity vector, $\vec{\mathbf{v}} = \frac{d\vec{\mathbf{r}}}{dt}$, and the second derivative is the acceleration vector, $\vec{\mathbf{a}} = \frac{d\vec{\mathbf{v}}}{dt} = \frac{d^2\vec{\mathbf{r}}}{dt^2}$ (Chapter 4). In this case, the unit tangent is $\hat{\mathbf{T}} = \frac{\vec{\mathbf{v}}}{\|\vec{\mathbf{v}}\|} = \frac{\vec{\mathbf{v}}}{v}$ (where $v = \|\vec{\mathbf{v}}\|$ is the speed), such that the velocity may be written as $\vec{\mathbf{v}} = v\hat{\mathbf{T}}$. The acceleration is $\vec{\mathbf{a}} = \frac{d\vec{\mathbf{v}}}{dt} = \frac{d}{dt}v\hat{\mathbf{T}} = \hat{\mathbf{T}}\frac{dv}{dt} + v\frac{d\hat{\mathbf{T}}}{dt}$ (using the product rule). The curvature is $\kappa = \frac{\left\|\frac{d\hat{\mathbf{T}}}{dt}\right\|}{\left\|\frac{d\vec{\mathbf{r}}}{dt}\right\|} = \frac{\left\|\frac{d\hat{\mathbf{T}}}{dt}\right\|}{v}$, such that $\left\|\frac{d\hat{\mathbf{T}}}{dt}\right\| = \kappa v$. The principal normal unit vector is $\hat{\mathbf{N}} = \frac{\vec{\mathbf{N}}}{\|\vec{\mathbf{N}}\|} = \frac{\frac{d\hat{\mathbf{T}}}{dt}}{\left\|\frac{d\hat{\mathbf{T}}}{dt}\right\|}$, such that $\frac{d\hat{\mathbf{T}}}{dt} = \left\|\frac{d\hat{\mathbf{T}}}{dt}\right\|\hat{\mathbf{N}} = \kappa v\hat{\mathbf{N}}$. The acceleration can then be expressed as $\vec{\mathbf{a}} = \hat{\mathbf{T}}\frac{dv}{dt} + \kappa v^2\hat{\mathbf{N}}$, which shows that the acceleration has a tangential component $a_T = \frac{dv}{dt}$ (which describes how the speed changes) and a centripetal component $a_N = \kappa v^2$ (which describes how the direction of the velocity changes). The scalar product between the velocity and acceleration vectors is $\vec{\mathbf{v}} \cdot \vec{\mathbf{a}} = v\frac{dv}{dt}$, such that the **tangential** component of acceleration is $a_T = \frac{dv}{dt} = \frac{\vec{\mathbf{v}}\cdot\vec{\mathbf{a}}}{v} = \frac{\frac{d\vec{\mathbf{r}}}{dt}\cdot\frac{d^2\vec{\mathbf{r}}}{dt^2}}{\left\|\frac{d\vec{\mathbf{r}}}{dt}\right\|}$. Since $\kappa = \frac{\left\|\frac{d\vec{\mathbf{r}}}{dt}\times\frac{d^2\vec{\mathbf{r}}}{dt^2}\right\|}{\left\|\frac{d\vec{\mathbf{r}}}{dt}\right\|^3}$, the **normal** (or **centripetal**) component of acceleration is $a_N = \kappa v^2 = \frac{\left\|\frac{d\vec{\mathbf{r}}}{dt}\times\frac{d^2\vec{\mathbf{r}}}{dt^2}\right\|}{\left\|\frac{d\vec{\mathbf{r}}}{dt}\right\|^3}\left\|\frac{d\vec{\mathbf{r}}}{dt}\right\|^2 = \frac{\left\|\frac{d\vec{\mathbf{r}}}{dt}\times\frac{d^2\vec{\mathbf{r}}}{dt^2}\right\|}{\left\|\frac{d\vec{\mathbf{r}}}{dt}\right\|} = \frac{\|\vec{\mathbf{v}}\times\vec{\mathbf{a}}\|}{v}$. In these forms, a_T and a_N have similar forms; the distinction is that a_T involves a scalar product $\left(a_T = \frac{\vec{\mathbf{v}}\cdot\vec{\mathbf{a}}}{v}\right)$ whereas a_N (also called a_c) involves a vector product $\left(a_N = \frac{\|\vec{\mathbf{v}}\times\vec{\mathbf{a}}\|}{v} = \kappa v^2\text{, such that } \kappa = \frac{\|\vec{\mathbf{v}}\times\vec{\mathbf{a}}\|}{v^3}\right)$.

For the **level surface** $f(x,y,z) = k$, where k is a constant, the gradient vector $\vec{\nabla} f$ evaluated at a point (x_0, y_0, z_0) lying on the surface is perpendicular to the surface at (x_0, y_0, z_0), meaning that the gradient is orthogonal to the tangent plane at (x_0, y_0, z_0). The gradient is normal to the level surface. An equation for the **tangent plane** at the point (x_0, y_0, z_0) lying on the surface is

$$(x - x_0)\left.\frac{\partial f}{\partial x}\right|_{x_0,y_0,z_0} + (y - y_0)\left.\frac{\partial f}{\partial y}\right|_{x_0,y_0,z_0} + (z - z_0)\left.\frac{\partial f}{\partial z}\right|_{x_0,y_0,z_0} = 0$$

where $\left.\frac{\partial f}{\partial x}\right|_{x_0,y_0,z_0}$ means to evaluate the partial derivative at the point (x_0, y_0, z_0). An equation for the **normal line** which is perpendicular to the tangent plane at (x_0, y_0, z_0) is given by the following symmetric equations:

$$\frac{x - x_0}{\left.\frac{\partial f}{\partial x}\right|_{x_0,y_0,z_0}} = \frac{y - y_0}{\left.\frac{\partial f}{\partial y}\right|_{x_0,y_0,z_0}} = \frac{z - z_0}{\left.\frac{\partial f}{\partial z}\right|_{x_0,y_0,z_0}}$$

Example. Find a unit vector that is orthogonal to both $\vec{\mathbf{A}} = \hat{\mathbf{i}} - 2\hat{\mathbf{j}} + 2\hat{\mathbf{k}}$ and $\vec{\mathbf{B}} = 3\hat{\mathbf{i}} - 6\hat{\mathbf{k}}$.
The vector product (Chapter 5) is orthogonal to both vectors.

$$\vec{\mathbf{n}} = \vec{\mathbf{A}} \times \vec{\mathbf{B}} = (A_y B_z - A_z B_y)\hat{\mathbf{i}} + (A_z B_x - A_x B_z)\hat{\mathbf{j}} + (A_x B_y - A_y B_x)\hat{\mathbf{k}}$$

$$\vec{\mathbf{n}} = [(-2)(-6) - (2)(0)]\hat{\mathbf{i}} + [(2)(3) - (1)(-6)]\hat{\mathbf{j}} + [(1)(0) - (-2)(3)]\hat{\mathbf{k}}$$

$$\vec{\mathbf{n}} = (12 - 0)\hat{\mathbf{i}} + (6 + 6)\hat{\mathbf{j}} + (0 + 6)\hat{\mathbf{k}} = 12\hat{\mathbf{i}} + 12\hat{\mathbf{j}} + 6\hat{\mathbf{k}}$$

The magnitude of the vector product is:

$$\|\vec{\mathbf{n}}\| = \sqrt{12^2 + 12^2 + 6^2} = \sqrt{144 + 144 + 36} = \sqrt{324} = 18$$

A unit vector orthogonal to both $\vec{\mathbf{A}}$ and $\vec{\mathbf{B}}$ is:

$$\hat{\mathbf{n}} = \frac{\vec{\mathbf{n}}}{\|\vec{\mathbf{n}}\|} = \frac{12\hat{\mathbf{i}} + 12\hat{\mathbf{j}} + 6\hat{\mathbf{k}}}{18} = \boxed{\frac{2\hat{\mathbf{i}}}{3} + \frac{2\hat{\mathbf{j}}}{3} + \frac{\hat{\mathbf{k}}}{3}}$$

Example. Write an equation for the plane that is orthogonal to the vector $\langle 2,5,8 \rangle$ and which passes through the point $(1,3,5)$.
The plane $2x + 5y + 8z + d = 0$ is orthogonal to the vector $\langle 2,5,8 \rangle$. To solve for d, plug in the coordinates of the point: $2(1) + 5(3) + 8(5) + d = 2 + 15 + 40 + d = 57 + d = 0$ such that $d = -57$. The plane $\boxed{2x + 5y + 8z - 57 = 0}$ is orthogonal to the vector $\langle 2,5,8 \rangle$ and passes through the point $(1,3,5)$.

Example. Find the angle between the planes $2x + y + z\sqrt{3} = 4$ and $2x - y\sqrt{3} + z = 9$. The normal vectors for these planes are $\vec{\mathbf{n}}_1 = \langle 2,1,\sqrt{3}\rangle$ and $\vec{\mathbf{n}}_2 = \langle 2,-\sqrt{3},1\rangle$. The scalar product is $\vec{\mathbf{n}}_1 \cdot \vec{\mathbf{n}}_2 = (2)(2) + (1)(-\sqrt{3}) + (\sqrt{3})(1) = 4$. The magnitudes of the vectors are $\sqrt{2^2 + 1^2 + (\sqrt{3})^2} = \sqrt{8}$ and $\sqrt{2^2 + (-\sqrt{3})^2 + 1^2} = \sqrt{8}$. The equation $|\vec{\mathbf{n}}_1 \cdot \vec{\mathbf{n}}_2| = \|\vec{\mathbf{n}}_1\|\|\vec{\mathbf{n}}_2\| \cos\theta$ is $4 = \sqrt{8}\sqrt{8}\cos\theta$, for which $\theta = \cos^{-1}\left(\frac{4}{8}\right) = \cos^{-1}\left(\frac{1}{2}\right) = \boxed{\frac{\pi}{3}} = \boxed{60°}$.

Example. Find the distance from the point $(7,0,0)$ to the plane $x + 2y + 2z = 1$. Write the equation as $x + 2y + 2z - 1 = 0$ to see that $a = 1$, $b = c = 2$, and $d = -1$.

$$\frac{|ax_0 + by_0 + cz_0 + d|}{\sqrt{a^2 + b^2 + c^2}} = \frac{|1(7) + 2(0) + 2(0) + (-1)|}{\sqrt{1^2 + 2^2 + 2^2}} = \frac{|7 - 1|}{\sqrt{1 + 4 + 4}} = \frac{6}{\sqrt{9}} = \frac{6}{3} = \boxed{2}$$

Example. Find the equation of the tangent plane and the symmetric equations for the normal line at the point $(1,1,\sqrt{2})$ on the sphere $x^2 + y^2 + z^2 = 4$.

The level surface is $f(x,y,z) = 4$. The partial derivatives are $\frac{\partial f}{\partial x} = \frac{\partial}{\partial x}(x^2 + y^2 + z^2) = 2x$, $\frac{\partial f}{\partial y} = \frac{\partial}{\partial y}(x^2 + y^2 + z^2) = 2y$, and $\frac{\partial f}{\partial z} = \frac{\partial}{\partial z}(x^2 + y^2 + z^2) = 2z$. The equation of the tangent plane at $(1,1,\sqrt{2})$ is:

$$(x - x_0)\left.\frac{\partial f}{\partial x}\right|_{x_0,y_0,z_0} + (y - y_0)\left.\frac{\partial f}{\partial y}\right|_{x_0,y_0,z_0} + (z - z_0)\left.\frac{\partial f}{\partial z}\right|_{x_0,y_0,z_0} = 0$$

$$(x - 1)2(1) + (y - 1)2(1) + (z - \sqrt{2})2(\sqrt{2}) = 0$$

$$2x - 2 + 2y - 2 + 2z\sqrt{2} - 4 = 0$$

$$\boxed{2x + 2y + 2z\sqrt{2} = 8} \quad \text{which reduces to} \quad \boxed{x + y + z\sqrt{2} = 4}$$

The symmetric equations for the normal line at $(1,1,\sqrt{2})$ are:

$$\frac{x - x_0}{\left.\frac{\partial f}{\partial x}\right|_{x_0,y_0,z_0}} = \frac{y - y_0}{\left.\frac{\partial f}{\partial y}\right|_{x_0,y_0,z_0}} = \frac{z - z_0}{\left.\frac{\partial f}{\partial z}\right|_{x_0,y_0,z_0}}$$

$$\frac{x - 1}{2(1)} = \frac{y - 1}{2(1)} = \frac{z - \sqrt{2}}{2(\sqrt{2})}$$

$$\boxed{\frac{x - 1}{2} = \frac{y - 1}{2} = \frac{z - \sqrt{2}}{2\sqrt{2}}} \quad \text{which is equivalent to} \quad \boxed{x - 1 = y - 1 = \frac{z - \sqrt{2}}{\sqrt{2}}}$$

Example. The position vector for an object is $\vec{\mathbf{r}} = \frac{t^3}{3}\hat{\mathbf{i}} + t^2\hat{\mathbf{j}} + 2t\hat{\mathbf{k}}$.

(A) What is the velocity?

$$\vec{\mathbf{v}} = \frac{d\vec{\mathbf{r}}}{dt} = \frac{d}{dt}\left(\frac{t^3}{3}\hat{\mathbf{i}} + t^2\hat{\mathbf{j}} + 2t\hat{\mathbf{k}}\right) = \boxed{t^2\hat{\mathbf{i}} + 2t\hat{\mathbf{j}} + 2\hat{\mathbf{k}}}$$

(B) What is the acceleration?

$$\vec{\mathbf{a}} = \frac{d\vec{\mathbf{v}}}{dt} = \frac{d}{dt}\left(t^2\hat{\mathbf{i}} + 2t\hat{\mathbf{j}} + 2\hat{\mathbf{k}}\right) = 2t\hat{\mathbf{i}} + 2\hat{\mathbf{j}} + 0 = \boxed{2t\hat{\mathbf{i}} + 2\hat{\mathbf{j}}}$$

(C) Find the unit tangent vector and principal normal unit vector at $t = 2$.

$$v = \|\vec{\mathbf{v}}\| = \sqrt{(t^2)^2 + (2t)^2 + 2^2} = \sqrt{t^4 + 4t^2 + 4} = \sqrt{(t^2+2)^2} = t^2 + 2$$

$$\hat{\mathbf{T}} = \frac{\vec{\mathbf{v}}}{\|\vec{\mathbf{v}}\|} = \frac{t^2\hat{\mathbf{i}} + 2t\hat{\mathbf{j}} + 2\hat{\mathbf{k}}}{t^2+2} \quad , \quad \hat{\mathbf{T}}(2) = \frac{2^2\hat{\mathbf{i}} + 2(2)\hat{\mathbf{j}} + 2\hat{\mathbf{k}}}{(2)^2+2} = \frac{4\hat{\mathbf{i}} + 4\hat{\mathbf{j}} + 2\hat{\mathbf{k}}}{6} = \boxed{\frac{2\hat{\mathbf{i}} + 2\hat{\mathbf{j}} + \hat{\mathbf{k}}}{3}}$$

$$\frac{d\hat{\mathbf{T}}}{dt} = \frac{d}{dt}\frac{t^2\hat{\mathbf{i}} + 2t\hat{\mathbf{j}} + 2\hat{\mathbf{k}}}{t^2+2} = \frac{(t^2+2)\frac{d}{dt}\left(t^2\hat{\mathbf{i}} + 2t\hat{\mathbf{j}} + 2\hat{\mathbf{k}}\right) - \left(t^2\hat{\mathbf{i}} + 2t\hat{\mathbf{j}} + 2\hat{\mathbf{k}}\right)\frac{d}{dt}(t^2+2)}{(t^2+2)^2}$$

$$\frac{d\hat{\mathbf{T}}}{dt} = \frac{(t^2+2)\left(2t\hat{\mathbf{i}} + 2\hat{\mathbf{j}}\right) - \left(t^2\hat{\mathbf{i}} + 2t\hat{\mathbf{j}} + 2\hat{\mathbf{k}}\right)(2t)}{(t^2+2)^2} = \frac{2t^3\hat{\mathbf{i}} + 2t^2\hat{\mathbf{j}} + 4t\hat{\mathbf{i}} + 4\hat{\mathbf{j}} - 2t^3\hat{\mathbf{i}} - 4t^2\hat{\mathbf{j}} - 4t\hat{\mathbf{k}}}{(t^2+2)^2}$$

$$\frac{d\hat{\mathbf{T}}}{dt} = \frac{4t\hat{\mathbf{i}} + (4-2t^2)\hat{\mathbf{j}} - 4t\hat{\mathbf{k}}}{(t^2+2)^2} \quad , \quad \left\|\frac{d\hat{\mathbf{T}}}{dt}\right\| = \frac{\sqrt{(4t)^2 + (4-2t^2)^2 + (-4t)^2}}{(t^2+2)^2}$$

$$\left\|\frac{d\hat{\mathbf{T}}}{dt}\right\| = \frac{\sqrt{16t^2 + 16 - 16t^2 + 4t^4 + 16t^2}}{(t^2+2)^2} = \frac{2\sqrt{t^4 + 4t^2 + 4}}{(t^2+2)^2} = \frac{2(t^2+2)}{(t^2+2)^2} = \frac{2}{t^2+2}$$

$$\hat{\mathbf{N}} = \frac{d\hat{\mathbf{T}}/dt}{\|d\hat{\mathbf{T}}/dt\|} = \frac{4t\hat{\mathbf{i}} + (4-2t^2)\hat{\mathbf{j}} - 4t\hat{\mathbf{k}}}{(t^2+2)^2} \div \frac{2}{t^2+2} = \frac{2t\hat{\mathbf{i}} + (2-t^2)\hat{\mathbf{j}} - 2t\hat{\mathbf{k}}}{t^2+2}$$

$$\hat{\mathbf{N}}(2) = \frac{2(2)\hat{\mathbf{i}} + (2-2^2)\hat{\mathbf{j}} - 2(2)\hat{\mathbf{k}}}{2^2+2} = \frac{4\hat{\mathbf{i}} - 2\hat{\mathbf{j}} - 4\hat{\mathbf{k}}}{6} = \boxed{\frac{2\hat{\mathbf{i}} - \hat{\mathbf{j}} - 2\hat{\mathbf{k}}}{3}}$$

(D) Find the curvature at $t = 2$.

$$\kappa = \frac{\left\|\frac{d\hat{\mathbf{T}}}{dt}\right\|}{\left\|\frac{d\vec{\mathbf{r}}}{dt}\right\|} = \frac{\|d\hat{\mathbf{T}}/dt\|}{v} = \frac{2}{t^2+2} \div (t^2+2) = \frac{2}{(t^2+2)^2} \quad , \quad \kappa(2) = \frac{2}{(2^2+2)^2} = \frac{2}{6^2} = \boxed{\frac{1}{18}}$$

Tip: If $\frac{d\hat{\mathbf{T}}}{dt}$ is particularly tedious, it may be simpler to apply the formula $\kappa = \frac{\|\vec{\mathbf{v}}\times\vec{\mathbf{a}}\|}{v^3}$. You can also use $\kappa = \frac{\|\vec{\mathbf{v}}\times\vec{\mathbf{a}}\|}{v^3}$ to check your answer for self-consistency.

Chapter 12 Exercises – Part A

Directions: Determine the indicated quantities.

❶ Find a unit vector that is orthogonal to both $\vec{\mathbf{A}} = 5\hat{\imath} + 2\hat{\jmath}$ and $\vec{\mathbf{B}} = 4\hat{\imath} - 3\hat{\mathbf{k}}$.

❷ Write an equation for the plane that is orthogonal to the vector $\langle 6,2,-4 \rangle$ and which passes through the point $(5,-7,3)$.

❸ Find a unit vector that is orthogonal to the plane that contains the points $(3,-1,2)$, $(6,4,-2)$, and $(0,8,4)$.

❹ Find the angle between the planes $x\sqrt{2} - z\sqrt{2} = \sqrt{3}$ and $y\sqrt{2} + z\sqrt{2} = \sqrt{5}$.

❺ Find the distance from the point $(5,9,10)$ to the plane $3x - 4y + 12z = 8$.

❖ Check your answers at the back of the book.

Chapter 12 Exercises – Part B

Directions: Determine the indicated quantities.

❻ Find the distance between planes $2x + y - 2z = -4$ and $6x + 3y - 6z = 9$, which are parallel.

❼ For the circular paraboloid $4z = 3x^2 + 3y^2$, find the equation of the tangent plane and the symmetric equations for the normal line at the point (2,2,6).

❽ Find the curvature of the parabola $y = x^2$ at the origin and at the point $(\sqrt{2}, 2)$.

❾ Find the curvature of $y = \cos x$ at the points $(0,1)$ and $\left(\frac{\pi}{2}, 0\right)$.

❖ Check your answers at the back of the book.

Chapter 12 Exercises – Part C

Directions: Determine the indicated quantities.

⑩ The position vector for an object is $\vec{\mathbf{r}} = 10t\hat{\mathbf{i}}\sqrt{3} + (10t - 5t^2)\hat{\mathbf{j}}$. Show that the path of the object is a parabola and derive equations for the velocity, acceleration, unit tangent vector, curvature, and the tangential and normal components of the acceleration. Also evaluate each of these quantities at $t = 2$.

⑪ The position vector for an object is $\vec{\mathbf{r}} = t^2\hat{\mathbf{r}}$, where $\frac{d\theta}{dt} = \omega$ is a constant and $\hat{\mathbf{r}}$ is the radial unit vector in 2D polar coordinates. Show that $\frac{d}{dt}\hat{\mathbf{r}} = \omega\widehat{\boldsymbol{\theta}}$ and $\frac{d}{dt}\widehat{\boldsymbol{\theta}} = -\omega\hat{\mathbf{r}}$. Derive equations for the velocity, acceleration, unit tangent vector, principal normal unit vector, curvature, and the tangential and normal components of the acceleration.

❖ Check your answers at the back of the book.

13 Line Integrals

If an object begins at (x_0, y_0, z_0) and ends at (x, y, z), the **arc length** s equals the total distance that the object travels, whereas the **net displacement** $\Delta\vec{\mathbf{r}}$ is a straight line from (x_0, y_0, z_0) to (x, y, z). The arc length is **path dependent** in that it depends on the path that the object takes, whereas the net displacement is **path-independent** because it is the same regardless of how the object travels from (x_0, y_0, z_0) to (x, y, z). The arc length and net displacement can be found from the following integrals:

$$s = \int_C ds \quad , \quad \Delta\vec{\mathbf{r}} = \int_i^f d\vec{\mathbf{s}}$$

The differential arc length ds is a **scalar**, whereas the differential displacement vector $d\vec{\mathbf{s}}$ is a **vector** (Chapter 4). The arc length integral is over the specific curve C (or path) that the object travels from (x_0, y_0, z_0) to (x, y, z), whereas the net displacement integral depends only on the initial values (x_0, y_0, z_0) and final values (x, y, z). The differential arc length is $ds = \sqrt{dx^2 + dy^2 + dz^2}$ in Cartesian coordinates, $ds = \sqrt{dr^2 + r^2 d\theta^2}$ in 2D polar coordinates, $ds = \sqrt{dr^2 + r^2 \sin^2\varphi\, d\theta^2 + r^2 d\varphi^2}$ in spherical coordinates, and $ds = \sqrt{dr^2 + r^2 d\theta^2 + dz^2}$ in cylindrical coordinates. These expressions simplify in some cases. For example, for a circular arc length, r is constant such that $ds = r d\theta$ in 2D polar coordinates. When the expression doesn't simplify to a single term, the trick is to **factor**. For example, $\sqrt{dx^2 + dy^2} = \sqrt{1 + \left(\frac{dy}{dx}\right)^2}\, dx$ for a curve in the xy plane. If the variables are each functions of a parameter t, factor out a dt. For example, in Cartesian coordinates $\sqrt{dx^2 + dy^2 + dz^2} = \sqrt{\left(\frac{dx}{dt}\right)^2 + \left(\frac{dy}{dt}\right)^2 + \left(\frac{dz}{dt}\right)^2}\, dt$.

The differential displacement vector is $d\vec{\mathbf{s}} = \hat{\mathbf{i}}\, dx + \hat{\mathbf{j}}\, dy + \hat{\mathbf{k}}\, dz$ in Cartesian coordinates. The net displacement integral gives the following result, regardless of the path taken.

$$\Delta\vec{\mathbf{r}} = \int_i^f d\vec{\mathbf{s}} = \hat{\mathbf{i}} \int_{x_0}^{x} dx + \hat{\mathbf{j}} \int_{y_0}^{y} dy + \hat{\mathbf{k}} \int_{z_0}^{z} dz = (x - x_0)\hat{\mathbf{i}} + (y - y_0)\hat{\mathbf{j}} + (z - z_0)\hat{\mathbf{k}}$$

The net displacement could alternatively be found via $\Delta\vec{\mathbf{r}} = \vec{\mathbf{r}} - \vec{\mathbf{r}}_0$, where $\vec{\mathbf{r}}$ is the position vector for the final position of the object and $\vec{\mathbf{r}}_0$ is the position vector for the initial position of the object (Chapter 4). The length of the net displacement is:

$$\|\Delta\vec{\mathbf{r}}\| = \sqrt{(x - x_0)^2 + (y - y_0)^2 + (z - z_0)^2}$$

An integral over a specific path is called a **line integral** (even though the path is often a curve). Line integrals often include a scalar or vector function in the integrand, like $\int_C f(x,y,z)ds$ or $\int_C \vec{\mathbf{A}}(x,y,z) \cdot d\vec{\mathbf{s}}$. For an integral of the form $\int_C \vec{\mathbf{A}}(x,y,z) \cdot d\vec{\mathbf{s}}$, use the scalar product (Chapter 5) to rewrite the integral in terms of components:

$$\int_C \vec{\mathbf{A}}(x,y,z) \cdot d\vec{\mathbf{s}} = \int_C A_x\, dx + \int_C A_y\, dy + \int_C A_z\, dz$$

If the path C is a closed path (meaning that the final position coincides with the initial position), then the integral is called a **closed integral**. The symbol $\oint ds$, which has a circle on the integration symbol, indicates a closed integral.

To determine whether or not a vector field $\vec{\mathbf{F}}(x,y,z)$ is **conservative** (throughout an open simply connected region), perform one of the following tests.

- $\frac{\partial F_x}{\partial y} = \frac{\partial F_y}{\partial x}$, $\frac{\partial F_x}{\partial z} = \frac{\partial F_z}{\partial x}$, and $\frac{\partial F_z}{\partial y} = \frac{\partial F_y}{\partial z}$ if $\vec{\mathbf{F}}$ is conservative. This is the simplest test when F_x, F_y, and F_z are known. If $\vec{\mathbf{F}}$ lies in the xy plane, just check if $\frac{\partial F_x}{\partial y} = \frac{\partial F_y}{\partial x}$.
- $\int_C \vec{\mathbf{F}}(x,y,z) \cdot d\vec{\mathbf{s}}$ is path-independent, meaning that it yields the same result for every possible path if $\vec{\mathbf{F}}$ is conservative. If this integral can be shown to give two different answers for two different paths, this proves that $\vec{\mathbf{F}}$ is nonconservative.
- $\oint_C \vec{\mathbf{F}}(x,y,z) \cdot d\vec{\mathbf{s}} = 0$ for every possible closed path if $\vec{\mathbf{F}}$ is conservative. If this integral can be shown to be nonzero for any possible closed path, this proves that $\vec{\mathbf{F}}$ is non-conservative.
- There exists a scalar function $f(x,y,z)$ such that $\vec{\mathbf{F}} = \vec{\nabla} f$ if $\vec{\mathbf{F}}$ is conservative. This follows from the first point such that $\frac{\partial^2 f}{\partial x \partial y} = \frac{\partial^2 f}{\partial y \partial x}$ (Clairaut's theorem).

One application of conservative fields is the work done by a force, $W = \int_C \vec{\mathbf{F}} \cdot d\vec{\mathbf{s}}$, which relates to conservation of energy. Another application of line integrals can be found in Maxwell's equations for electromagnetism (see Chapter 14).

Example. Find the arc length and the net displacement from the origin to (4,8) along the curve $y = x^{3/2}$. Also find the magnitude of the net displacement.

Perform the arc length integral. Factor out dx.

$$s = \int_C ds = \int_C \sqrt{dx^2 + dy^2} = \int_C \sqrt{dx^2\left[1 + \left(\frac{dy}{dx}\right)^2\right]} = \int_{x=0}^{4} \sqrt{1 + \left(\frac{dy}{dx}\right)^2}\, dx$$

Plug in the given equation, $y = x^{3/2}$.

$$s = \int_{x=0}^{4} \sqrt{1 + \left(\frac{d}{dx}x^{3/2}\right)^2}\, dx = \int_{x=0}^{4} \sqrt{1 + \left(\frac{3}{2}x^{1/2}\right)^2}\, dx = \int_{x=0}^{4} \sqrt{1 + \frac{9x}{4}}\, dx$$

Make the substitution $u = \frac{9x}{4} + 1$ such that $du = \frac{9}{4}dx$ and $\frac{4}{9}du = dx$. The new limits are from $u(0) = \frac{9(0)}{4} + 1 = 0 + 1 = 1$ to $u(4) = \frac{9(4)}{4} + 1 = 9 + 1 = 10$.

$$s = \frac{4}{9}\int_{u=1}^{10} \sqrt{u}\, du = \frac{4}{9}\int_{u=1}^{10} u^{1/2}\, du = \frac{4}{9}\left[\frac{2u^{3/2}}{3}\right]_{u=1}^{10} = \left(\frac{4}{9}\right)\left(\frac{2}{3}\right)\left(10^{3/2} - 1^{3/2}\right)$$

$$s = \frac{8}{27}\left(\sqrt{1000} - 1\right) = \boxed{\frac{8}{27}\left(10\sqrt{10} - 1\right)} \approx 9.073$$

The net displacement depends only on the initial and final points.

$$\Delta\vec{\mathbf{r}} = \int_i^f d\vec{\mathbf{s}} = \hat{\mathbf{i}}\int_{x_0}^{x} dx + \hat{\mathbf{j}}\int_{y_0}^{y} dy = (x - x_0)\hat{\mathbf{i}} + (y - y_0)\hat{\mathbf{j}}$$

$$\Delta\vec{\mathbf{r}} = (4 - 0)\hat{\mathbf{i}} + (8 - 0)\hat{\mathbf{j}} = \boxed{4\hat{\mathbf{i}} + 8\hat{\mathbf{j}}}$$

$$\|\Delta\vec{\mathbf{r}}\| = \sqrt{(x - x_0)^2 + (y - y_0)^2} = \sqrt{4^2 + 8^2} = \sqrt{16 + 64} = \sqrt{80} = \boxed{4\sqrt{5}}$$

Note that $\|\Delta\vec{\mathbf{r}}\| = 4\sqrt{5} \approx 8.944$ is less than $s \approx 9.073$. The arc length is always greater than the magnitude of the net displacement, except when the path is a single straight line segment (in which case they are equal).

Example. Find the arc length from the origin to $\left(\frac{\pi}{2}, 1\right)$ along the curve $r = \sin\theta$ in 2D polar coordinates.

Use 2D polar coordinate formulas to find the arc length. Factor out $d\theta$.

$$s = \int_C ds = \int_C \sqrt{dr^2 + r^2 d\theta^2} = \int_C \sqrt{\left[\left(\frac{dr}{d\theta}\right)^2 + r^2\right] d\theta^2} = \int_{\theta=0}^{\pi/2} \sqrt{\left(\frac{dr}{d\theta}\right)^2 + r^2}\, d\theta$$

Plug in the given equation, $r = \sin\theta$.

$$s = \int_{\theta=0}^{\pi/2} \sqrt{\left(\frac{d}{d\theta}\sin\theta\right)^2 + (\sin\theta)^2}\, d\theta = \int_{\theta=0}^{\pi/2} \sqrt{\cos^2\theta + \sin^2\theta}\, d\theta = \int_{\theta=0}^{\pi/2} d\theta = \boxed{\frac{\pi}{2}}$$

Example. Evaluate $\int_C \vec{\mathbf{F}} \cdot d\vec{\mathbf{s}}$ for $\vec{\mathbf{F}} = x^2y^2\hat{\mathbf{i}} + x^3y\hat{\mathbf{j}}$ from the origin to $(1,2)$ along the line $y = 2x$ and also along the route $(0,0) \to (1,0) \to (1,2)$. Is $\vec{\mathbf{F}}$ conservative?

Express the scalar product in terms of the components $F_x = x^2y^2$ and $F_y = x^3y$.

$$\int_C \vec{\mathbf{F}} \cdot d\vec{\mathbf{s}} = \int_C F_x\, dx + \int_C F_y\, dy = \int_C x^2y^2\, dx + \int_C x^3y\, dy$$

To perform these integrals, we need to write each integrand as a function of a single variable that matches the differential element. For the path $y = 2x$, use this equation to replace y with $2x$ in the first integral and to replace x with $\frac{y}{2}$ in the second integral. Going from $(0,0)$ to $(1,2)$, x varies from 0 to 1 and y varies from 0 to 2.

$$\int_{C_1} \vec{\mathbf{F}} \cdot d\vec{\mathbf{s}} = \int_{x=0}^{1} x^2(2x)^2\, dx + \int_{y=0}^{2} \left(\frac{y}{2}\right)^3 y\, dy = 2^2 \int_{x=0}^{1} x^4\, dx + \frac{1}{8}\int_{y=0}^{2} y^4\, dy$$

$$\int_{C_1} \vec{\mathbf{F}} \cdot d\vec{\mathbf{s}} = 4\left[\frac{x^5}{5}\right]_{x=0}^{1} + \frac{1}{8}\left[\frac{y^5}{5}\right]_{y=0}^{2} = \frac{4}{5}(1^5 - 0^5) + \frac{1}{40}(2^5 - 0^5)$$

$$\int_{C_1} \vec{\mathbf{F}} \cdot d\vec{\mathbf{s}} = \frac{4}{5} + \frac{32}{40} = \frac{4}{5} + \frac{32 \div 8}{40 \div 8} = \frac{4}{5} + \frac{4}{5} = \boxed{\frac{8}{5}}$$

For the second path, $y = 0$ from $(0,0)$ to $(1,0)$, while $x = 1$ going from $(1,0)$ to $(1,2)$.

$$\int_{C_2} \vec{\mathbf{F}} \cdot d\vec{\mathbf{s}} = \int_{x=0}^{1} x^2 0^2\, dx + \int_{y=0}^{2} 1^3 y\, dy = 1\int_{y=0}^{2} y\, dy = \left[\frac{y^2}{2}\right]_{y=0}^{2} = \frac{1}{2}(2^2 - 0^2) = \frac{1}{2}(4) = \boxed{2}$$

Since the line integral equals $\frac{8}{5}$ for the first path and 2 for the second path, $\vec{\mathbf{F}}$ is clearly nonconservative. Although this suffices to show that a field is nonconservative, if the two line integrals had been the same, it wouldn't be satisfactory to show that the field was conservative. One would need to integrate over every possible path, for which there are an infinite number. The partial derivative test can be used in that case. $\vec{\mathbf{F}}$ is nonconservative because $\frac{\partial F_x}{\partial y} = \frac{\partial}{\partial y} x^2 y^2 = 2x^2 y$ doesn't equal $\frac{\partial F_y}{\partial x} = \frac{\partial}{\partial x} x^3 y = 3x^2 y$.

Example. Evaluate $\oint_C \vec{\mathbf{F}} \cdot d\vec{\mathbf{s}}$ for $\vec{\mathbf{F}} = y\hat{\mathbf{i}} + x\hat{\mathbf{j}}$ along $(0,1) \to (1,1) \to (0,2) \to (0,1)$.

Perform the integral along each path: $y = 1$ from $(0,1)$ to $(1,1)$, $y = -x + 2$ from $(1,1)$ to $(0,2)$ since $m = \frac{2-1}{0-1} = \frac{1}{-1} = -1$ and the y-intercept is 2, and $x = 0$ from $(0,2)$ to $(0,1)$. Since $\vec{\mathbf{F}} = y\hat{\mathbf{i}} + x\hat{\mathbf{j}}$, in this example $F_x = y$ and $F_y = x$.

$$\oint_C \vec{\mathbf{F}} \cdot d\vec{\mathbf{s}} = \int_{C_1} F_x\,dx + \int_{C_1} F_y\,dy + \int_{C_2} F_x\,dx + \int_{C_2} F_y\,dy + \int_{C_3} F_x\,dx + \int_{C_3} F_y\,dy$$

$$\oint_C \vec{\mathbf{F}} \cdot d\vec{\mathbf{s}} = \int_{x=0}^{1} 1\,dx + \int_{y=1}^{1} x\,dy + \int_{x=1}^{0} y\,dx + \int_{y=1}^{2} x\,dy + \int_{x=0}^{0} y\,dx + \int_{y=2}^{1} 0\,dy$$

The integrals where the lower and upper limits are the same equal zero, and the last integral is zero because the integrand is zero. For the second path, use the equation of the line to replace y with $-x + 2$ or to replace x with $x = 2 - y$.

$$\oint_C \vec{\mathbf{F}} \cdot d\vec{\mathbf{s}} = \int_{x=0}^{1} 1\,dx + 0 + \int_{x=1}^{0} (-x + 2)\,dx + \int_{y=1}^{2} (2 - y)\,dy + 0 + 0$$

Pay close attention to the limits, as x goes from 1 to 0 in the second path.

$$\oint_C \vec{\mathbf{F}} \cdot d\vec{\mathbf{s}} = [x]_{x=0}^{1} + \left[-\frac{x^2}{2} + 2x\right]_{x=1}^{0} + \left[2y - \frac{y^2}{2}\right]_{y=1}^{2}$$

$$= 1 - 0 - \frac{0^2}{2} + \frac{1^2}{2} + 2(0) - 2(1) + 2(2) - 2(1) - \frac{2^2}{2} + \frac{1^2}{2}$$

$$\oint_C \vec{\mathbf{F}} \cdot d\vec{\mathbf{s}} = 1 + \frac{1}{2} - 2 + 4 - 2 - \frac{4}{2} + \frac{1}{2} = \boxed{0}$$

In this example, $\frac{\partial F_x}{\partial y} = \frac{\partial}{\partial y} y = 1$ equals $\frac{\partial F_y}{\partial x} = \frac{\partial}{\partial x} x = 1$, such that $\vec{\mathbf{F}}$ is conservative, which is why $\oint_C \vec{\mathbf{F}} \cdot d\vec{\mathbf{s}} = 0$.

Example. Given $\vec{\mathbf{F}} = xy^2\hat{\mathbf{i}} + (x^2y - 2y)\hat{\mathbf{j}}$, find a scalar function $f(x,y)$ such that $\vec{\mathbf{F}} = \vec{\nabla} f$.

Comparing the given expression, $\vec{\mathbf{F}} = xy^2\hat{\mathbf{i}} + (x^2y - 2y)\hat{\mathbf{j}}$, with the definition of the gradient from Chapter 9, $\vec{\mathbf{F}} = \vec{\nabla} f = \hat{\mathbf{i}}\frac{\partial f}{\partial x} + \hat{\mathbf{j}}\frac{\partial f}{\partial y}$, gives the following equations:

$$\frac{\partial f}{\partial x} = F_x = xy^2 \quad , \quad \frac{\partial f}{\partial y} = F_y = x^2y - 2y$$

Integrate $\frac{\partial f}{\partial x} = xy^2$ over the variable x, treating y as if it were a constant. (Why? When we take the partial derivative $\frac{\partial f}{\partial x}$ with respect to x, we treat the independent variable y as if it were a constant. Therefore, we do the same thing when we integrate both sides of an equation that has one first-order partial derivative.)

$$f(x,y) = \frac{x^2y^2}{2} + g(y)$$

The "constant" of integration, $g(y)$, is not necessarily a constant; it may be a function of y because we treated y as if it were a constant when we integrated. Next, take a partial derivative of the above expression for $f(x,y)$ with respect to y.

$$\frac{\partial f}{\partial y} = x^2y + \frac{dg}{dy}$$

Compare this to the previous expression $\frac{\partial f}{\partial y} = x^2y - 2y$. By comparison, $\frac{dg}{dy} = -2y$. Integrate both sides of $\frac{dg}{dy} = -2y$ to determine that $g = -y^2 + c$, where the constant of integration c really is a constant. Our final answer for $f(x,y)$ is:

$$f(x,y) = \boxed{\frac{x^2y^2}{2} - y^2 + c}$$

Tip: It is easy to check the answer. Verify that the gradient $(\vec{\nabla} f)$ is equal to $\vec{\mathbf{F}}$.

Note: If $\vec{\mathbf{F}}$ has three components, when integrating both sides of $\frac{\partial f}{\partial x}$, the "constant" of integration may have two variables, $g(y,z)$. Next, integrating both sides of $\frac{\partial f}{\partial y}$, a second "constant" of integration may have one variable, $h(z)$. Apply the partial derivatives $\frac{\partial f}{\partial x}$ and $\frac{\partial f}{\partial y}$ to narrow $g(y,z)$ and $h(z)$ down to a constant (similar to this example).

Note: One application of this technique is used in physics to find **potential energy**. If $\vec{\mathbf{F}}$ represents a conservative force (like gravitational force, but unlike friction which is nonconservative), there exists a potential energy (U) such that $\vec{\mathbf{F}} = -\vec{\nabla} U$.

Chapter 13 Exercises – Part A

Directions: Find the arc length along the given curve over the specified interval.

❶ $y = \sqrt{1 - x^2}, 0 \leq x \leq 1$

❷ $y = x^2, 0 \leq x \leq \frac{\sqrt{3}}{2}$

❸ $r = e^\theta, 0 \leq \theta \leq \pi$

❹ $r = \theta, 0 \leq \theta \leq 1$ rad

❖ Check your answers at the back of the book.

Chapter 13 Exercises – Part B

Directions: Perform the line integral $\int_C \vec{\mathbf{F}} \cdot d\vec{\mathbf{s}}$ for the given field along the specified path. Also determine whether each force is conservative or nonconservative.

❺ $\vec{\mathbf{F}} = x^4 y^2 \hat{\mathbf{i}} + x^2 y^4 \hat{\mathbf{j}}$, along $y = x^2$ from $(0,0)$ to $(2,4)$

❻ $\vec{\mathbf{F}} = \vec{\nabla} x^3 y$, along $y = 1 - x$ from $(-1,2)$ to $(1,0)$

❖ Check your answers at the back of the book.

Chapter 13 Exercises – Part C

Directions: Perform the closed line integral $\oint_C \vec{\mathbf{F}} \cdot d\vec{\mathbf{s}}$ for the given field along the specified path. Also determine whether each force is conservative or nonconservative.

❼ $\vec{\mathbf{F}} = x^4 y^2 \hat{\mathbf{i}} + x^5 y \hat{\mathbf{j}}$, along the path $(1,1) \to (1,-1) \to (-1,1) \to (1,1)$

❽ $\vec{\mathbf{F}} = r\widehat{\boldsymbol{\theta}}$, starting and finishing at $(2,0)$ along the counterclockwise circle $r = 2$

❖ Check your answers at the back of the book.

Chapter 13 Exercises – Part D

Directions: For each vector field, show that it is conservative and find a scalar function $f(x,y)$ such that $\vec{\mathbf{F}} = \vec{\nabla} f$.

❾ $\vec{\mathbf{F}} = (2xy - 3)\hat{\mathbf{i}} + (x^2 - y^2)\hat{\mathbf{j}}$

❿ $\vec{\mathbf{F}} = 2x^5y^3\hat{\mathbf{i}} + (x^6y^2 - y^8)\hat{\mathbf{j}}$

⓫ $\vec{\mathbf{F}} = yz\hat{\mathbf{i}} + xz\hat{\mathbf{j}} + xy\hat{\mathbf{k}}$

⓬ $\vec{\mathbf{F}} = r\hat{\mathbf{r}}$ (in 2D polar coordinates)

❖ Check your answers at the back of the book.

14 Surface and Volume Integrals

One way to find **surface area** is to integrate over the differential area element dA. In the simple case that the surface is **flat** and lies entirely within the xy plane, $dA = dxdy$. The surface area S is found by integrating over dA for the region S. If the region S is not rectangular, the integration limits for one of the coordinates (either x or y) are functions. This point, which is typical of multiple integrals, is illustrated in the examples.

$$S = \iint_S dA$$

In the more general case, the surface is **curved**. If the surface can be expressed as $z = z(x, y)$, the surface area can be found with the following integral.

$$S = \iint_S \sqrt{1 + \left(\frac{\partial z}{\partial x}\right)^2 + \left(\frac{\partial z}{\partial y}\right)^2}\, dxdy$$

One way to find **volume** is to integrate over the differential volume element, dV, where $dV = dxdydz$. The volume V is found by integrating over dV for the region V. For the general case, the integration limits for one or two of the coordinates are functions.

$$V = \iiint_V dV$$

Surface and volume integrals often include a scalar or vector function in the integrand, like $\iint_S f(x, y, z)\, dA$, $\iint_S \vec{\mathbf{F}} \cdot d\vec{\mathbf{A}}$, or $\iiint_V f(x, y, z)\, dV$. For the case $\iint_S \vec{\mathbf{F}} \cdot d\vec{\mathbf{A}}$, the direction of the oriented differential area element, $d\vec{\mathbf{A}}$, is normal to the surface: $d\vec{\mathbf{A}} = \hat{\mathbf{n}} dA$, where $\hat{\mathbf{n}}$ is a unit normal vector (see Chapter 12), which is orthogonal to the surface. If the surface is curved, $\hat{\mathbf{n}}$ is **not** a constant (as it will point in different directions at different points on the surface).

For some shapes, like spheres or cylinders, the integral for surface area or volume is simpler using 2D polar coordinates, spherical coordinates, or cylindrical coordinates. The variables of a multiple integral can be transformed using the **Jacobian**, which is a determinant formed by the partial derivatives. For an area integral in the xy plane over x and y, where $x = x(u, v)$ and $y = y(u, v)$, the Jacobian for the transformation is:

$$\frac{\partial(x,y)}{\partial(u,v)} = \begin{vmatrix} \frac{\partial x}{\partial u} & \frac{\partial x}{\partial v} \\ \frac{\partial y}{\partial u} & \frac{\partial y}{\partial v} \end{vmatrix} = \frac{\partial x}{\partial u}\frac{\partial y}{\partial v} - \frac{\partial x}{\partial v}\frac{\partial y}{\partial u}$$

The above Jacobian allows an integral of the form $\iint_S f(x,y)\, dxdy$ to be written as:

$$\iint\limits_S f(x,y)\, dxdy = \iint\limits_S f(u,v) \left|\frac{\partial(x,y)}{\partial(u,v)}\right| dudv$$

For example, $x = r\cos\theta$ and $y = r\sin\theta$ relate the Cartesian coordinates (x,y) to the **2D polar coordinates** (r,θ). The Jacobian for this transformation is:

$$\frac{\partial(x,y)}{\partial(r,\theta)} = \begin{vmatrix} \frac{\partial x}{\partial r} & \frac{\partial x}{\partial \theta} \\ \frac{\partial y}{\partial r} & \frac{\partial y}{\partial \theta} \end{vmatrix} = \begin{vmatrix} \frac{\partial}{\partial r} r\cos\theta & \frac{\partial}{\partial \theta} r\cos\theta \\ \frac{\partial}{\partial r} r\sin\theta & \frac{\partial}{\partial \theta} r\sin\theta \end{vmatrix} = \begin{vmatrix} \cos\theta & -r\sin\theta \\ \sin\theta & r\cos\theta \end{vmatrix}$$

$$\frac{\partial(x,y)}{\partial(r,\theta)} = \cos\theta\, r\cos\theta - (-r\sin\theta)\sin\theta = r\cos^2\theta + r\sin^2\theta = r$$

Therefore, $dA = dxdy$ in Cartesian coordinates is equivalent to $dA = rdrd\theta$ in 2D polar coordinates.

$$\iint\limits_S f(x,y)\, dxdy = \iint\limits_S f(r,\theta)\, rdrd\theta$$

If a surface can be expressed as $z = z(x,y)$, the Jacobian can be used to transform the surface area integral into coordinates u and v, where $x = x(u,v)$ and $y = y(u,v)$.

$$\iint\limits_S \sqrt{1 + \left(\frac{\partial z}{\partial x}\right)^2 + \left(\frac{\partial z}{\partial y}\right)^2}\, dxdy = \iint\limits_S \sqrt{1 + \left(\frac{\partial z}{\partial x}\right)^2 + \left(\frac{\partial z}{\partial y}\right)^2} \left|\frac{\partial(x,y)}{\partial(u,v)}\right| dudv$$

For a volume integral over x, y, and z, where $x = x(u,v,w)$, $y = y(u,v,w)$, and $z = z(u,v,w)$, the Jacobian for the transformation is:

$$\frac{\partial(x,y,z)}{\partial(u,v,w)} = \begin{vmatrix} \frac{\partial x}{\partial u} & \frac{\partial x}{\partial v} & \frac{\partial x}{\partial w} \\ \frac{\partial y}{\partial u} & \frac{\partial y}{\partial v} & \frac{\partial y}{\partial w} \\ \frac{\partial z}{\partial u} & \frac{\partial z}{\partial v} & \frac{\partial z}{\partial w} \end{vmatrix}$$

$$\frac{\partial(x,y,z)}{\partial(u,v,w)} = \frac{\partial x}{\partial u}\left(\frac{\partial y}{\partial v}\frac{\partial z}{\partial w} - \frac{\partial y}{\partial w}\frac{\partial z}{\partial v}\right) - \frac{\partial x}{\partial v}\left(\frac{\partial y}{\partial u}\frac{\partial z}{\partial w} - \frac{\partial y}{\partial w}\frac{\partial z}{\partial u}\right) + \frac{\partial x}{\partial w}\left(\frac{\partial y}{\partial u}\frac{\partial z}{\partial v} - \frac{\partial y}{\partial v}\frac{\partial z}{\partial u}\right)$$

The 3D Jacobian allows an integral of the form $\iiint_V f(x,y,z)\, dxdydz$ to be written as:

$$\iiint_V f(x,y,z)\, dxdydz = \iiint_V f(u,v,w) \left|\frac{\partial(x,y,z)}{\partial(u,v,w)}\right| dudvdw$$

For example, $x = r\cos\theta\sin\varphi$, $y = r\sin\theta\sin\varphi$, and $z = r\cos\varphi$ relate the Cartesian coordinates (x,y,z) to the **spherical coordinates** (r,θ,φ) in common math notation (for common physics notation, swap θ and φ). The Jacobian for this transformation is:

$$\frac{\partial(x,y,z)}{\partial(r,\theta,\varphi)} = \begin{vmatrix} \frac{\partial x}{\partial r} & \frac{\partial x}{\partial \theta} & \frac{\partial x}{\partial \varphi} \\ \frac{\partial y}{\partial r} & \frac{\partial y}{\partial \theta} & \frac{\partial y}{\partial \varphi} \\ \frac{\partial z}{\partial r} & \frac{\partial z}{\partial \theta} & \frac{\partial z}{\partial \varphi} \end{vmatrix} = \begin{vmatrix} \frac{\partial}{\partial r} r\cos\theta\sin\varphi & \frac{\partial}{\partial \theta} r\cos\theta\sin\varphi & \frac{\partial}{\partial \varphi} r\cos\theta\sin\varphi \\ \frac{\partial}{\partial r} r\sin\theta\sin\varphi & \frac{\partial}{\partial \theta} r\sin\theta\sin\varphi & \frac{\partial}{\partial \varphi} r\sin\theta\sin\varphi \\ \frac{\partial}{\partial r} r\cos\varphi & \frac{\partial}{\partial \theta} r\cos\varphi & \frac{\partial}{\partial \varphi} r\cos\varphi \end{vmatrix}$$

$$\frac{\partial(x,y,z)}{\partial(r,\theta,\varphi)} = \begin{vmatrix} \cos\theta\sin\varphi & -r\sin\theta\sin\varphi & r\cos\theta\cos\varphi \\ \sin\theta\sin\varphi & r\cos\theta\sin\varphi & r\sin\theta\cos\varphi \\ \cos\varphi & 0 & -r\sin\varphi \end{vmatrix}$$

$$\frac{\partial(x,y,z)}{\partial(r,\theta,\varphi)} = -r^2\cos^2\theta\sin^3\varphi - r^2\sin^2\theta\sin^3\varphi - r^2\sin^2\theta\sin\varphi\cos^2\varphi - r^2\cos^2\theta\sin\varphi\cos^2\varphi$$

$$\frac{\partial(x,y,z)}{\partial(r,\theta,\varphi)} = -r^2\sin^3\varphi - r^2\sin\varphi\cos^2\varphi = -r^2\sin\varphi$$

We used the trig identities $\sin^2\theta + \cos^2\theta = 1$ and $\sin^2\varphi + \cos^2\varphi = 1$. For example, $-r^2\sin^3\varphi - r^2\sin\varphi\cos^2\varphi = -r^2\sin\varphi(\sin^2\varphi - \cos^2\varphi) = -r^2\sin\varphi$. The volume element $dV = dxdydz$ in Cartesian coordinates is equivalent to $dV = r^2\sin\varphi\, drd\theta d\varphi$ in spherical coordinates (since there are absolute values, $\left|\frac{\partial(x,y,z)}{\partial(r,\theta,\varphi)}\right|$, on the Jacobian in the integrand).

$$\iiint_V f(x,y,z)\, dxdydz = \iiint_V f(r,\theta,\varphi)\, r^2\sin\varphi\, drd\theta d\varphi$$

Note: Recall that φ is the polar (or zenith) angle and θ is the azimuthal angle in common math notation. For common physics notation, swap φ and θ in spherical coordinates.

Cylindrical **coordinates** are similar to 2D polar coordinates in that $dV = r_c dr_c d\theta dz$.

$$\iiint_V f(x,y,z)\, dxdydz = \iiint_V f(r_c,\theta,\varphi)\, r_c dr_c d\theta dz$$

If there are two coordinates, (u, v), which allow the position vector $\vec{\mathbf{r}} = x\hat{\mathbf{i}} + y\hat{\mathbf{j}} + z\hat{\mathbf{k}}$ to map every point on a surface via the transformation $x = x(u, v)$, $y = y(u, v)$, and $z = z(u, v)$, the surface area integral transforms according to:

$$\iint_S f(x, y)\, dxdy = \iint_S f(u, v)\, \|\vec{\mathbf{r}}_u \times \vec{\mathbf{r}}_v\| dudv$$

where $\vec{\mathbf{r}}_u = \hat{\mathbf{i}}\frac{\partial x}{\partial u} + \hat{\mathbf{j}}\frac{\partial y}{\partial u} + \hat{\mathbf{k}}\frac{\partial z}{\partial u}$ and $\vec{\mathbf{r}}_v = \hat{\mathbf{i}}\frac{\partial x}{\partial v} + \hat{\mathbf{j}}\frac{\partial y}{\partial v} + \hat{\mathbf{k}}\frac{\partial z}{\partial v}$. For example, on the surface of a sphere centered about the origin, $r = a$ is a constant such that $x = a\cos\theta\sin\varphi$, $y = a\sin\theta\sin\varphi$, and $z = a\cos\varphi$ allow the two spherical coordinates θ and φ to map every point on the sphere. In this case,

$$\vec{\mathbf{r}}_\varphi \times \vec{\mathbf{r}}_\theta = \begin{vmatrix} \hat{\mathbf{i}} & \hat{\mathbf{j}} & \hat{\mathbf{k}} \\ \frac{\partial x}{\partial\varphi} & \frac{\partial y}{\partial\varphi} & \frac{\partial z}{\partial\varphi} \\ \frac{\partial x}{\partial\theta} & \frac{\partial y}{\partial\theta} & \frac{\partial z}{\partial\theta} \end{vmatrix} = \begin{vmatrix} \hat{\mathbf{i}} & \hat{\mathbf{j}} & \hat{\mathbf{k}} \\ \frac{\partial}{\partial\varphi} a\cos\theta\sin\varphi & \frac{\partial}{\partial\varphi} a\sin\theta\sin\varphi & \frac{\partial}{\partial\varphi} a\cos\varphi \\ \frac{\partial}{\partial\theta} a\cos\theta\sin\varphi & \frac{\partial}{\partial\theta} a\sin\theta\sin\varphi & \frac{\partial}{\partial\theta} a\cos\varphi \end{vmatrix}$$

$$\vec{\mathbf{r}}_\varphi \times \vec{\mathbf{r}}_\theta = \begin{vmatrix} \hat{\mathbf{i}} & \hat{\mathbf{j}} & \hat{\mathbf{k}} \\ a\cos\theta\cos\varphi & a\sin\theta\cos\varphi & -a\sin\varphi \\ -a\sin\theta\sin\varphi & a\cos\theta\sin\varphi & 0 \end{vmatrix}$$

$$\vec{\mathbf{r}}_\varphi \times \vec{\mathbf{r}}_\theta = a^2\hat{\mathbf{i}}\cos\theta\sin^2\varphi + a^2\hat{\mathbf{j}}\sin\theta\sin^2\varphi + a^2\hat{\mathbf{k}}\sin^2\theta\sin\varphi\cos\varphi + a^2\hat{\mathbf{k}}\cos^2\theta\sin\varphi\cos\varphi$$

$$\vec{\mathbf{r}}_\varphi \times \vec{\mathbf{r}}_\theta = a^2\hat{\mathbf{i}}\cos\theta\sin^2\varphi + a^2\hat{\mathbf{j}}\sin\theta\sin^2\varphi + a^2\hat{\mathbf{k}}\sin\varphi\cos\varphi$$

$$\|\vec{\mathbf{r}}_\varphi \times \vec{\mathbf{r}}_\theta\| = \sqrt{a^4\cos^2\theta\sin^4\varphi + a^4\sin^2\theta\sin^4\varphi + a^4\sin^2\varphi\cos^2\varphi}$$

$$\|\vec{\mathbf{r}}_\varphi \times \vec{\mathbf{r}}_\theta\| = \sqrt{a^4\sin^4\varphi + a^4\sin^2\varphi\cos^2\varphi} = \sqrt{a^4\sin^2\varphi} = a^2\sin\varphi$$

The **flux** of a vector field $\vec{\mathbf{F}}$ through a region S on a surface is $\iint_S \vec{\mathbf{F}} \cdot d\vec{\mathbf{A}}$. Recall that $d\vec{\mathbf{A}} = \hat{\mathbf{n}}dA$ and $\hat{\mathbf{n}}$ is a unit normal vector (see Chapter 12), which is orthogonal to the surface. For a curved surface, $\hat{\mathbf{n}}$ is **outward**; for a flat surface, the orientation must be specified. A few common examples of flux include electric flux, magnetic flux, and heat flux. If there are two coordinates, (u, v), which allow the position vector $\vec{\mathbf{r}} = x\hat{\mathbf{i}} + y\hat{\mathbf{j}} + z\hat{\mathbf{k}}$ to map every point on a surface via the transformation $x = x(u, v)$, $y = y(u, v)$, and $z = z(u, v)$, the flux integral transforms according to (where $\vec{\mathbf{r}}_u \times \vec{\mathbf{r}}_v$ is **outward**):

$$\iint_S \vec{\mathbf{F}} \cdot d\vec{\mathbf{A}} = \iint_S \vec{\mathbf{F}} \cdot \hat{\mathbf{n}}dA = \iint_S \vec{\mathbf{F}} \cdot (\vec{\mathbf{r}}_u \times \vec{\mathbf{r}}_v) dudv$$

Note: Some texts use $d\vec{\mathbf{A}}$, others use $d\vec{\mathbf{S}}$, and in others $d\vec{\mathbf{A}}$ is flat while $d\vec{\mathbf{S}}$ is curved. This book uses $d\vec{\mathbf{A}}$ to mean the general surface, whether curved or flat.

If a surface is described by $z = z(x, y)$, the parameters u and v are x and y, such that $\vec{\mathbf{r}}_x = \hat{\mathbf{i}}\frac{\partial x}{\partial x} + \hat{\mathbf{j}}\frac{\partial y}{\partial x} + \hat{\mathbf{k}}\frac{\partial z}{\partial x} = \hat{\mathbf{i}} + \hat{\mathbf{k}}\frac{\partial z}{\partial x}$, $\vec{\mathbf{r}}_y = \hat{\mathbf{i}}\frac{\partial x}{\partial y} + \hat{\mathbf{j}}\frac{\partial y}{\partial y} + \hat{\mathbf{k}}\frac{\partial z}{\partial y} = \hat{\mathbf{j}} + \hat{\mathbf{k}}\frac{\partial z}{\partial y}$, and

$$\vec{\mathbf{r}}_x \times \vec{\mathbf{r}}_y = \begin{vmatrix} \hat{\mathbf{i}} & \hat{\mathbf{j}} & \hat{\mathbf{k}} \\ 1 & 0 & \frac{\partial z}{\partial x} \\ 0 & 1 & \frac{\partial z}{\partial y} \end{vmatrix} = -\frac{\partial z}{\partial x}\hat{\mathbf{i}} - \frac{\partial z}{\partial y}\hat{\mathbf{j}} + \hat{\mathbf{k}}$$

In this case, the flux through the surface can be written as follows for **upward** orientation (for a surface that is oriented downward, multiply by negative one):

$$\iint_S \vec{\mathbf{F}} \cdot d\vec{\mathbf{A}} = \iint_S \left(-F_x\frac{\partial z}{\partial x} - F_y\frac{\partial z}{\partial y} + F_z\right) dx dy$$

If C represents the counterclockwise traversal of a simple smooth curve lying in the xy plane and if S represents the region bounded by C, **Green's theorem** relates the line integral for the vector field $\vec{\mathbf{F}} = F_x\hat{\mathbf{i}} + F_y\hat{\mathbf{j}}$ (which is often written with P and Q in place of F_x and F_y) to a surface integral (for the case that F_x and F_y have continuous partial derivatives):

$$\oint_C \vec{\mathbf{F}} \cdot d\vec{\mathbf{s}} = \oint_C F_x\, dx + \oint_C F_y\, dy = \iint_S \left(\frac{\partial F_y}{\partial x} - \frac{\partial F_x}{\partial y}\right) dA = \iint_S \left(\vec{\nabla} \times \vec{\mathbf{F}}\right)_z dA$$

Green's theorem is analogous to the fundamental theorem of calculus, but for double integrals. A notable special case of Green's theorem occurs when $F_x = 0$ and $F_y = x$, when $F_x = -y$ and $F_y = 0$, or when $F_x = -\frac{y}{2}$ and $F_y = \frac{x}{2}$. In these cases, $\frac{\partial F_y}{\partial x} - \frac{\partial F_x}{\partial y} = 1$, such that $\iint_S \left(\frac{\partial F_y}{\partial x} - \frac{\partial F_x}{\partial y}\right) dA = \iint_S dA = A$. It follows that the following integrals are formulas for area: $A = \oint_C x\, dy = -\oint_C y\, dx = \frac{1}{2}\oint_C x\, dy - \frac{1}{2}\oint_C x\, dx$.

Two other theorems generalize Green's theorem to higher dimensions in two different ways. **Stokes's theorem** (often written Stokes' theorem) generalizes Green's theorem to the case where the bounding curve C is not necessarily planar, but may be a curve in 3D space, and where the surface S may be a curved surface in 3D space bounded by C.

$$\oint_C \vec{\mathbf{F}} \cdot d\vec{\mathbf{s}} = \iint_S \vec{\nabla} \times \vec{\mathbf{F}}\, dA$$

The **divergence theorem** relates the net (outward) flux through a closed surface to the divergence of the field, where the volume V is bounded by the surface S. Note that the surface integral is closed for the divergence theorem (as the surface must be closed in order to bound a volume), whereas the surface integral is not closed for Stokes's theorem (in the case of Stokes's theorem, the line integral is closed, as the path must be closed in order to bound a surface).

$$\oiint_S \vec{\mathbf{F}} \cdot d\vec{\mathbf{A}} = \iiint_V \vec{\nabla} \cdot \vec{\mathbf{F}}\, dV$$

A notable application of Stokes's theorem and the divergence theorem can be found in electromagnetism. **Maxwell's equations** below (in SI units) describe electromagnetic fields, where $\vec{\mathbf{E}}$ represents the electric field and $\vec{\mathbf{B}}$ represents the magnetic field.

$$\oiint_S \vec{\mathbf{E}} \cdot d\vec{\mathbf{A}} = \iiint_V \vec{\nabla} \cdot \vec{\mathbf{E}}\, dV = \frac{q_{enc}}{\varepsilon_0} \quad , \quad \oint_C \vec{\mathbf{E}} \cdot d\vec{\mathbf{s}} = \iint_S \vec{\nabla} \times \vec{\mathbf{E}}\, dA = -\frac{\partial}{\partial t} \iint_S \vec{\mathbf{B}} \cdot d\vec{\mathbf{A}}$$

$$\oiint_S \vec{\mathbf{B}} \cdot d\vec{\mathbf{A}} = \iiint_V \vec{\nabla} \cdot \vec{\mathbf{B}}\, dV = 0 \quad , \quad \oint_C \vec{\mathbf{B}} \cdot d\vec{\mathbf{s}} = \iint_S \vec{\nabla} \times \vec{\mathbf{B}}\, dA = \mu_0 I_{enc} + \varepsilon_0 \mu_0 \frac{\partial}{\partial t} \iint_S \vec{\mathbf{E}} \cdot d\vec{\mathbf{A}}$$

- **Gauss's law** (top left) states that the net electric flux, $\Phi_e = \oiint_S \vec{\mathbf{E}} \cdot d\vec{\mathbf{A}}$, through any closed surface is proportional to the charge enclosed by the surface, q_{enc}.
- **Gauss's law in magnetism** (bottom left) states that the net magnetic flux, $\Phi_m = \oiint_S \vec{\mathbf{B}} \cdot d\vec{\mathbf{A}}$, through any closed surface is always zero. The reason for this is that no magnetic monopoles (which would be the magnetic equivalent of electric charge) have ever been observed. (What makes a magnetic field? Current does.)
- **Faraday's law** (top right) states that a changing magnetic flux, $\Phi_m = \oiint_S \vec{\mathbf{B}} \cdot d\vec{\mathbf{A}}$, through the area of a closed loop induces an emf in the loop (which gives rise to an induced current in the loop). The induced electric field in $\oint_C \vec{\mathbf{E}} \cdot d\vec{\mathbf{s}}$ causes charges in the wire to accelerate, which causes the induced current.
- **Ampère's law** (bottom right) states that the line integral of the magnetic field, $\oint_C \vec{\mathbf{B}} \cdot d\vec{\mathbf{s}}$, is proportional to the net current enclosed by the closed path, I_{enc}. The quantity $\varepsilon_0 \mu_0 \frac{\partial}{\partial t} \iint_S \vec{\mathbf{E}} \cdot d\vec{\mathbf{A}}$ is referred to as the displacement current, which shows that a changing electric flux can induce a magnetic field.

Maxwell's equations can also be expressed in differential form (these are in SI units):

$$\vec{\nabla}\cdot\vec{\mathbf{E}} = \frac{\rho}{\varepsilon_0} \quad , \quad \vec{\nabla}\cdot\vec{\mathbf{B}} = 0 \quad , \quad \vec{\nabla}\times\vec{\mathbf{E}} = -\frac{\partial\vec{\mathbf{B}}}{\partial t} \quad , \quad \vec{\nabla}\times\vec{\mathbf{B}} = \mu_0\vec{\mathbf{J}} + \varepsilon_0\mu_0\frac{\partial\vec{\mathbf{E}}}{\partial t}$$

The permittivity of free space ($\varepsilon_0 = \frac{1}{4\pi k}$, where $k = 9.0 \times 10^9 \frac{\text{Nm}^2}{\text{C}^2}$), which is a constant relating to electric fields, and the permeability of free space ($\mu_0 = 4\pi \times 10^{-7}\frac{\text{Tm}}{\text{A}}$), which is a constant relating to magnetic fields, combine together to form the speed of light (which is an electromagnetic wave) in vacuum as follows: $c = \frac{1}{\sqrt{\varepsilon_0\mu_0}}$.

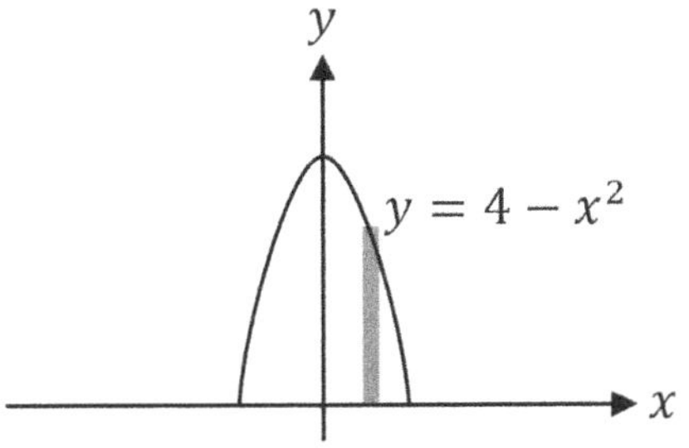

Example. Evaluate $\iint_S x^2 y\, dA$ for the region between $y = 4 - x^2$ and the x-axis.

In the region between $y = 4 - x^2$ and the x-axis, x varies from -2 to 2. For a given value of x, y varies from 0 to $4 - x^2$ (from the x-axis to the curve $y = 4 - x^2$).

$$I = \int_{x=-2}^{2}\int_{y=0}^{4-x^2} x^2 y\, dxdy$$

Since y has a function in its limit, we must integrate over y first. When integrating over y, treat the independent variable x as if it were a constant.

$$I = \int_{x=-2}^{2} x^2 \int_{y=0}^{4-x^2} y\, dy\, dx = \int_{x=-2}^{2} x^2 \left[\frac{y^2}{2}\right]_{y=0}^{4-x^2} dx = \frac{1}{2}\int_{x=-2}^{2} x^2(4-x^2)^2\, dx$$

$$I = \frac{1}{2}\int_{x=-2}^{2} x^2(16 - 8x^2 + x^4)\, dx = 8\int_{x=-2}^{2} x^2\, dx - 4\int_{x=-2}^{2} x^4\, dx + \frac{1}{2}\int_{x=-2}^{2} x^6\, dx$$

$$I = 8\left[\frac{x^3}{3}\right]_{x=-2}^{2} - 4\left[\frac{x^5}{5}\right]_{x=-2}^{2} + \frac{1}{2}\left[\frac{x^7}{7}\right]_{x=-2}^{2} = \frac{8(2)^3}{3} - \frac{8(-2)^3}{3} - \frac{4(2^5)}{5} + \frac{4(-2)^5}{5} + \frac{(2)^7}{2(7)} - \frac{(-2)^7}{2(7)}$$

$$I = \frac{8(8)}{3} - \frac{8(-8)}{3} - \frac{4(32)}{5} + \frac{4(-32)}{5} + \frac{64}{7} - \frac{-64}{7} = \frac{64}{3} + \frac{64}{3} - \frac{128}{5} - \frac{128}{5} + \frac{64}{7} + \frac{64}{7}$$

$$I = \frac{128}{3} - \frac{256}{5} + \frac{128}{7} = \frac{128(5)(7)}{(3)(5)(7)} - \frac{256(3)(7)}{(3)(5)(7)} + \frac{128(3)(5)}{(3)(5)(7)} = \frac{4480 - 5376 + 1920}{105} = \boxed{\frac{1024}{105}}$$

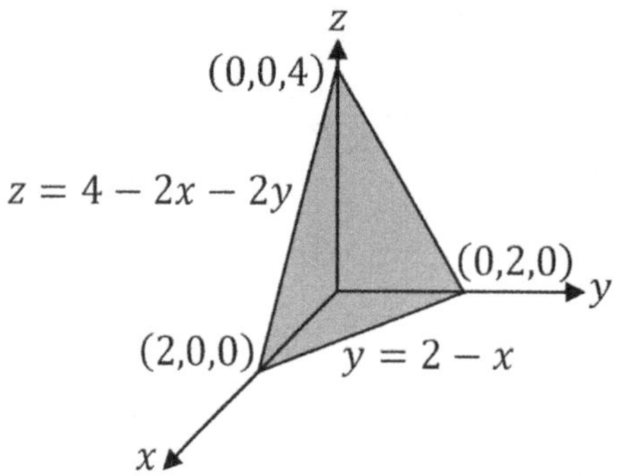

Example. Evaluate $\iint_S xy\sqrt{1+\left(\frac{\partial z}{\partial x}\right)^2+\left(\frac{\partial z}{\partial y}\right)^2}\,dxdy$ for the portion of the plane $z = 4 - 2x - 2y$ that lies in the first octant.

The plane $z = 4 - 2x - 2y$ intersects the xy plane along the line $x + y = 2$ (which can be found by setting $z = 0$). When x lies between 0 and 2 and when y lies between 0 and $2 - x$ (where the upper value comes from solving $x + y = 2$ for y), the given plane lies in the first octant.

$$I = \int_{x=0}^{2}\int_{y=0}^{2-x} xy\sqrt{1+\left[\frac{\partial}{\partial x}(4-2x-2y)\right]^2+\left[\frac{\partial}{\partial y}(4-2x-2y)\right]^2}\,dx\,dy$$

$$I = \int_{x=0}^{2}\int_{y=0}^{2-x} xy\sqrt{1+(-2)^2+(-2)^2}\,dx\,dy = \int_{x=0}^{2}\int_{y=0}^{2-x} xy\sqrt{9}\,dx\,dy = 3\int_{x=0}^{2}\int_{y=0}^{2-x} xy\,dx\,dy$$

Since y has a function in its limit, we must integrate over y first. When integrating over y, treat the independent variable x as if it were a constant.

$$I = 3\int_{x=0}^{2} x\int_{y=0}^{2-x} y\,dy\,dx = 3\int_{x=0}^{2} x\left[\frac{y^2}{2}\right]_{y=0}^{2-x} dx = \frac{3}{2}\int_{x=0}^{2} x\,(2-x)^2 dx$$

$$I = \frac{3}{2}\int_{x=0}^{2} x\,(4-4x+x^2)dx = 6\int_{x=0}^{2} x\,dx - 6\int_{x=0}^{2} x^2\,dx + \frac{3}{2}\int_{x=0}^{2} x^3\,dx$$

$$I = 6\left[\frac{x^2}{2}\right]_{x=0}^{2} - 6\left[\frac{x^3}{3}\right]_{x=0}^{2} + \frac{3}{2}\left[\frac{x^4}{4}\right]_{x=0}^{2} = \frac{6(2)^2}{2} - 0 - \frac{6(2)^3}{3} + 0 + \frac{3(2)^4}{2(4)} - 0$$

$$I = \frac{24}{2} - \frac{48}{3} + \frac{48}{8} = 12 - 16 + 6 = \boxed{2}$$

Example. Evaluate $\iiint_V z\,dV$ for the region between $z = 9 - x^2 - y^2$ and the xy plane. This problems is simpler in cylindrical coordinates. Since $x^2 + y^2 = r_c^2$, the region lies between $z = 9 - r_c^2$ and the xy plane. The equation $z = 9 - r_c^2$ represents a circular paraboloid with an apex of $(0,0,9)$. The circular paraboloid intersects the xy plane at the circle $r_c = 3$. The volume is fully mapped by letting r_c vary outward from 0 to 3, θ vary from 0 to 2π, and z vary from 0 to $9 - r_c^2$. Recall that $dV = r_c dr_c d\theta dz$ in cylindrical coordinates.

$$I = \int_{r_c=0}^{3} \int_{\theta=0}^{2\pi} \int_{z=0}^{9-r_c^2} z\, r_c dr_c\, d\theta\, dz$$

Since z has a function in its limit, we must integrate over z before we integrate over r_c. When integrating over z, treat the independent variables as if they were constants.

$$I = \int_{r_c=0}^{3} \int_{\theta=0}^{2\pi} \int_{z=0}^{9-r_c^2} z\, dz\, r_c dr_c\, d\theta = \int_{r_c=0}^{3} \int_{\theta=0}^{2\pi} \left[\frac{z^2}{2}\right]_{z=0}^{9-r_c^2} r_c dr_c\, d\theta$$

$$I = \frac{1}{2} \int_{r_c=0}^{3} \int_{\theta=0}^{2\pi} (9 - r_c^2)^2\, r_c dr_c\, d\theta = \frac{1}{2} \int_{r_c=0}^{3} \int_{\theta=0}^{2\pi} (81 - 18r_c^2 + r_c^4)\, r_c dr_c\, d\theta$$

$$I = \frac{1}{2} \int_{r_c=0}^{3} \int_{\theta=0}^{2\pi} d\theta\, (81r_c - 18r_c^3 + r_c^5)\, dr_c = \frac{1}{2} \int_{r_c=0}^{3} 2\pi(81r_c - 18r_c^3 + r_c^5)\, dr_c$$

$$I = \pi \left[\frac{81r_c^2}{2} - \frac{9r_c^4}{2} + \frac{r_c^6}{6}\right]_{r_c=0}^{3} = \frac{81\pi(3)^2}{2} - 0 - \frac{9\pi(3)^4}{2} + 0 + \frac{3^6\pi}{6} - 0$$

$$I = \frac{729\pi}{2} - \frac{729\pi}{2} + \frac{243\pi}{2} = \boxed{\frac{243\pi}{2}}$$

Example. Evaluate $\iiint_V dV$ to find the volume of a sphere with radius a in spherical coordinates.

Note: Unlike the previous examples, this integrand does not have a function. The answer to this problem will be the volume of the sphere (whereas the previous problems did not find area or volume because they had functions in the integrand). This example will apply calculus to show that the volume of a sphere equals $\frac{4}{3}\pi a^3$.

Recall that in spherical coordinates (Chapter 7), $0 \le \varphi \le \pi$ whereas $0 \le \theta \le 2\pi$. The reason that φ only varies up to π can be understood by visualizing the cone formed by the equation $\varphi = \alpha$ (where α is a constant). When α is zero, the cone shrinks down to a semi-infinite line along the $+z$-axis. As α grows, the cone grows wider. When α equals $\frac{\pi}{2}$ (or 90°), it widens so much that it becomes the xy plane. As α passes $\frac{\pi}{2}$, the cone goes below the xy plane. As α continues to grow, the cone gets narrower. When α is π, the cone shrinks down to a semi-infinite line along the $-z$-axis. Going from 0 to π covers every unique possibility for φ. **Note**: Recall that θ and φ are backwards in math compared to physics.

$$V = \int_{r=0}^{a} \int_{\theta=0}^{2\pi} \int_{\varphi=0}^{\pi} r^2 \sin\varphi \, dr \, d\theta \, d\varphi$$

Since all of the limits are constant, the order of the integration does not matter.

$$V = \left[\frac{r^3}{3}\right]_{r=0}^{a} [\theta]_{\theta=0}^{2\pi} [-\cos\varphi]_{\varphi=0}^{\pi} = \frac{a^3}{3}(2\pi)(-\cos\pi + \cos 0) = \frac{2\pi a^3}{3}[-(-1) + 1]$$

$$V = \frac{2\pi a^3}{3}(1+1) = \frac{2\pi a^3}{3}(2) = \boxed{\frac{4\pi a^3}{3}}$$

Example. Find the flux of $\vec{\mathbf{F}} = z\hat{\mathbf{i}} - x\hat{\mathbf{k}}$ through the sphere $x^2 + y^2 + z^2 = 4$.
The two angles of spherical coordinates, (θ, φ), allow the position vector $\vec{\mathbf{r}} = x\hat{\mathbf{i}} + y\hat{\mathbf{j}} + z\hat{\mathbf{k}}$ to map every point on the sphere via $x = 2\cos\theta\sin\varphi$, $y = 2\sin\theta\sin\varphi$, and $z = 2\cos\varphi$ (since this sphere has a radius of $a = 2$). Earlier in this chapter, we showed that $\vec{\mathbf{r}}_\varphi \times \vec{\mathbf{r}}_\theta = a^2\hat{\mathbf{i}}\cos\theta\sin^2\varphi + a^2\hat{\mathbf{j}}\sin\theta\sin^2\varphi + a^2\hat{\mathbf{k}}\sin\varphi\cos\varphi$ for the case of a sphere. The flux integral is $\iint_S \vec{\mathbf{F}} \cdot d\vec{\mathbf{A}} = \iint_S \vec{\mathbf{F}} \cdot \hat{\mathbf{n}} dA = \iint_S \vec{\mathbf{F}} \cdot (\vec{\mathbf{r}}_\varphi \times \vec{\mathbf{r}}_\theta) d\theta d\varphi$.

$$\vec{\mathbf{F}} \cdot (\vec{\mathbf{r}}_\varphi \times \vec{\mathbf{r}}_\theta) = (z\hat{\mathbf{i}} - x\hat{\mathbf{k}}) \cdot (2^2\hat{\mathbf{i}}\cos\theta\sin^2\varphi + 2^2\hat{\mathbf{j}}\sin\theta\sin^2\varphi + 2^2\hat{\mathbf{k}}\sin\varphi\cos\varphi)$$

$$\vec{\mathbf{F}} \cdot (\vec{\mathbf{r}}_\varphi \times \vec{\mathbf{r}}_\theta) = 4z\cos\theta\sin^2\varphi - 4x\sin\varphi\cos\varphi$$

$$\Phi = \iint_S \vec{\mathbf{F}} \cdot (\vec{\mathbf{r}}_\varphi \times \vec{\mathbf{r}}_\theta) d\theta d\varphi = 4\int_{\theta=0}^{2\pi}\int_{\varphi=0}^{\pi} z\cos\theta\sin^2\varphi \, d\theta \, d\varphi - 4\int_{\theta=0}^{2\pi}\int_{\varphi=0}^{\pi} x\sin\varphi\cos\varphi \, d\theta \, d\varphi$$

Since $a = 2$, $x = 2\cos\theta\sin\varphi$ and $z = 2\cos\varphi$. Observe that the two terms cancel out.

$$\Phi = 4\int_{\theta=0}^{2\pi}\int_{\varphi=0}^{\pi} 2\cos\theta\sin^2\varphi\cos\varphi \, d\theta \, d\varphi - 4\int_{\theta=0}^{2\pi}\int_{\varphi=0}^{\pi} 2\cos\theta\sin^2\varphi\cos\varphi \, d\theta \, d\varphi = \boxed{0}$$

Chapter 14 Exercises – Part A

Directions: Use a double integral to find each surface area.

❶ the (smaller) area between the line $y = 1 - x$ and the circle $x^2 + y^2 = 1$

❷ the cardioid $r = 1 + \sin\theta$, where $0 \leq \theta \leq 2\pi$

❸ the portion of $z = x^2 - y^2$ that lies above the disc $x^2 + y^2 \leq 4$

❹ the (total) surface of a hemisphere with radius a (including its base area)

❖ Check your answers at the back of the book.

Chapter 14 Exercises – Part B

Directions: Use a triple integral to find each volume.

❺ between $z = x^2 + y^2$ and the plane $z = 9$

❻ the portion of $z = \sin x \cos y$ that lies above the square $0 \leq x \leq \frac{\pi}{2}, 0 \leq y \leq \frac{\pi}{2}$

❼ the tetrahedron with vertices at $(0,0,0)$, $(1,0,0)$, $(0,1,0)$, and $(0,0,1)$

❽ the volume of a right-circular cone with radius a and height h

❖ Check your answers at the back of the book.

Chapter 14 Exercises – Part C

Directions: Evaluate each integral over the indicated region.

❾ $\iint_S xy\, dA$ for the triangle with vertices at (1,1), (2,1), and (1,2)

❿ $\iiint_V z^2\, dV$ for the hemisphere $r = 4$ where $z > 0$

⓫ $\iint_S xy\sqrt{1 + \left(\frac{\partial z}{\partial x}\right)^2 + \left(\frac{\partial z}{\partial y}\right)^2}\, dxdy$ for the portion of $z = x^2 + y$ that lies above the rectangle with vertices at (0,0,0), (2,0,0), (0,4,0), and (2,4,0)

❖ Check your answers at the back of the book.

Chapter 14 Exercises – Part D

Directions: Find the flux of each field through the indicated surface.

⓬ $\vec{\mathbf{F}} = x\hat{\mathbf{i}} + y\hat{\mathbf{j}} + z\hat{\mathbf{k}}$ through the part of $z = 6 - 3x - 2y$ that lies in the first octant (an open surface)

⓭ $\vec{\mathbf{F}} = z^3\hat{\mathbf{k}}$ through $x^2 + y^2 + z^2 = 9$ (a closed surface)

⓮ $\vec{\mathbf{F}} = y\hat{\mathbf{i}} - z\hat{\mathbf{k}}$ through the region enclosed by $z = x^2 + y^2$ and $z = 9$ (a closed surface)

❖ Check your answers at the back of the book.

15 Center of Mass and Moment of Inertia

The **center of mass** of a continuous body has the following Cartesian coordinates

$$x_{cm} = \frac{1}{m}\int x\,dm \quad , \quad y_{cm} = \frac{1}{m}\int y\,dm \quad , \quad z_{cm} = \frac{1}{m}\int y\,dm$$

where $m = \int dm$ is the total mass of the object and the differential mass element is:

$$dm = \begin{cases} \lambda ds & \text{along an arc length} \\ \sigma dA & \text{on a surface} \\ \rho dV & \text{in a volume} \end{cases}$$

where λ is the linear mass density, σ is the mass per unit area, and ρ is the density of a three-dimensional solid. For an object that has uniform density, λ, σ, or ρ is constant and equals the total mass of the object (m) divided by its total length, total area, or total volume, respectively. For an object that has non-uniform density, λ, σ, or ρ is not a constant, but is generally given as a function of the coordinates in the problem.

The **moment of inertia** of a continuous body is:

$$I = \int r_\perp^2\,dm$$

where $r_\perp$ is the distance between the axis of rotation (which is a line about which the object rotates or is to be rotated, usually specified in a problem) and each infinitesimal dm of the integral (imagine dividing the body up into an infinite number of dm's). For a specific problem, express $r_\perp$ in terms of coordinates that apply to every dm that makes up the object (as illustrated in the examples). A larger **moment of inertia** means that more torque is required to achieve a given angular acceleration.

For an integral over an arc length, recall the expressions for ds from Chapter 13. For example, ds becomes dx for a straight line parallel to the x-axis and ds becomes $rd\theta$ for a circular arc in the xy plane with the center of the circle at the origin. For an integral over a surface or volume, recall the expressions for dA and dV from Chapter 14. For example, dA becomes $dxdy$ for a planar surface in the xy plane, dA becomes $rdrd\theta$ in 2D polar coordinates, dA becomes $a^2 \sin\varphi\, d\theta d\varphi$ for a thin sphere centered about the origin, dV becomes $dxdydz$ in Cartesian coordinates, dV becomes $r_c dr_c d\theta dz$ in cylindrical coordinates, and dV becomes $r^2 \sin\varphi\, drd\theta d\varphi$ in spherical coordinates.

Example. Find the center of mass of a thin rod lying on the x-axis with endpoints at the origin and $(L, 0)$ if the rod has non-uniform density $\lambda = kx$, where k is a constant. Express the final answer in terms of L only.

The center of mass integral can be performed starting with a series of substitutions. It pays to do these substitutions carefully one step at a time (otherwise, it is easy to drop an important factor along the way). For a long thin rod, $dm = \lambda ds$. For a straight rod along the x-axis, $ds = dx$. For a non-uniform rod, it would be a mistake to pull λ out of the integral; instead, we must use the equation $\lambda = kx$ given in the problem.

$$x_{cm} = \frac{1}{m}\int x\, dm = \frac{1}{m}\int x\, \lambda ds = \frac{1}{m}\int_{x=0}^{L} x\, \lambda dx = \frac{1}{m}\int_{x=0}^{L} x\,(kx) dx = \frac{k}{m}\int_{x=0}^{L} x^2\, dx$$

$$x_{cm} = \frac{k}{m}\left[\frac{x^3}{3}\right]_{x=0}^{L} = \frac{k}{m}\left(\frac{L^3}{3} - \frac{0^3}{3}\right) = \frac{kL^3}{3m}$$

To eliminate k and m from the answer, perform the integral $m = \int dm$ using the same substitutions as before.

$$m = \int dm = \int \lambda\, ds = \int_{x=0}^{L} \lambda\, dx = \int_{x=0}^{L} kx\, dx = k\int_{x=0}^{L} x\, dx = k\left[\frac{x^2}{2}\right]_{x=0}^{L} = \frac{kL^2}{2}$$

Isolate k in the above equation to see that $\frac{2m}{L^2} = k$. Plug this into the equation for x_{cm}.

$$x_{cm} = \frac{kL^3}{3m} = \frac{2m}{L^2}\frac{L^3}{3m} = \boxed{\frac{2L}{3}}$$

If you think about the answer, it should make sense. If the rod were uniform, it would have a center of mass at $\left(\frac{L}{2}, 0\right)$. Since the rod has non-uniform density $\lambda = kx$, which is proportional to x, there is less mass near the origin and more mass near the other end. The answer $\frac{2L}{3}$ is greater than $\frac{L}{2}$, which agrees with this observation.

Example. A uniform rod lies on the x-axis with endpoints at the origin and $(L, 0)$. The rod will rotate about an axis that is parallel to the y-axis and which passes through $\left(\frac{L}{2}, 0\right)$. Find the moment of inertia of the rod about this axis. Express the answer in terms of the mass of the rod and L only.

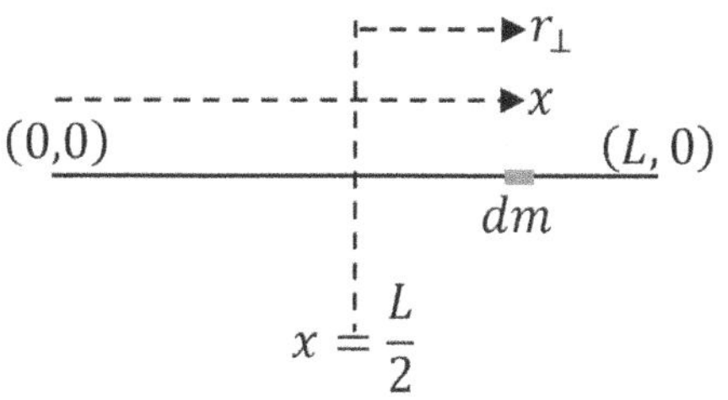

In the figure above, the axis of rotation is the vertical dashed line where $x = \frac{L}{2}$. Since the origin lies at the left end of the rod, x is measured from the origin to dm, whereas $r_\perp$ is measured from the axis of rotation to dm. In this example, $r_\perp = x - \frac{L}{2}$. (Since $r_\perp$ will get squared in the integral, it doesn't matter whether we use $x - \frac{L}{2}$ or $\frac{L}{2} - x$.) For a rod, $dm = \lambda ds$. For a straight rod along the x-axis, $ds = dx$. For a uniform rod, $\lambda = \frac{m}{L}$ is a constant (equal to the mass per unit length).

$$I = \int r_\perp^2\, dm = \int \left(x - \frac{L}{2}\right)^2 \lambda ds = \int_{x=0}^{L} \left(x - \frac{L}{2}\right)^2 \left(\frac{m}{L}\right) dx = \frac{m}{L} \int_{x=0}^{L} \left(x - \frac{L}{2}\right)^2 dx$$

$$I = \frac{m}{L} \int_{x=0}^{L} \left(x^2 - xL + \frac{L^2}{4}\right) dx = \frac{m}{L}\left[\frac{x^3}{3} - \frac{x^2 L}{2} + \frac{xL^2}{4}\right]_{x=0}^{L} = \frac{m}{L}\left(\frac{L^3}{3} - \frac{L^3}{2} + \frac{L^3}{4}\right)$$

$$I = \frac{mL^3}{L}\left(\frac{4}{12} - \frac{6}{12} + \frac{3}{12}\right) = mL^2\left(\frac{1}{12}\right) = \boxed{\frac{mL^2}{12}}$$

Example. One-half of a solid disc with radius a lies in the xy plane as shown below. Find its center of mass. Express the final answer in terms of a only.

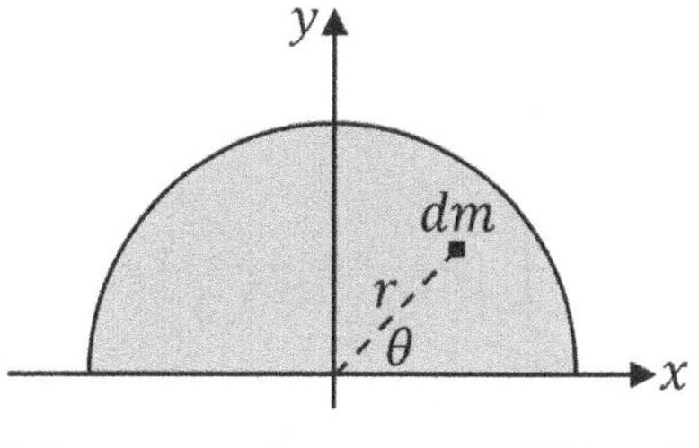

For a solid disc, $dm = \sigma dA$. It is convenient to use 2D polar coordinates: $dA = r dr d\theta$. For a uniform solid disc, $\sigma = \frac{m}{A}$ is a constant (equal to the mass per unit area). For one-half of a solid disc, $A = \frac{\pi a^2}{2}$ and $0 \leq \theta \leq \pi$. In 2D polar coordinates, $y = r \sin\theta$.

$$y_{cm} = \frac{1}{m}\int y\,dm = \frac{1}{m}\int y\,\sigma dA = \frac{1}{m}\int_{r=0}^{a}\int_{\theta=0}^{\pi}(r\sin\theta)\left(\frac{m}{A}\right)rdrd\theta = \frac{1}{A}\int_{r=0}^{a}\int_{\theta=0}^{\pi} r^2 \sin\theta\,dr\,d\theta$$

$$y_{cm} = \frac{1}{\pi a^2/2}\left[\frac{r^3}{3}\right]_{r=0}^{a}[-\cos\theta]_{\theta=0}^{\pi} = \frac{2}{\pi a^2}\frac{a^3}{3}(-\cos\pi + \cos 0) = \frac{2a}{3\pi}(1+1) = \boxed{\frac{4a}{3\pi}}$$

By symmetry, it should be clear that $x_{cm} = \boxed{0}$. It should make sense that $\frac{4a}{3\pi} \approx 0.4244a$ is less than one-half of the radius because there is more mass at the bottom of the half-disc than at its top.

Example. A uniform solid disc with radius a lies in the xy plane with its center at the origin. Find the moment of inertia of the disc about the x-axis and about the z-axis. Express the final answers in terms of the mass of the disc and a only.

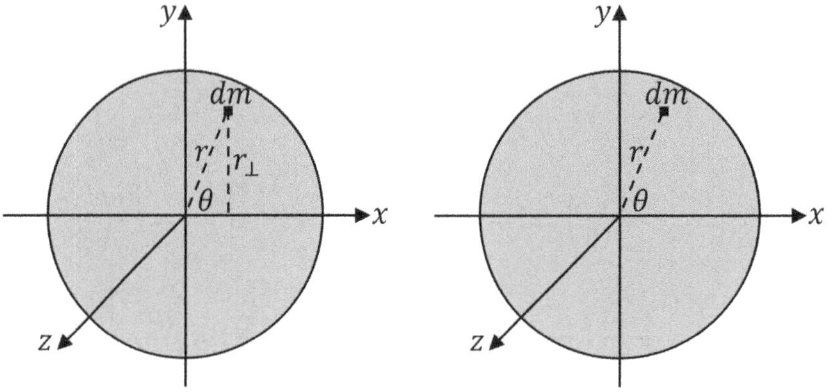

For a solid disc, $dm = \sigma dA$. It is convenient to use 2D polar coordinates: $dA = rdrd\theta$. For a uniform solid disc, $\sigma = \frac{m}{A}$ is a constant (equal to the mass per unit area). For a solid disc, $A = \pi a^2$. If the x-axis is the axis of rotation, $r_\perp = y = r\sin\theta$ because that is the distance from the x-axis to each dm (left figure above).

$$I_x = \int r_\perp^2\,dm = \int y^2\,\sigma dA = \int_{r=0}^{a}\int_{\theta=0}^{2\pi}(r\sin\theta)^2\left(\frac{m}{A}\right)rdrd\theta = \frac{m}{A}\int_{r=0}^{a}\int_{\theta=0}^{2\pi} r^3\sin^2\theta\,dr\,d\theta$$

Recall the trig identity $\sin^2\theta = \frac{1-\cos 2\theta}{2}$.

$$I_x = \frac{m}{\pi a^2}\left[\frac{r^4}{4}\right]_{r=0}^{a}\int_{\theta=0}^{2\pi}\frac{1-\cos 2\theta}{2}d\theta = \frac{m}{\pi a^2}\frac{a^4}{4}\left[\frac{\theta}{2} - \frac{\sin 2\theta}{4}\right]_{\theta=0}^{2\pi}$$

$$I_x = \frac{ma^2}{4\pi}\left(\frac{2\pi}{2} - \frac{0}{2} - \frac{\sin 4\pi}{4} + \frac{\sin 0}{4}\right) = \frac{ma^2}{4\pi}(\pi - 0) = \frac{ma^2}{4\pi}(\pi) = \boxed{\frac{ma^2}{4}}$$

If the z-axis is the axis of rotation, $r_\perp = r$ (whereas $r_\perp = y = r\sin\theta$ if the x-axis is the axis of rotation). It instructive to compare the integral below with the integral on the previous page.

$$I_z = \int r_\perp^2\, dm = \int r^2\, \sigma dA = \int_{r=0}^{a}\int_{\theta=0}^{2\pi} r^2 \left(\frac{m}{A}\right) r dr d\theta = \frac{m}{A}\int_{r=0}^{a}\int_{\theta=0}^{2\pi} r^3\, dr\, d\theta$$

$$I_z = \frac{m}{\pi a^2}\left[\frac{r^4}{4}\right]_{r=0}^{a} [\theta]_{\theta=0}^{2\pi} = \frac{m}{\pi a^2}\left(\frac{a^4}{4}\right)(2\pi) = \boxed{\frac{ma^2}{2}}$$

The moment of inertia is larger in rolling mode $\left(I_z = \frac{ma^2}{2}\right)$ than it is in flipping mode $\left(I_x = I_y = \frac{ma^2}{4}\right)$ because a greater percentage of the mass is farther away from the axis of rotation (on average) in rolling mode. For example, you can see that only the center of the disc lies on the axis of rotation in rolling mode, whereas an entire diameter (on the x-axis) lies on the axis of rotation in flipping mode.

Example. A uniform ball (which is a solid sphere) with radius a has its center at the origin. Find the moment of inertia of the ball about the z-axis. Express the final answer in terms of the mass of the sphere and a only.

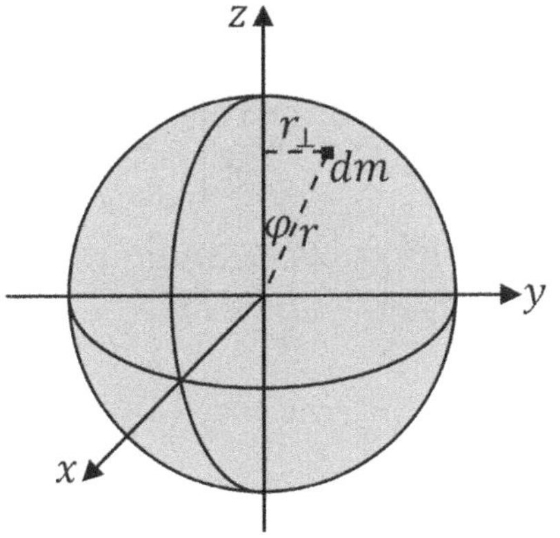

For a solid sphere, $dm = \rho dV$. In spherical coordinates, $dV = r^2 \sin\varphi\, dr d\theta d\varphi$. For a uniform solid sphere, $\rho = \frac{m}{V}$ is a constant (equal to the mass per unit volume). For a sphere, $V = \frac{4\pi a^3}{3}$. Since the z-axis is the axis of rotation, $r_\perp = r\sin\varphi$ because that is the distance from the z-axis to each dm. Observe that $r_\perp$ is opposite to φ in the right triangle shown in the previous diagram. Recall that the polar angle (or zenith angle) lies in the interval $0 \le \varphi \le \pi$ whereas the azimuthal angle lies in the interval $0 \le \theta \le 2\pi$ (Chapter 7).

$$I = \int r_\perp^2\, dm = \int (r \sin\varphi)^2 \rho dV = \int_{r=0}^{a} \int_{\theta=0}^{2\pi} \int_{\varphi=0}^{\pi} r^2 \sin^2\varphi \left(\frac{m}{V}\right) r^2 \sin\varphi\, dr d\theta d\varphi$$

$$I = \frac{m}{V} \int_{r=0}^{a} \int_{\theta=0}^{2\pi} \int_{\varphi=0}^{\pi} r^4 \sin^3\varphi\, dr\, d\theta\, d\varphi = \frac{m}{4\pi a^3/3} \left[\frac{r^5}{5}\right]_{r=0}^{a} [\theta]_{\theta=0}^{2\pi} \int_{\varphi=0}^{\pi} \sin^3\varphi\, d\varphi$$

Recall the trig identity $\sin^2\varphi = 1 - \cos^2\varphi$. Note that the volume of a sphere is $\frac{4\pi a^3}{3}$.

$$I = \frac{3m}{4\pi a^3}\left(\frac{a^5}{5}\right)(2\pi) \int_{\varphi=0}^{\pi} \sin\varphi\,(1 - \cos^2\varphi)\, d\varphi$$

$$I = \frac{3ma^2}{10} \int_{\varphi=0}^{\pi} \sin\varphi\, d\varphi - \frac{3ma^2}{10} \int_{\varphi=0}^{\pi} \sin\varphi \cos^2\varphi\, d\varphi$$

Let $u = \cos\varphi$ such that $du = -\sin\varphi\, d\varphi$. When $\varphi = 0$, $u = 1$. When $\varphi = \pi$, $u = -1$.

$$I = \frac{3ma^2}{10}[-\cos\varphi]_{\varphi=0}^{\pi} - \frac{3ma^2}{10} \int_{u=1}^{-1} u^2\,(-du) = \frac{3ma^2}{10}(-\cos\pi + 1) + \frac{3ma^2}{10}\left[\frac{u^3}{3}\right]_{u=1}^{-1}$$

Note: The two minus signs made a plus sign for the second term.

$$I = \frac{3ma^2}{10}(1+1) + \frac{3ma^2}{10}\left[\frac{(-1)^3}{3} - \frac{1^3}{3}\right] = \frac{3ma^2}{10}(2) + \frac{3ma^2}{10}\left(-\frac{1}{3} - \frac{1}{3}\right)$$

$$I = \frac{3ma^2}{5} + \frac{3ma^2}{10}\left(-\frac{2}{3}\right) = \frac{3ma^2}{5} - \frac{ma^2}{5} = \boxed{\frac{2ma^2}{5}}$$

Chapter 15 Exercises – Part A

Directions: Express the center of mass of each object in terms of a characteristic length.

❶ a non-uniform rod with endpoints at $(0,0)$ and $(0, L)$, where $\lambda = k\sqrt{y}$

❷ a thin uniform semicircular arc with radius a with its apex at $(0, a)$ and endpoints at $(\pm a, 0)$

❸ a solid uniform quarter disc with radius a in the first quadrant with its edges along the coordinate axes

❹ a solid uniform triangular sheet with endpoints at $(0,0)$, $(b, 0)$, and $(0, h)$

❖ Check your answers at the back of the book.

Chapter 15 Exercises – Part B

Directions: Express the center of mass of each object in terms of a characteristic length.

❺ one-half of a solid non-uniform disc with radius a with its base along the y-axis and its apex at $(a, 0)$, where $\sigma = kr$

❻ a solid uniform region between the paraboloid $z = r_c^2$ and the plane $z = 9$

❼ a solid uniform hemisphere with radius a with its base in the xy plane, centered about the z-axis with its apex at $(0,0,a)$

❽ a solid uniform cone with radius a and height h with its base in the xy plane and its apex at $(0,0,h)$

❖ Check your answers at the back of the book.

Chapter 15 Exercises – Part C

Directions: Find the moment of inertia of each object about the indicated axis. Express each answer as a number times mass times a characteristic length squared.

❾ a uniform rod with endpoints at $(0,0)$ and $(0, L)$ about the x-axis

❿ a non-uniform rod with endpoints at $(0,0)$ and $(L, 0)$ about the line $x = \frac{L}{4}$, where $\lambda = kx$

⓫ a very thin uniform ring with radius a lying in the xy plane, centered about the origin, about the y-axis

⓬ a solid non-uniform disc with radius a lying in the xy plane, centered about the origin, about the z-axis, where $\sigma = kr$

❖ Check your answers at the back of the book.

Chapter 15 Exercises – Part D

Directions: Find the moment of inertia of each object about the indicated axis. Express each answer as a number times mass times a characteristic length squared.

⓭ a solid uniform very thin hollow sphere with radius a centered about the origin, about the z-axis

⓮ a solid uniform triangular sheet with endpoints at $(0,0)$, $(b, 0)$, and $(0, h)$, about the y-axis

⓯ a non-uniform ball (which is a solid sphere) with radius a centered about the origin, about the z-axis, where $\rho = kr$

⓰ a solid uniform cone with radius a and height h with its base in the xy plane and its apex at $(0,0, h)$, about the z-axis

❖ Check your answers at the back of the book.

Solutions

Chapter 1, Part A

❶ $\frac{\partial z}{\partial x} = \frac{\partial}{\partial x}\frac{x^3y^6}{3} = \frac{y^6}{3}\frac{\partial}{\partial x}x^3 = \frac{y^6}{3}(3x^2) = \boxed{x^2y^6}$

$\frac{\partial z}{\partial y} = \frac{\partial}{\partial y}\frac{x^3y^6}{3} = \frac{x^3}{3}\frac{\partial}{\partial y}y^6 = \frac{x^3}{3}(6y^5) = \boxed{2x^3y^5}$

❷ $\frac{\partial z}{\partial x} = \frac{\partial}{\partial x}\frac{x}{y} = \frac{1}{y}\frac{\partial}{\partial x}x = \frac{1}{y}(1) = \boxed{\frac{1}{y}}$

$\frac{\partial z}{\partial y} = \frac{\partial}{\partial y}\frac{x}{y} = x\frac{\partial}{\partial y}\frac{1}{y} = x\frac{\partial}{\partial y}y^{-1} = x(-y^{-2}) = x\left(-\frac{1}{y^2}\right) = \boxed{-\frac{x}{y^2}}$

❸ $\frac{\partial f}{\partial x} = \frac{\partial}{\partial x}x\sqrt{y} = \sqrt{y}\frac{\partial}{\partial x}x = \sqrt{y}(1) = \boxed{\sqrt{y}}$

$\frac{\partial f}{\partial y} = \frac{\partial}{\partial y}x\sqrt{y} = x\frac{\partial}{\partial y}\sqrt{y} = x\frac{\partial}{\partial y}y^{1/2} = x\left(\frac{1}{2}y^{-1/2}\right) = x\left(\frac{1}{2y^{1/2}}\right) = x\left(\frac{1}{2\sqrt{y}}\right) = \frac{x}{2\sqrt{y}}$

$= \frac{x}{2\sqrt{y}}\frac{\sqrt{y}}{\sqrt{y}} = \boxed{\frac{x\sqrt{y}}{2y}}$

Note: To put the final answer in standard form, we multiplied by $\frac{\sqrt{y}}{\sqrt{y}}$ in order to rationalize the denominator. The answers $\frac{x}{2\sqrt{y}}$ and $\frac{x\sqrt{y}}{2y}$ are otherwise equivalent.

❹ $\frac{\partial w}{\partial t} = \frac{\partial}{\partial t}\sin t\cos u = \cos u\frac{\partial}{\partial t}\sin t = \cos u\,(\cos t) = \boxed{\cos t\cos u}$

$\frac{\partial w}{\partial u} = \frac{\partial}{\partial u}\sin t\cos u = \sin t\frac{\partial}{\partial u}\cos u = \sin u\,(-\sin t) = \boxed{-\sin t\sin u}$

Chapter 1, Part B

❺ $\frac{\partial g}{\partial x} = \frac{\partial}{\partial x}e^y\ln x = e^y\frac{\partial}{\partial x}\ln x = e^y\left(\frac{1}{x}\right) = \boxed{\frac{e^y}{x}}$

$\frac{\partial g}{\partial y} = \frac{\partial}{\partial y}e^y\ln x = \ln x\frac{\partial}{\partial y}e^y = \ln x\,(e^y) = \boxed{e^y\ln x}$

❻ $\frac{\partial z}{\partial x} = \frac{\partial}{\partial x}(x^4 + 2x^2y^2) = \frac{\partial}{\partial x}x^4 + 2y^2\frac{\partial}{\partial x}x^2 = 4x^3 + 2y^2(2x) = \boxed{4x^3 + 4xy^2}$

$\frac{\partial z}{\partial y} = \frac{\partial}{\partial y}(x^4 + 2x^2y^2) = x^4\frac{\partial}{\partial y}(1) + 2x^2\frac{\partial}{\partial y}y^2 = x^4(0) + 2x^2(2y) = \boxed{4x^2y}$

7 $\frac{\partial u}{\partial p} = \frac{\partial}{\partial p}\sqrt{p^2 - q^2} = \frac{1}{2}\frac{2p}{\sqrt{p^2-q^2}} = \boxed{\frac{p}{\sqrt{p^2-q^2}}}$

$\frac{\partial u}{\partial q} = \frac{\partial}{\partial q}\sqrt{p^2 - q^2} = \frac{1}{2}\frac{-2q}{\sqrt{p^2-q^2}} = \boxed{\frac{-q}{\sqrt{p^2-q^2}}}$

Note: Recall the chain rule from calculus. Let $u = p^2 - q^2$ and $f = \sqrt{u}$ such that $\frac{df}{dp} = \frac{d}{dp}\sqrt{u} = \frac{df}{du}\frac{du}{dp} = \left(\frac{d}{du}\sqrt{u}\right)\left(\frac{du}{dp}\right) = \left(\frac{d}{du}u^{1/2}\right)\left[\frac{d}{dp}(p^2 - q^2)\right] = \frac{1}{2}u^{-1/2}(2p) = \frac{p}{u^{1/2}} = \frac{p}{\sqrt{u}} = \frac{p}{\sqrt{p^2-q^2}}$ and similarly for the derivative with respect to q. Since we are treating q as a constant for $\frac{\partial u}{\partial p}$, we may use the chain rule for a function of one variable.

8 $\frac{\partial h}{\partial t} = \frac{\partial}{\partial t}\ln(t^2 + tu) = \frac{1}{t^2+tu}\frac{\partial}{\partial t}(t^2 + tu) = \boxed{\frac{2t+u}{t^2+tu}}$

$\frac{\partial h}{\partial u} = \frac{\partial}{\partial u}\ln(t^2 + tu) = \frac{1}{t^2+tu}\frac{\partial}{\partial u}(t^2 + tu) = \boxed{\frac{t}{t^2+tu}}$

Note: As in the solution to Exercise 7, we applied the chain rule.

Chapter 1, Part C

9 $\frac{\partial f}{\partial x} = \frac{\partial}{\partial x}\frac{x^4}{y^2} = \frac{1}{y^2}\frac{\partial}{\partial x}x^4 = \frac{1}{y^2}(4x^3) = \frac{4x^3}{y^2}$

$\frac{\partial^2 f}{\partial x^2} = \frac{\partial}{\partial x}\left(\frac{\partial f}{\partial x}\right) = \frac{\partial}{\partial x}\frac{4x^3}{y^2} = \frac{4}{y^2}\frac{\partial}{\partial x}x^3 = \frac{4}{y^2}(3x^2) = \boxed{\frac{12x^2}{y^2}}$

$\frac{\partial f}{\partial y} = \frac{\partial}{\partial y}\frac{x^4}{y^2} = x^4\frac{\partial}{\partial y}\frac{1}{y^2} = x^4\frac{\partial}{\partial y}y^{-2} = x^4(-2y^{-3}) = -\frac{2x^4}{y^3}$

$\frac{\partial^2 f}{\partial y^2} = \frac{\partial}{\partial y}\left(\frac{\partial f}{\partial y}\right) = \frac{\partial}{\partial y}\left(-\frac{2x^4}{y^3}\right) = -2x^4\frac{\partial}{\partial y}\frac{1}{y^3} = -2x^4\frac{\partial}{\partial y}y^{-3} = -2x^4(-3y^{-4}) = \boxed{\frac{6x^4}{y^4}}$

10 $\frac{\partial w}{\partial t} = \frac{\partial}{\partial t}t^2\sin u = \sin u\frac{\partial}{\partial t}t^2 = \sin u\,(2t) = 2t\sin u$

$\frac{\partial^2 w}{\partial t^2} = \frac{\partial}{\partial t}\left(\frac{\partial w}{\partial t}\right) = \frac{\partial}{\partial t}2t\sin u = 2\sin u\frac{\partial}{\partial t}t = 2\sin u\,(1) = \boxed{2\sin u}$

$\frac{\partial w}{\partial u} = \frac{\partial}{\partial u}t^2\sin u = t^2\frac{\partial}{\partial u}\sin u = t^2\cos u$

$\frac{\partial^2 w}{\partial u^2} = \frac{\partial}{\partial u}\left(\frac{\partial w}{\partial u}\right) = \frac{\partial}{\partial u}t^2\cos u = t^2\frac{\partial}{\partial u}\cos u = t^2(-\sin u) = \boxed{-t^2\sin u}$

Chapter 1, Part D

11 $\frac{\partial z}{\partial x} = \frac{\partial}{\partial x}\frac{x^8y^4}{4} = \frac{y^4}{4}\frac{\partial}{\partial x}x^8 = \frac{y^4}{4}(8x^7) = 2x^7y^4$

$\frac{\partial^2 z}{\partial y \partial x} = \frac{\partial}{\partial y}\left(\frac{\partial z}{\partial x}\right) = \frac{\partial}{\partial y}2x^7y^4 = 2x^7\frac{\partial}{\partial y}y^4 = 2x^7(4y^3) = \boxed{8x^7y^3}$

$\frac{\partial z}{\partial y} = \frac{\partial}{\partial y}\frac{x^8y^4}{4} = \frac{x^8}{4}\frac{\partial}{\partial y}y^4 = \frac{x^8}{4}(4y^3) = x^8y^3$

$\frac{\partial^2 z}{\partial x \partial y} = \frac{\partial}{\partial x}\left(\frac{\partial z}{\partial y}\right) = \frac{\partial}{\partial x}x^8y^3 = y^3\frac{\partial}{\partial x}x^8 = y^3(8x^7) = \boxed{8x^7y^3}$

Note: For most common standard functions, the mixed second partial derivatives $\frac{\partial^2 z}{\partial y \partial x}$ and $\frac{\partial^2 z}{\partial x \partial y}$ are equal, except near discontinuities, in accordance with Clairaut's theorem. In Chapter 13, we will see that this relates to conservative fields.

12 $\frac{\partial z}{\partial x} = \frac{\partial}{\partial x}e^{xy} = ye^{xy}$

$\frac{\partial^2 z}{\partial y \partial x} = \frac{\partial}{\partial y}\left(\frac{\partial z}{\partial x}\right) = \frac{\partial}{\partial y}ye^{xy} = e^{xy}\frac{\partial}{\partial y}y + y\frac{\partial}{\partial y}e^{xy} = \boxed{e^{xy} + xye^{xy}} = \boxed{(1+xy)e^{xy}}$

$\frac{\partial z}{\partial y} = \frac{\partial}{\partial y}e^{xy} = xe^{xy}$

$\frac{\partial^2 z}{\partial x \partial y} = \frac{\partial}{\partial x}\left(\frac{\partial z}{\partial y}\right) = \frac{\partial}{\partial x}xe^{xy} = e^{xy}\frac{\partial}{\partial x}x + x\frac{\partial}{\partial x}e^{xy} = \boxed{e^{xy} + xye^{xy}} = \boxed{(1+xy)e^{xy}}$

Notes: Use the chain rule, $\frac{dz}{dx} = \frac{dz}{du}\frac{du}{dx}$, with $u = xy$ to show that $\frac{d}{dx}e^{xy} = \frac{d}{dx}e^u = \frac{d}{du}e^u\frac{du}{dx} = e^u\left(\frac{d}{dx}xy\right) = ye^u = ye^{xy}$. Similarly, $\frac{d}{dy}e^{xy} = xe^{xy}$. See the note to Exercise 7 regarding the chain rule.

Recall the product rule: $\frac{d}{dx}(pq) = p\frac{dq}{dx} + q\frac{dp}{dx}$. For example, let $p = x$ and $q = e^{xy}$ to see that $\frac{d}{dx}xe^{xy} = \frac{d}{dx}pq = p\frac{dq}{dx} + q\frac{dp}{dx} = x\frac{d}{dx}e^{xy} + e^{xy}\frac{d}{dx}x = xy\,e^{xy} + e^{xy} = e^{xy} + xye^{xy}$. Similarly, $\frac{d}{dy}ye^{xy} = e^{xy} + xye^{xy}$. (When this is applies to the partial derivatives, note that we are treating the other independent variable as a constant.)

Chapter 2, Part A

1 $\frac{\partial z}{\partial s} = \frac{\partial z}{\partial x}\frac{\partial x}{\partial s} + \frac{\partial z}{\partial y}\frac{\partial y}{\partial s} = \left(\frac{\partial}{\partial x}x^5\sqrt{y}\right)\left[\frac{\partial}{\partial s}(s^4+t^2)\right] + \left(\frac{\partial}{\partial y}x^5\sqrt{y}\right)\left[\frac{\partial}{\partial s}(s^4-t^4)\right]$

$\frac{\partial z}{\partial s} = (5x^4\sqrt{y})(4s^3) + \left(\frac{x^5}{2\sqrt{y}}\right)(4s^3) = 20s^3(s^4+t^2)^4\sqrt{s^4-t^4} + \frac{2s^3(s^4+t^2)^5}{\sqrt{s^4-t^4}}$

$\frac{\partial z}{\partial s} = \boxed{20s^3(s^4+t^2)^4\sqrt{s^4-t^4} + \frac{2s^3(s^4+t^2)^5\sqrt{s^4-t^4}}{(s^4-t^4)}}$

$\frac{\partial z}{\partial t} = \frac{\partial z}{\partial x}\frac{\partial x}{\partial t} + \frac{\partial z}{\partial y}\frac{\partial y}{\partial t} = \left(\frac{\partial}{\partial x}x^5\sqrt{y}\right)\left[\frac{\partial}{\partial t}(s^4+t^2)\right] + \left(\frac{\partial}{\partial y}x^5\sqrt{y}\right)\left[\frac{\partial}{\partial t}(s^4-t^4)\right]$

$\frac{\partial z}{\partial t} = (5x^4\sqrt{y})(2t) + \left(\frac{x^5}{2\sqrt{y}}\right)(-4t^3) = 10t(s^4+t^2)^4\sqrt{s^4-t^4} - \frac{2t^3(s^4+t^2)^5}{\sqrt{s^4-t^4}}$

$\frac{\partial z}{\partial t} = \boxed{10t(s^4+t^2)^4\sqrt{s^4-t^4} - \frac{2t^3(s^4+t^2)^5\sqrt{s^4-t^4}}{(s^4-t^4)}}$

Notes: In the last step, we multiplied by $\frac{\sqrt{s^4-t^4}}{\sqrt{s^4-t^4}}$ in order to rationalize the denominator. Note that $\frac{d}{dy}\sqrt{y} = \frac{d}{dy}y^{1/2} = \frac{1}{2}y^{-1/2} = \frac{1}{2y^{1/2}} = \frac{1}{2\sqrt{y}}$.

2 $\frac{\partial f}{\partial p} = \frac{\partial f}{\partial x}\frac{\partial x}{\partial p} + \frac{\partial f}{\partial y}\frac{\partial y}{\partial p} = \left(\frac{\partial}{\partial x}\ln x\cos y\right)\left(\frac{\partial}{\partial p}p^3q^2\right) + \left(\frac{\partial}{\partial y}\ln x\cos y\right)\left(\frac{\partial}{\partial p}p^2q^3\right)$

$\frac{\partial f}{\partial p} = \left(\frac{\cos y}{x}\right)(3p^2q^2) + (-\ln x\sin y)(2pq^3) = \frac{3p^2q^2}{p^3q^2}\cos(p^2q^3) - 2pq^3\ln(p^3q^2)\sin(p^2q^3)$

$\frac{\partial f}{\partial p} = \boxed{\frac{3\cos(p^2q^3)}{p} - 2pq^3\ln(p^3q^2)\sin(p^2q^3)}$

$\frac{\partial f}{\partial q} = \frac{\partial f}{\partial x}\frac{\partial x}{\partial q} + \frac{\partial f}{\partial y}\frac{\partial y}{\partial q} = \left(\frac{\partial}{\partial x}\ln x\cos y\right)\left(\frac{\partial}{\partial q}p^3q^2\right) + \left(\frac{\partial}{\partial y}\ln x\cos y\right)\left(\frac{\partial}{\partial q}p^2q^3\right)$

$\frac{\partial f}{\partial q} = \left(\frac{\cos y}{x}\right)(2p^3q) + (-\ln x\sin y)(3p^2q^2) = \frac{2p^3q}{p^3q^2}\cos(p^2q^3) - 3p^2q^2\ln(p^3q^2)\sin(p^2q^3)$

$\frac{\partial f}{\partial p} = \boxed{\frac{2\cos(p^2q^3)}{q} - 3p^2q^2\ln(p^3q^2)\sin(p^2q^3)}$

3 $\frac{\partial w}{\partial s} = \frac{\partial w}{\partial x}\frac{\partial x}{\partial s} + \frac{\partial w}{\partial y}\frac{\partial y}{\partial s} + \frac{\partial w}{\partial z}\frac{\partial z}{\partial s}$

$\frac{\partial w}{\partial s} = \left(\frac{\partial}{\partial x}xy^2z^3\right)\left(\frac{\partial}{\partial s}s\cos t\sin u\right) + \left(\frac{\partial}{\partial y}xy^2z^3\right)\left(\frac{\partial}{\partial s}s\sin t\sin u\right) + \left(\frac{\partial}{\partial z}xy^2z^3\right)\left(\frac{\partial}{\partial s}s\cos u\right)$

$\frac{\partial w}{\partial s} = (y^2z^3)(\cos t\sin u) + (2xyz^3)(\sin t\sin u) + (3xy^2z^2)(\cos u)$

$\frac{\partial w}{\partial s} = s^5\sin^2 t\cos t\sin^3 u\cos^3 u + 2s^5\sin^2 t\cos t\sin^3 u\cos^3 u + 3s^5\sin^2 t\cos t\sin^3 u\cos^3 u$

$\frac{\partial w}{\partial s} = \boxed{6s^5\sin^2 t\cos t\sin^3 u\cos^3 u}$

$$\frac{\partial w}{\partial t} = \frac{\partial w}{\partial x}\frac{\partial x}{\partial t} + \frac{\partial w}{\partial y}\frac{\partial y}{\partial t} + \frac{\partial w}{\partial z}\frac{\partial z}{\partial t}$$

$$\frac{\partial w}{\partial t} = \left(\frac{\partial}{\partial x}xy^2z^3\right)\left(\frac{\partial}{\partial t}s\cos t\sin u\right) + \left(\frac{\partial}{\partial y}xy^2z^3\right)\left(\frac{\partial}{\partial t}s\sin t\sin u\right) + \left(\frac{\partial}{\partial z}xy^2z^3\right)\left(\frac{\partial}{\partial t}s\cos u\right)$$

$$\frac{\partial w}{\partial t} = (y^2z^3)(-s\sin t\sin u) + (2xyz^3)(s\cos t\sin u) + (3xy^2z^2)(0)$$

$$\frac{\partial w}{\partial t} = \boxed{-s^6\sin^3 t\sin^3 u\cos^3 u + 2s^6\sin t\cos^2 t\sin^3 u\cos^3 u}$$

$$\frac{\partial w}{\partial u} = \frac{\partial w}{\partial x}\frac{\partial x}{\partial u} + \frac{\partial w}{\partial y}\frac{\partial y}{\partial u} + \frac{\partial w}{\partial z}\frac{\partial z}{\partial u}$$

$$\frac{\partial w}{\partial u} = \left(\frac{\partial}{\partial x}xy^2z^3\right)\left(\frac{\partial}{\partial u}s\cos t\sin u\right) + \left(\frac{\partial}{\partial y}xy^2z^3\right)\left(\frac{\partial}{\partial u}s\sin t\sin u\right) + \left(\frac{\partial}{\partial z}xy^2z^3\right)\left(\frac{\partial}{\partial u}s\cos u\right)$$

$$\frac{\partial w}{\partial u} = (y^2z^3)(s\cos t\cos u) + (2xyz^3)(s\sin t\cos u) + (3xy^2z^2)(-s\sin u)$$

$$\frac{\partial w}{\partial u} = s^6\sin^2 t\cos t\sin^2 u\cos^4 u + 2s^6\sin^2 t\cos t\sin^2 u\cos^4 u - 3s^6\sin^2 t\cos t\sin^4 u\cos^2 u$$

$$\frac{\partial w}{\partial u} = \boxed{3s^6\sin^2 t\cos t\sin^2 u\cos^4 u - 3s^6\sin^2 t\cos t\sin^4 u\cos^2 u} = \boxed{3s^6\sin^2 t\cos t\sin^2 u\cos^2 u\cos(2u)}$$

Note: Recall the trig identity $\cos(2u) = \cos^2 u - \sin^2 u$.

Chapter 2, Part B

❹ $$\frac{dz}{dt} = \frac{\partial z}{\partial x}\frac{dx}{dt} + \frac{\partial z}{\partial y}\frac{dy}{dt} = \left(\frac{\partial}{\partial x}\frac{x^3}{y}\right)\left(\frac{d}{dt}\sin t\right) + \left(\frac{\partial}{\partial y}\frac{x^3}{y}\right)\left(\frac{d}{dt}\cos t\right)$$

$$\frac{dz}{dt} = \frac{3x^2}{y}\cos t + \left(-\frac{x^3}{y^2}\right)(-\sin t) = \frac{3\sin^2 t}{\cos t}\cos t + \frac{\sin^3 t}{\cos^2 t}\sin t = \boxed{3\sin^2 t + \frac{\sin^4 t}{\cos^2 t}}$$

❺ $$\frac{dz}{dt} = \frac{\partial z}{\partial x}\frac{dx}{dt} + \frac{\partial z}{\partial y}\frac{dy}{dt} = \left(\frac{\partial}{\partial x}\sec x\tan y\right)\left[\frac{d}{dt}(1+t^2)\right] + \left(\frac{\partial}{\partial y}\sec x\tan y\right)\left[\frac{d}{dt}(1-t^2)\right]$$

$$\frac{dz}{dt} = \boxed{2t\sec(1+t^2)\tan(1+t^2)\tan(1-t^2) - 2t\sec(1+t^2)\sec^2(1-t^2)}$$

❻ $$\frac{dw}{dt} = \frac{\partial w}{\partial x}\frac{dx}{dt} + \frac{\partial w}{\partial y}\frac{dy}{dt} + \frac{\partial w}{\partial z}\frac{dz}{dt} = \left(\frac{\partial}{\partial x}e^x e^{-y}\ln z\right)\left[\frac{d}{dt}(t^2+3t)\right] +$$

$$\left(\frac{\partial}{\partial y}e^x e^{-y}\ln z\right)\left[\frac{d}{dt}(t^3+t^2)\right] + \left(\frac{\partial}{\partial z}e^x e^{-y}\ln z\right)\left(\frac{d}{dt}3t^2\right)$$

$$\frac{dz}{dt} = (2t+3)e^{t^2+3t}e^{-t^3-t^2}\ln(3t^2) - (3t^2+2t)e^{t^2+3t}e^{-t^3-t^2}\ln(3t^2) + \frac{6t}{3t^2}e^{t^2+3t}e^{-t^3-t^2}$$

$$\frac{dz}{dt} = (2t+3)e^{-t^3+3t}\ln(3t^2) - (3t^2+2t)e^{-t^3+3t}\ln(3t^2) + \left(\frac{2}{t}\right)e^{-t^3+3t}$$

$$\frac{dz}{dt} = (2t+3-3t^2-2t)e^{-t^3+3t}\ln(3t^2) + \left(\frac{2}{t}\right)e^{-t^3+3t}$$

$$\frac{dz}{dt} = (-3t^2+3)e^{-t^3+3t}\ln(3t^2) + \left(\frac{2}{t}\right)e^{-t^3+3t}$$

$$\frac{dz}{dt} = \boxed{3(-t^2+1)e^{-t^3+3t}\ln(3t^2) + \left(\frac{2}{t}\right)e^{-t^3+3t}}$$

Note: $e^m e^n = e^{m+n}$ such that $e^{t^2+3t}e^{-t^3-t^2} = e^{-t^3+3t}$.

Chapter 3, Part A

1 $\frac{\partial z}{\partial x} = \frac{\partial}{\partial x}(x^2 + 2xy - y^2) = 2x + 2y = 0$ Divide both sides by 2 to get $x + y = 0$.

$\frac{\partial z}{\partial y} = \frac{\partial}{\partial y}(x^2 + 2xy - y^2) = 2x - 2y = 0$ Divide both sides by 2 to get $x - y = 0$.

Add the two equations together: $2x = 0$. Simplify: $x = 0$. Plug this into $x + y = 0$ to see that $y = 0$. The critical point is $(0,0)$.

$\frac{\partial^2 z}{\partial x^2} = \frac{\partial}{\partial x}(2x + 2y) = 2 \quad , \quad \frac{\partial^2 z}{\partial y \partial x} = \frac{\partial}{\partial y}(2x + 2y) = 2$

$\frac{\partial^2 z}{\partial x \partial y} = \frac{\partial}{\partial x}(2x - 2y) = 2 \quad , \quad \frac{\partial^2 z}{\partial y^2} = \frac{\partial}{\partial y}(2x - 2y) = -2$

$D = \frac{\partial^2 f}{\partial x^2}\frac{\partial^2 f}{\partial y^2} - \frac{\partial^2 f}{\partial x \partial y}\frac{\partial^2 f}{\partial y \partial x} = (2)(-2) - (2)(2) = -4 - 4 = -8$

$(0,0)$ is a **saddle point** since $D < 0$. There are no local minima or maxima.

Evaluate $z = x^2 + 2xy - y^2$ over the square $-1 \le x \le 1$ and $-1 \le y \le 1$:

- Top edge ($y = 1$): $z = x^2 + 2x(1) - 1^2 = x^2 + 2x - 1$.
- Right edge ($x = 1$): $z = 1^2 + 2(1)y - y^2 = 1 + 2y - y^2$.
- Bottom edge ($y = -1$): $z = x^2 + 2x(-1) - (-1)^2 = x^2 - 2x - 1$.
- Left edge ($x = -1$): $z = (-1)^2 + 2(-1)y - y^2 = 1 - 2y - y^2$.

Along the boundary of the square, the minimum value of z is -2 and occurs at $(-1,1)$ and $(1,-1)$ and the maximum value of z is 2 and occurs at $(1,1)$ and $(-1,-1)$. Since z doesn't have any local minima or maxima, the **absolute minimum** is -2 at $(-1,1,-2)$ and $(1,-1,-2)$ and the **absolute maximum** is 2 at $(1,1,2)$ and $(-1,-1,2)$.

Note: To find the minimum and maximum values along the edges of the square, first apply the usual single-variable first and second derivative tests to the function for each edge (for example, at the top edge, where z simplifies to $z = x^2 + 2x - 1$, set $\frac{dz}{dx} = 0$ to find that the top edge has a minimum of -2 when $x = -1$). Then also find the value of z at each vertex. For the absolute minimum and maximum, look at the minimum and maximum values along the boundary and also look at the local minimum and maximum (this problem is special in that it didn't have any).

2 $\frac{\partial z}{\partial x} = \frac{\partial}{\partial x}\left(e^{-x^2-y^2}\right) = -2xe^{-x^2-y^2} = 0$ This is only true if $x = 0$, $x \to \infty$, or $y \to \infty$.

$\frac{\partial z}{\partial y} = \frac{\partial}{\partial y}\left(e^{-x^2-y^2}\right) = -2ye^{-x^2-y^2}$ This is only true if $y = 0$. The critical point is $(0,0)$.

$\frac{\partial^2 z}{\partial x^2} = \frac{\partial}{\partial x}\left(-2xe^{-x^2-y^2}\right) = -2e^{-x^2-y^2} + 4x^2e^{-x^2-y^2} = 2(2x^2-1)e^{-x^2-y^2}$

$\frac{\partial^2 z}{\partial y \partial x} = \frac{\partial}{\partial y}\left(-2xe^{-x^2-y^2}\right) = 4xye^{-x^2-y^2}$, $\frac{\partial^2 z}{\partial x \partial y} = \frac{\partial}{\partial x}\left(-2ye^{-x^2-y^2}\right) = 4xye^{-x^2-y^2}$

$\frac{\partial^2 z}{\partial y^2} = \frac{\partial}{\partial y}\left(-2ye^{-x^2-y^2}\right) = -2e^{-x^2-y^2} + 4y^2e^{-x^2-y^2} = 2(2y^2-1)e^{-x^2-y^2}$

$D = \frac{\partial^2 f}{\partial x^2}\frac{\partial^2 f}{\partial y^2} - \frac{\partial^2 f}{\partial x \partial y}\frac{\partial^2 f}{\partial y \partial x} = 2(2x^2-1)e^{-x^2-y^2}2(2y^2-1)e^{-x^2-y^2} - \left(4xye^{-x^2-y^2}\right)^2$

$D = (16x^2y^2 - 8x^2 - 8y^2 + 4)e^{-2(x^2+y^2)} - 16x^2y^2e^{-2(x^2+y^2)}$

$D = (-8x^2 - 8y^2 + 4)e^{-2(x^2+y^2)} = -4(2x^2 + 2y^2 - 1)e^{-2(x^2+y^2)}$

For $x = 0$ and $y = 0$, the value of D is $D = -4(-1)e^0 = (-4)(-1)(1) = 4$ and the value of $\frac{\partial^2 z}{\partial x^2}$ is $\frac{\partial^2 z}{\partial x^2} = 2(-1)e^0 = 2(-1)(1) = -2$. Since $D = 4 > 0$ and $\frac{\partial^2 z}{\partial x^2} = -2 < 0$ at the critical point $(0,0)$, z has a local maximum at $(0,0)$. The value of z at the critical point is $z(0,0) = e^0 = 1$. The **local maximum** of z equals 1 at $(0,0,1)$. Note that z also approaches a **minimum of zero** as x or y become infinite.

Evaluate $z = e^{-x^2-y^2}$ over the disc $x^2 + y^2 \leq 1$. At the boundary of the disc, $x^2 + y^2 = 1$. Plug this into z at the boundary: $z = e^{-(x^2+y^2)} = e^{-1} = \frac{1}{e} \approx 0.37$ at every point on the boundary. The **absolute minimum** is $e^{-1} = \frac{1}{e} \approx 0.37$ on the boundary of the disc and the **absolute maximum** is 1 at $(0,0,1)$.

Notes: Recall that $e^0 = 1$. We applied the product rule to find $\frac{\partial^2 z}{\partial x^2}$ and $\frac{\partial^2 z}{\partial y^2}$. Also, see the note to the solution to Problem 1.

Chapter 3, Part B

3 $\frac{\partial z}{\partial x} = \frac{\partial}{\partial x}(x^3 - 6xy + y^3) = 3x^2 - 6y = 0$ Simplify: $x^2 = 2y$.

$\frac{\partial z}{\partial y} = \frac{\partial}{\partial y}(x^3 - 6xy + y^3) = -6x + 3y^2 = 0$ Simplify: $y^2 = 2x$.

Plug $x = \frac{y^2}{2}$ from the second equation into the first equation: $\frac{y^4}{4} = 2y$. Multiply by 4 on both sides: $y^4 = 8y$. Factor: $y(y^3 - 8) = 0$. Either $y = 0$ or $y^3 = 8$. Cube root both sides: $y = 0$ or $y = 2$. Plug $y = 2$ into the second equation: $2^2 = 4 = 2x$. Divide by 2 on both sides: $x = 2$. The critical points are $(0,0)$ and $(2,2)$.

$$\frac{\partial^2 z}{\partial x^2} = \frac{\partial}{\partial x}(3x^2 - 6y) = 6x \quad , \quad \frac{\partial^2 z}{\partial y \partial x} = \frac{\partial}{\partial y}(3x^2 - 6y) = -6$$

$$\frac{\partial^2 z}{\partial x \partial y} = \frac{\partial}{\partial x}(-6x + 3y^2) = -6 \quad , \quad \frac{\partial^2 z}{\partial y^2} = \frac{\partial}{\partial y}(-6x + 3y^2) = 6y$$

$$D = \frac{\partial^2 f}{\partial x^2}\frac{\partial^2 f}{\partial y^2} - \frac{\partial^2 f}{\partial x \partial y}\frac{\partial^2 f}{\partial y \partial x} = (6x)(6y) - (-6)(-6) = 36xy - 36 = 36(xy - 1)$$

For $x = 0$ and $y = 0$, the value of D is $D = 36(0 - 1) = 36(-1) = -36$. There is a **saddle point** at (0,0).

For $x = 2$ and $y = 2$, the value of D is $D = 36[(2)(2) - 1] = 36(3) = 108$ and the value of $\frac{\partial^2 z}{\partial x^2}$ is $\frac{\partial^2 z}{\partial x^2} = 6(2) = 12$. Since $D = 108 > 0$ and $\frac{\partial^2 z}{\partial x^2} = 12 > 0$ at the critical point (0,0), z has a local minimum at (2,2). The value of z at the critical point is $z(2,2) = 2^3 - 6(2)(2) + 2^3 = 8 - 24 + 8 = -8$. The **local minimum** of z equals -8 at $(2,2,-8)$.

Evaluate $z = x^3 - 6xy + y^3$ over the triangle with vertices at (0,0), (4,0), and (4,4):

- Bottom edge ($y = 0$): $z = x^3 - 6x(0) + 0^3 = x^3$.
- Right edge ($x = 4$): $z = 4^3 - 6(4)y + y^3 = 64 - 24y + y^3$.
- Hypotenuse ($y = x$): $z = x^3 - 6(x)(x) + x^3 = 2x^3 - 6x^2$.

Along the boundary of the triangle, the minimum value of z is -8 and occurs at (2,2) along the hypotenuse and the maximum value of z is 64 and occurs at (4,0). In this problem, the local minimum happens to coincide with the midpoint of the hypotenuse on the boundary of the region of interest. The **absolute minimum** is -8 at $(2,2,-8)$ and the **absolute maximum** is 64 at (4,0,64).

Notes: The equation for the hypotenuse is $y = x$ because the slope of the hypotenuse is 1 and the y-intercept is zero. Also, see the note to the solution to Problem 1 (regarding how to determine that the minimum value of $2x^3 - 6x^2$ occurs at $x = 2$ by using the single-variable extreme value derivative tests).

4 $\frac{\partial z}{\partial x} = \frac{\partial}{\partial x}(\cos x \cos y) = -\sin x \cos y = 0$ Either $\sin x = 0$ or $\cos y = 0$.

Either $x = 0, x = \pi, x = 2\pi, y = \frac{\pi}{2}$, or $y = \frac{3\pi}{2}$.

$\frac{\partial z}{\partial y} = \frac{\partial}{\partial y}(\cos x \cos y) = -\cos x \sin y = 0$ Either $\cos x = 0$ or $\sin y = 0$.

Either $x = \frac{\pi}{2}, x = \frac{3\pi}{2}, y = 0, y = \pi$, or $y = 2\pi$.

Combine these results. Each critical point has x from one set and y from the other set.

The critical points are $(0,0)$, $(0,\pi)$, $(0,2\pi)$, $(\pi,0)$, (π,π), $(\pi,2\pi)$, $(2\pi,0)$, $(2\pi,\pi)$, $(2\pi,2\pi)$, $\left(\frac{\pi}{2},\frac{\pi}{2}\right)$, $\left(\frac{\pi}{2},\frac{3\pi}{2}\right)$, $\left(\frac{3\pi}{2},\frac{\pi}{2}\right)$, and $\left(\frac{3\pi}{2},\frac{3\pi}{2}\right)$.

$\frac{\partial^2 z}{\partial x^2} = \frac{\partial}{\partial x}(-\sin x \cos y) = -\cos x \cos y$, $\frac{\partial^2 z}{\partial y \partial x} = \frac{\partial}{\partial y}(-\sin x \cos y) = \sin x \sin y$

$\frac{\partial^2 z}{\partial x \partial y} = \frac{\partial}{\partial x}(-\cos x \sin y) = \sin x \sin y$, $\frac{\partial^2 z}{\partial y^2} = \frac{\partial}{\partial y}(-\cos x \sin y) = -\cos x \cos y$

$$D = \frac{\partial^2 f}{\partial x^2}\frac{\partial^2 f}{\partial y^2} - \frac{\partial^2 f}{\partial x \partial y}\frac{\partial^2 f}{\partial y \partial x} = \cos^2 x \cos^2 y - \sin^2 x \sin^2 y$$

Evaluate D and $\frac{\partial^2 f}{\partial x^2}$ at each critical point to determine the nature of each critical point.

- There are **local minima** of $z = -1$ at $(0,\pi)$, $(\pi,0)$, $(\pi,2\pi)$, and $(2\pi,\pi)$ because $D = 1 > 0$ and $\frac{\partial^2 z}{\partial x^2} = 1 > 0$.
- There are **local maxima** of $z = 1$ at $(0,0)$, $(0,2\pi)$, (π,π), $(2\pi,0)$, and $(2\pi,2\pi)$ because $D = 1 > 0$ and $\frac{\partial^2 z}{\partial x^2} = -1 < 0$.
- There are **saddle points** at $\left(\frac{\pi}{2},\frac{\pi}{2}\right)$, $\left(\frac{\pi}{2},\frac{3\pi}{2}\right)$, $\left(\frac{3\pi}{2},\frac{\pi}{2}\right)$, and $\left(\frac{3\pi}{2},\frac{3\pi}{2}\right)$ because $D = -1 < 0$.

There are actually an infinite number of critical points. Simply add or subtract any integer number of 2π's to any value of x or y (or both) above to obtain another critical point.

Evaluate $z = \cos x \cos y$ over the square $\pi \le x \le 2\pi$ and $\pi \le y \le 2\pi$:

- Bottom edge $(y = \pi)$: $z = \cos x \cos \pi = -\cos x$.
- Left edge $(x = \pi)$: $z = \cos \pi \cos y = -\cos y$.
- Top edge $(y = 2\pi)$: $\cos x \cos 2\pi = \cos x$.
- Right edge $(x = 2\pi)$: $z = \cos 2\pi \cos y = \cos y$.

Along the boundary of the square, the minimum value of z is -1 and occurs at $(2\pi,\pi)$ and $(\pi,2\pi)$, and the maximum value of z is 1 and occurs at (π,π) and $(2\pi,2\pi)$. In this case, the absolute extrema are also local extrema.

Note: See the note to the solution to Problem 1.

Chapter 4, Part A

❶ $A = \|\vec{\mathbf{A}}\| = \sqrt{A_x^2 + A_y^2} = \sqrt{(-\sqrt{2})^2 + (-\sqrt{2})^2} = \sqrt{2+2} = \sqrt{4} = \boxed{2}$

$\theta = \tan^{-1}\left(\frac{A_y}{A_x}\right) = \tan^{-1}\left(\frac{-\sqrt{2}}{-\sqrt{2}}\right) = \tan^{-1}(1) = \boxed{\frac{5\pi}{4}} = \boxed{225°}$

Note: θ lies in Quadrant III because $A_x < 0$ and $A_y < 0$.

❷ $B = \|\vec{\mathbf{B}}\| = \sqrt{B_x^2 + B_y^2} = \sqrt{(-1)^2 + (\sqrt{3})^2} = \sqrt{1+3} = \sqrt{4} = \boxed{2}$

$\theta = \tan^{-1}\left(\frac{B_y}{B_x}\right) = \tan^{-1}\left(\frac{\sqrt{3}}{-1}\right) = \tan^{-1}(-\sqrt{3}) = \boxed{\frac{2\pi}{3}} = \boxed{120°}$

Note: θ lies in Quadrant II because $B_x < 0$ and $B_y > 0$.

❸ $C_x = C\cos\theta_C = 6\cos 210° = 6\left(-\frac{\sqrt{3}}{2}\right) = \boxed{-3\sqrt{3}}$

$C_y = C\sin\theta_C = 6\sin 210° = 6\left(-\frac{1}{2}\right) = \boxed{-3}$

Chapter 4, Part B

❹ $D = \|\vec{\mathbf{D}}\| = \sqrt{D_x^2 + D_y^2 + D_z^2} = \sqrt{2^2 + (\sqrt{5})^2 + (-4)^2} = \sqrt{4+5+16} = \sqrt{25} = \boxed{5}$

$\hat{\mathbf{D}} = \frac{\vec{\mathbf{D}}}{\|\vec{\mathbf{D}}\|} = \frac{2\hat{\mathbf{i}} + \hat{\mathbf{j}}\sqrt{5} - 4\hat{\mathbf{k}}}{5} = \boxed{\frac{2}{5}\hat{\mathbf{i}} + \frac{\sqrt{5}}{5}\hat{\mathbf{j}} - \frac{4}{5}\hat{\mathbf{k}}}$

❺ $\vec{\mathbf{E}} + \vec{\mathbf{F}} = \langle 7, -4, 6\rangle + \langle 5, 9, -8\rangle = \langle 7+5, -4+9, 6+(-8)\rangle = \boxed{\langle 12, 5, -2\rangle}$

❻ $2\vec{\mathbf{G}} - 5\vec{\mathbf{H}} = 2(4\hat{\mathbf{i}} + 2\hat{\mathbf{j}} - 3\hat{\mathbf{k}}) - 5(3\hat{\mathbf{i}} - \hat{\mathbf{k}}) = 8\hat{\mathbf{i}} + 4\hat{\mathbf{j}} - 6\hat{\mathbf{k}} - (15\hat{\mathbf{i}} - 5\hat{\mathbf{k}})$

$2\vec{\mathbf{G}} - 5\vec{\mathbf{H}} = 8\hat{\mathbf{i}} + 4\hat{\mathbf{j}} - 6\hat{\mathbf{k}} - 15\hat{\mathbf{i}} + 5\hat{\mathbf{k}} = (8-15)\hat{\mathbf{i}} + 4\hat{\mathbf{j}} + (-6+5)\hat{\mathbf{k}} = \boxed{-7\hat{\mathbf{i}} + 4\hat{\mathbf{j}} - \hat{\mathbf{k}}}$

Chapter 4, Part C

❼ $A_x = A\cos\theta_A = 6\cos 150° = 6\left(-\frac{\sqrt{3}}{2}\right) = -3\sqrt{3}$

$B_x = B\cos\theta_B = 12\cos 270° = 12(0) = 0$

$A_y = A\sin\theta_A = 6\sin 150° = 6\left(\frac{1}{2}\right) = 3$

$B_y = B\sin\theta_B = 12\sin 270° = 12(-1) = -12$

$R_x = A_x + B_x = -3\sqrt{3} + 0 = -3\sqrt{3}$
$R_y = A_y + B_y = 3 + (-12) = -9$

$R = \|\vec{\mathbf{R}}\| = \sqrt{R_x^2 + R_y^2} = \sqrt{\left(-3\sqrt{3}\right)^2 + (-9)^2} = \sqrt{(9)(3) + 81} = \sqrt{108} = \sqrt{(36)(3)} = \boxed{6\sqrt{3}}$

$\theta_R = \tan^{-1}\left(\frac{R_y}{R_x}\right) = \tan^{-1}\left(\frac{-9}{-3\sqrt{3}}\right) = \tan^{-1}\left(\frac{3}{\sqrt{3}}\right) = \tan^{-1}(\sqrt{3}) = \boxed{\frac{4\pi}{3}} = \boxed{240°}$

Note that θ_R lies in Quadrant III because $R_x < 0$ and $R_y < 0$. We factored the perfect square 36 out of $\sqrt{108}$ to put the answer in standard form: $\sqrt{108} = 6\sqrt{3}$.

8 $C_x = C\cos\theta_C = 4\cos 210° = 4\left(-\frac{\sqrt{3}}{2}\right) = -2\sqrt{3}$
$D_x = D\cos\theta_D = 4\sqrt{3}\cos 180° = 4\sqrt{3}(-1) = -4\sqrt{3}$
$C_y = C\sin\theta_C = 4\sin 210° = 4\left(-\frac{1}{2}\right) = -2$
$D_y = D\sin\theta_D = 4\sqrt{3}\sin 180° = 8\sqrt{3}(0) = 0$
$\vec{\mathbf{S}} = \vec{\mathbf{D}} - \vec{\mathbf{C}} = \vec{\mathbf{D}} + (-\vec{\mathbf{C}})$, where $-\vec{\mathbf{C}}$ is the reverse of $\vec{\mathbf{C}}$. The components of $-\vec{\mathbf{C}}$ are opposite to the components of $\vec{\mathbf{C}}$. Therefore, instead of $D_x + C_x$ and $D_y + C_y$, we need to subtract the components of $\vec{\mathbf{C}}$.
$S_x = D_x - C_x = -4\sqrt{3} - (-2\sqrt{3}) = -4\sqrt{3} + 2\sqrt{3} = -2\sqrt{3}$
$S_y = D_y - C_y = 0 - (-2) = 0 + 2 = 2$

$S = \|\vec{\mathbf{S}}\| = \sqrt{S_x^2 + S_y^2} = \sqrt{\left(-2\sqrt{3}\right)^2 + 2^2} = \sqrt{(4)(3) + 4} = \sqrt{16} = \boxed{4}$

$\theta_S = \tan^{-1}\left(\frac{S_y}{S_x}\right) = \tan^{-1}\left(\frac{2}{-2\sqrt{3}}\right) = \tan^{-1}\left(\frac{1}{-\sqrt{3}}\right) = \boxed{\frac{5\pi}{6}} = \boxed{150°}$

Note that θ_S lies in Quadrant II because $S_x < 0$ and $S_y > 0$.

Chapter 4, Part D

9 $\vec{\mathbf{v}}(t) = \frac{d\vec{\mathbf{r}}}{dt} = \frac{d}{dt}\left(\hat{\mathbf{i}}\sqrt{t} - 2\hat{\mathbf{j}}\right) = \hat{\mathbf{i}}\frac{d}{dt}\sqrt{t} - \hat{\mathbf{j}}\frac{d}{dt}2 = \hat{\mathbf{i}}\frac{d}{dt}t^{\frac{1}{2}} - 0\hat{\mathbf{j}} = \frac{t^{-1/2}}{2}\hat{\mathbf{i}} = \frac{\hat{\mathbf{i}}}{2t^{1/2}} = \frac{\hat{\mathbf{i}}}{2\sqrt{t}}$

$\vec{\mathbf{v}}(4) = \frac{\hat{\mathbf{i}}}{2\sqrt{4}} = \frac{\hat{\mathbf{i}}}{2(2)} = \boxed{\frac{\hat{\mathbf{i}}}{4}}$

$\vec{\mathbf{a}}(t) = \frac{d\vec{\mathbf{v}}}{dt} = \frac{d}{dt}\frac{t^{-1/2}}{2}\hat{\mathbf{i}} = \frac{\hat{\mathbf{i}}}{2}\frac{d}{dt}t^{-1/2} = -\frac{\hat{\mathbf{i}}}{4}t^{-3/2} = -\frac{\hat{\mathbf{i}}}{4t^{3/2}}$

$\vec{\mathbf{a}}(4) = -\frac{\hat{\mathbf{i}}}{4(4)^{3/2}} = -\frac{\hat{\mathbf{i}}}{4(4^3)^{1/2}} = -\frac{\hat{\mathbf{i}}}{4(64)^{1/2}} = -\frac{\hat{\mathbf{i}}}{4(8)} = \boxed{-\frac{\hat{\mathbf{i}}}{32}}$ (taking the positive root)

10 The initial velocity is $\vec{\mathbf{v}}_0 = 4\hat{\mathbf{i}}$.

$$\vec{\mathbf{v}} = \vec{\mathbf{v}}_0 + \int_{t=0}^{t} \vec{\mathbf{a}}\, dt = 4\hat{\mathbf{i}} + \int_{t=0}^{t} 6t\hat{\mathbf{j}}\, dt = 4\hat{\mathbf{i}} + 6\hat{\mathbf{j}} \int_{t=0}^{t} t\, dt = 4\hat{\mathbf{i}} + 6\hat{\mathbf{j}} \left[\frac{t^2}{2}\right]_{t=0}^{2}$$

$$\vec{\mathbf{v}} = 4\hat{\mathbf{i}} + 6\hat{\mathbf{j}}\left(\frac{2^2}{2} - \frac{0^2}{2}\right) = 4\hat{\mathbf{i}} + 6\hat{\mathbf{j}}\left(\frac{4}{2}\right) = 4\hat{\mathbf{i}} + 6\hat{\mathbf{j}}(2) = \boxed{4\hat{\mathbf{i}} + 12\hat{\mathbf{j}}}$$

$$\Delta\vec{\mathbf{r}} = \int_{t=0}^{t} \vec{\mathbf{v}}\, dt = \int_{t=0}^{2} \left(4\hat{\mathbf{i}} + 6\hat{\mathbf{j}}\frac{t^2}{2}\right) dt = 4\hat{\mathbf{i}} \int_{t=0}^{2} dt + 3\hat{\mathbf{j}} \int_{t=0}^{2} t^2\, dt$$

$$\Delta\vec{\mathbf{r}} = 4\hat{\mathbf{i}}[t]_{t=0}^{2} + 3\hat{\mathbf{j}}\left[\frac{t^3}{3}\right]_{t=0}^{2} = 4\hat{\mathbf{i}}(2-0) + 3\hat{\mathbf{j}}\left(\frac{2^3}{3} - \frac{0^3}{3}\right) = 8\hat{\mathbf{i}} + 3\hat{\mathbf{j}}\left(\frac{8}{3}\right) = \boxed{8\hat{\mathbf{i}} + 8\hat{\mathbf{j}}}$$

Note: Plug the expression for $\vec{\mathbf{v}}$ that is a function of time, $4\hat{\mathbf{i}} + 6\hat{\mathbf{j}}\frac{t^2}{2}$, into the integrand for $\Delta\vec{\mathbf{r}}$. It would be a mistake to plug the final velocity, $4\hat{\mathbf{i}} + 12\hat{\mathbf{j}}$, in for $\vec{\mathbf{v}}$ in $\int_{t=0}^{t} \vec{\mathbf{v}}\, dt$.

11 $\vec{\mathbf{a}}(t) = \frac{d\vec{\mathbf{v}}}{dt} = \frac{d}{dt}[8\hat{\mathbf{i}}\sin(2t) - 4\hat{\mathbf{j}}] = 8\hat{\mathbf{i}}\frac{d}{dt}\sin(2t) - \hat{\mathbf{j}}\frac{d}{dt}4 = 16\hat{\mathbf{i}}\cos(2t) - 0\hat{\mathbf{j}} = 16\hat{\mathbf{i}}\cos(2t)$

$$\vec{\mathbf{a}}\left(\frac{\pi}{6}\right) = 16\hat{\mathbf{i}}\cos\left[2\left(\frac{\pi}{6}\right)\right] = 16\hat{\mathbf{i}}\cos\left(\frac{\pi}{3}\right) = 16\hat{\mathbf{i}}\left(\frac{1}{2}\right) = \boxed{8\hat{\mathbf{i}}}$$

$$\Delta\vec{\mathbf{r}} = \int_{t=0}^{t} \vec{\mathbf{v}}\, dt = \int_{t=0}^{\pi/6} [8\hat{\mathbf{i}}\sin(2t) - 4\hat{\mathbf{j}}]\, dt = 8\hat{\mathbf{i}} \int_{t=0}^{\pi/6} \sin(2t)\, dt - 4\hat{\mathbf{j}} \int_{t=0}^{\pi/6} dt$$

$$\Delta\vec{\mathbf{r}} = 8\hat{\mathbf{i}}\left[-\frac{\cos(2t)}{2}\right]_{t=0}^{\pi/6} - 4\hat{\mathbf{j}}[t]_{t=0}^{\frac{\pi}{6}} = -4\hat{\mathbf{i}}[\cos(2t)]_{t=0}^{\pi/6} - 4\hat{\mathbf{j}}[t]_{t=0}^{\pi/6}$$

$$\Delta\vec{\mathbf{r}} = -4\hat{\mathbf{i}}\left\{\cos\left[2\left(\frac{\pi}{6}\right)\right] + \cos[2(0)]\right\} - 4\hat{\mathbf{j}}\left(\frac{\pi}{6} - 0\right)$$

$$\Delta\vec{\mathbf{r}} = -4\hat{\mathbf{i}}\left[\cos\left(\frac{\pi}{3}\right) - \cos 0\right] - \frac{2\pi}{3}\hat{\mathbf{j}} = -4\hat{\mathbf{i}}\left(\frac{1}{2} - 1\right) - \frac{2\pi}{3}\hat{\mathbf{j}} = -4\hat{\mathbf{i}}\left(-\frac{1}{2}\right) - \frac{2\pi}{3}\hat{\mathbf{j}} = \boxed{2\hat{\mathbf{i}} - \frac{2\pi}{3}\hat{\mathbf{j}}}$$

Chapter 5, Part A

❶ $\vec{\mathbf{A}} \cdot \vec{\mathbf{B}} = A_x B_x + A_y B_y + A_z B_z$

$\vec{\mathbf{A}} \cdot \vec{\mathbf{B}} = (5)(6) + (2)(-3) + (-4)(-1) = 30 - 6 + 4 = \boxed{28}$

$\vec{\mathbf{A}} \times \vec{\mathbf{B}} = (A_y B_z - A_z B_y)\hat{\mathbf{i}} + (A_z B_x - A_x B_z)\hat{\mathbf{j}} + (A_x B_y - A_y B_x)\hat{\mathbf{k}}$

$\vec{\mathbf{A}} \times \vec{\mathbf{B}} = [(2)(-1) - (-4)(-3)]\hat{\mathbf{i}} + [(-4)(6) - (5)(-1)]\hat{\mathbf{j}} + [(5)(-3) - (2)(6)]\hat{\mathbf{k}}$

$\vec{\mathbf{A}} \times \vec{\mathbf{B}} = (-2 - 12)\hat{\mathbf{i}} + (-24 + 5)\hat{\mathbf{j}} + (-15 - 12)\hat{\mathbf{k}} = \boxed{-14\hat{\mathbf{i}} - 19\hat{\mathbf{j}} - 27\hat{\mathbf{k}}}$

❷ $\vec{\mathbf{C}} \cdot \vec{\mathbf{D}} = C_x D_x + C_y D_y + C_z D_z$

$\vec{\mathbf{C}} \cdot \vec{\mathbf{D}} = (8)(9) + (-3)(0) + (6)(-7) = 72 - 0 - 42 = \boxed{30}$

$\vec{\mathbf{C}} \times \vec{\mathbf{D}} = (C_y D_z - C_z D_y)\hat{\mathbf{i}} + (C_z D_x - C_x D_z)\hat{\mathbf{j}} + (C_x D_y - C_y D_x)\hat{\mathbf{k}}$

$\vec{\mathbf{C}} \times \vec{\mathbf{D}} = [(-3)(-7) - (6)(0)]\hat{\mathbf{i}} + [(6)(9) - (8)(-7)]\hat{\mathbf{j}} + [(8)(0) - (-3)(9)]\hat{\mathbf{k}}$

$\vec{\mathbf{C}} \times \vec{\mathbf{D}} = (21 - 0)\hat{\mathbf{i}} + (54 + 56)\hat{\mathbf{j}} + (0 + 27)\hat{\mathbf{k}} = \boxed{21\hat{\mathbf{i}} + 110\hat{\mathbf{j}} + 27\hat{\mathbf{k}}}$

❸ $\vec{\mathbf{E}} \cdot \vec{\mathbf{F}} = E_x F_x + E_y F_y + E_z F_z$

$\vec{\mathbf{E}} \cdot \vec{\mathbf{F}} = (4)(-3) + (1)(5) + (-2)(-2) = -12 + 5 + 4 = \boxed{-3}$

$\vec{\mathbf{E}} \times \vec{\mathbf{F}} = (E_y F_z - E_z F_y)\hat{\mathbf{i}} + (E_z F_x - E_x F_z)\hat{\mathbf{j}} + (E_x F_y - E_y F_x)\hat{\mathbf{k}}$

$\vec{\mathbf{E}} \times \vec{\mathbf{F}} = [(1)(-2) - (-2)(5)]\hat{\mathbf{i}} + [(-2)(-3) - (4)(-2)]\hat{\mathbf{j}} + [(4)(5) - (1)(-3)]\hat{\mathbf{k}}$

$\vec{\mathbf{E}} \times \vec{\mathbf{F}} = (-2 + 10)\hat{\mathbf{i}} + (6 + 8)\hat{\mathbf{j}} + (20 + 3)\hat{\mathbf{k}} = \boxed{8\hat{\mathbf{i}} + 14\hat{\mathbf{j}} + 23\hat{\mathbf{k}}}$

Chapter 5, Part B

❹ $\vec{\mathbf{A}} \cdot \vec{\mathbf{B}} = \|\vec{\mathbf{A}}\|\|\vec{\mathbf{B}}\| \cos\theta = (6)(12)\cos 150° = 72\left(-\frac{\sqrt{3}}{2}\right) = \boxed{-36\sqrt{3}}$

$\|\vec{\mathbf{A}} \times \vec{\mathbf{B}}\| = \|\vec{\mathbf{A}}\|\|\vec{\mathbf{B}}\| \sin\theta = (6)(12)\sin 150° = 72\left(\frac{1}{2}\right) = \boxed{36}$

❺ $\vec{\mathbf{C}} \cdot \vec{\mathbf{D}} = C_x D_x + C_y D_y + C_z D_z$

$\vec{\mathbf{C}} \cdot \vec{\mathbf{D}} = (\sqrt{3})(1) + (1)(-\sqrt{3}) + (-2)(2) = \sqrt{3} - \sqrt{3} - 4 = -4$

$\|\vec{\mathbf{C}}\| = \sqrt{C_x^2 + C_y^2 + C_z^2} = \sqrt{(\sqrt{3})^2 + 1^2 + (-2)^2} = \sqrt{3 + 1 + 4} = \sqrt{8} = \sqrt{(4)(2)} = 2\sqrt{2}$

$\|\vec{\mathbf{D}}\| = \sqrt{D_x^2 + D_y^2 + D_z^2} = \sqrt{1^2 + (-\sqrt{3})^2 + 2^2} = \sqrt{1 + 3 + 4} = \sqrt{8} = \sqrt{(4)(2)} = 2\sqrt{2}$

$$\vec{\mathbf{C}} \cdot \vec{\mathbf{D}} = \|\vec{\mathbf{C}}\|\|\vec{\mathbf{D}}\| \cos\theta \rightarrow -4 = (2\sqrt{2})(2\sqrt{2}) \cos\theta \rightarrow -4 = 4(2) \cos\theta \rightarrow -\frac{1}{2} = \cos\theta$$

$$\theta = \cos^{-1}\left(-\frac{1}{2}\right) = \boxed{\frac{2\pi}{3}} = \boxed{120°}$$

Note: Since $\cos\theta < 0$, the condition $0 \leq \theta \leq \pi$ requires θ to lie in Quadrant II.

Chapter 5, Part C

❻ Make the definition $\vec{\mathbf{D}} \equiv \vec{\mathbf{B}} \times \vec{\mathbf{C}}$.

$$\vec{\mathbf{D}} = \vec{\mathbf{B}} \times \vec{\mathbf{C}} = (B_y C_z - B_z C_y)\hat{\mathbf{i}} + (B_z C_x - B_x C_z)\hat{\mathbf{j}} + (B_x C_y - B_y C_x)\hat{\mathbf{k}}$$

$$\vec{\mathbf{D}} = [(-3)(4) - (-1)(0)]\hat{\mathbf{i}} + [(-1)(-3) - (2)(4)]\hat{\mathbf{j}} + [(2)(0) - (-3)(-3)]\hat{\mathbf{k}}$$

$$\vec{\mathbf{D}} = (-12 + 0)\hat{\mathbf{i}} + (3 - 8)\hat{\mathbf{j}} + (0 - 9)\hat{\mathbf{k}} = -12\hat{\mathbf{i}} - 5\hat{\mathbf{j}} - 9\hat{\mathbf{k}}$$

$$\vec{\mathbf{A}} \cdot (\vec{\mathbf{B}} \times \vec{\mathbf{C}}) = \vec{\mathbf{A}} \cdot \vec{\mathbf{D}} = A_x D_x + A_y D_y + A_z D_z$$

$$\vec{\mathbf{A}} \cdot (\vec{\mathbf{B}} \times \vec{\mathbf{C}}) = (4)(-12) + (-2)(-5) + (3)(-9) = -48 + 10 - 27 = \boxed{-65}$$

$$\vec{\mathbf{A}} \times (\vec{\mathbf{B}} \times \vec{\mathbf{C}}) = \vec{\mathbf{A}} \times \vec{\mathbf{D}} = (A_y D_z - A_z D_y)\hat{\mathbf{i}} + (A_z D_x - A_x D_z)\hat{\mathbf{j}} + (A_x D_y - A_y D_x)\hat{\mathbf{k}}$$

$$\vec{\mathbf{A}} \times (\vec{\mathbf{B}} \times \vec{\mathbf{C}}) = [(-2)(-9) - (3)(-5)]\hat{\mathbf{i}} + [(3)(-12) - (4)(-9)]\hat{\mathbf{j}} + [(4)(-5) - (-2)(-12)]\hat{\mathbf{k}}$$

$$\vec{\mathbf{A}} \times (\vec{\mathbf{B}} \times \vec{\mathbf{C}}) = (18 + 15)\hat{\mathbf{i}} + (-36 + 36)\hat{\mathbf{j}} + (-20 - 24)\hat{\mathbf{k}} = 33\hat{\mathbf{i}} + 0\hat{\mathbf{j}} - 44\hat{\mathbf{k}} = \boxed{33\hat{\mathbf{i}} - 44\hat{\mathbf{k}}}$$

❼ Make the definition $\vec{\mathbf{D}} \equiv \vec{\mathbf{B}} \times \vec{\mathbf{C}}$.

$$\vec{\mathbf{D}} = \vec{\mathbf{B}} \times \vec{\mathbf{C}} = (B_y C_z - B_z C_y)\hat{\mathbf{i}} + (B_z C_x - B_x C_z)\hat{\mathbf{j}} + (B_x C_y - B_y C_x)\hat{\mathbf{k}}$$

$$\vec{\mathbf{D}} = [(0)(2) - (-4)(-4)]\hat{\mathbf{i}} + [(-4)(8) - (4)(2)]\hat{\mathbf{j}} + [(4)(-4) - (0)(8)]\hat{\mathbf{k}}$$

$$\vec{\mathbf{D}} = (0 - 16)\hat{\mathbf{i}} + (-32 - 8)\hat{\mathbf{j}} + (-16 - 0)\hat{\mathbf{k}} = -16\hat{\mathbf{i}} - 40\hat{\mathbf{j}} - 16\hat{\mathbf{k}}$$

$$\vec{\mathbf{A}} \cdot (\vec{\mathbf{B}} \times \vec{\mathbf{C}}) = \vec{\mathbf{A}} \cdot \vec{\mathbf{D}} = A_x D_x + A_y D_y + A_z D_z$$

$$\vec{\mathbf{A}} \cdot (\vec{\mathbf{B}} \times \vec{\mathbf{C}}) = (6)(-16) + (2)(-40) + (-4)(-16) = -96 - 80 + 64 = \boxed{-112}$$

$$\vec{\mathbf{A}} \times (\vec{\mathbf{B}} \times \vec{\mathbf{C}}) = \vec{\mathbf{A}} \times \vec{\mathbf{D}} = (A_y D_z - A_z D_y)\hat{\mathbf{i}} + (A_z D_x - A_x D_z)\hat{\mathbf{j}} + (A_x D_y - A_y D_x)\hat{\mathbf{k}}$$

$$\vec{\mathbf{A}} \times (\vec{\mathbf{B}} \times \vec{\mathbf{C}}) = [(2)(-16) - (-4)(-40)]\hat{\mathbf{i}} + [(-4)(-16) - (6)(-16)]\hat{\mathbf{j}} + [(6)(-40) - (2)(-16)]\hat{\mathbf{k}}$$

$$\vec{\mathbf{A}} \times (\vec{\mathbf{B}} \times \vec{\mathbf{C}}) = (-32 - 160)\hat{\mathbf{i}} + (64 + 96)\hat{\mathbf{j}} + (-240 + 32)\hat{\mathbf{k}} = \boxed{-192\hat{\mathbf{i}} + 160\hat{\mathbf{j}} - 208\hat{\mathbf{k}}}$$

$$\vec{\mathbf{A}} \times (\vec{\mathbf{B}} \times \vec{\mathbf{C}}) = \boxed{\langle -192, 160, -208 \rangle}$$

Chapter 6, Part A

❶ $x = r\cos\theta = 1\cos\frac{5\pi}{6} = 1\left(-\frac{\sqrt{3}}{2}\right) = \boxed{-\frac{\sqrt{3}}{2}}$

$y = r\sin\theta = 1\sin\frac{5\pi}{6} = 1\left(\frac{1}{2}\right) = \boxed{\frac{1}{2}}$

❷ $x = r\cos\theta = 8\cos\frac{4\pi}{3} = 8\left(-\frac{1}{2}\right) = \boxed{-4}$

$y = r\sin\theta = 8\sin\frac{4\pi}{3} = 8\left(-\frac{\sqrt{3}}{2}\right) = \boxed{-4\sqrt{3}}$

❸ $r = \sqrt{x^2 + y^2} = \sqrt{\left(\sqrt{3}\right)^2 + (-1)^2} = \sqrt{3+1} = \sqrt{4} = \boxed{2}$

$\theta = \tan^{-1}\left(\frac{y}{x}\right) = \tan^{-1}\left(\frac{-1}{\sqrt{3}}\right) = \boxed{-\frac{\pi}{6}} = \boxed{-30°}$

Notes: θ lies in Quadrant IV because $x > 0$ and $y < 0$. The answer for θ is equivalent to $\frac{11\pi}{6}$ rad or 330°.

❹ $r = \sqrt{x^2 + y^2} = \sqrt{0^2 + (-3)^2} = \sqrt{0+9} = \sqrt{9} = \boxed{3}$

$\theta = \tan^{-1}\left(\frac{y}{x}\right) = \tan^{-1}\left(\frac{-3}{0}\right) = \boxed{\frac{3\pi}{2}} = \boxed{270°}$

Note: Although $\frac{-3}{0}$ is undefined, θ is defined and clearly equals 270° because $(0, -3)$ corresponds to the $-y$-axis. The answer for θ is equivalent to $-\frac{\pi}{2}$ rad or $-90°$. Recall from trig that $\tan(270°)$ is undefined and recall from calculus that $\tan\theta$ approaches negative infinity as θ approaches $\frac{3\pi}{2}$ rad.

❺ Recall the trig identity $\cos(2\theta) = \cos^2\theta - \sin^2\theta$.

$r = \cos^2\theta - \sin^2\theta$ Now use the equations $\cos\theta = \frac{x}{r}$ and $\sin\theta = \frac{y}{r}$.

$r = \frac{x^2}{r^2} - \frac{y^2}{r^2}$ Multiply by r^2 on both sides: $r^3 = x^2 - y^2$.

Use the equation $r = \sqrt{x^2 + y^2} = (x^2 + y^2)^{1/2}$ to get $(x^2 + y^2)^{3/2} = x^2 - y^2$.

Square both sides: $(x^2 + y^2)^3 = (x^2 - y^2)^2$. Expand each side.

$\boxed{x^6 + 3x^4y^2 + 3x^2y^4 + y^6 = x^4 - 2x^2y^2 + y^4}$

$r = \cos(2\theta)$ represents a four-petaled rose centered about the origin.

❻ Use $\sin\theta = \frac{y}{r}$ to write $r = 1 + \frac{y}{r}$. Multiply by r on both sides: $r^2 = r + y$.

Use the equation $r = \sqrt{x^2 + y^2}$ to get $x^2 + y^2 = \sqrt{x^2 + y^2} + y$.

Subtract y from both sides: $x^2 + y^2 - y = \sqrt{x^2 + y^2}$.

Square both sides: $x^4 + 2x^2y^2 + y^4 - 2y^3 + y^2 - 2x^2y = x^2 + y^2$.

$\boxed{x^4 - x^2 + 2x^2y^2 + y^4 - 2y^3 - 2x^2y = 0}$

$r = 1 + \sin\theta$ represents a cardioid that is symmetric about the y-axis.

❼ Use $x = r\cos\theta$ and $r = \sqrt{x^2 + y^2}$ to get $\sqrt{x^2 + y^2} = 1 + x$.

Square both sides: $x^2 + y^2 = 1 + 2x + x^2$.

$\boxed{y^2 = 2x + 1}$ represents a parabola that is symmetric about the x-axis with its apex at $\left(-\frac{1}{2}, 0\right)$.

❽ Recall the trig identities $\tan\theta = \frac{\sin\theta}{\cos\theta}$ and $\sec\theta = \frac{1}{\cos\theta}$.

$r = \frac{\sin\theta}{\cos\theta}\frac{1}{\cos\theta}$. Multiply both sides by $\cos^2\theta$ to get $r\cos^2\theta = \sin\theta$.

Multiply by r on both sides: $r^2\cos^2\theta = r\sin\theta$.

Use $x = r\cos\theta$ and $y = r\sin\theta$ to get $\boxed{x^2 = y}$.

$r = \tan\theta\sec\theta$ represents a parabola that is symmetric about the y-axis with its apex at the origin.

Chapter 6, Part B

❾ Use $x = r\cos\theta$ and $y = r\sin\theta$ to get $r\sin\theta = \frac{1}{r\cos\theta}$.

Multiply both sides by $r\cos\theta$ to get $\boxed{r^2\sin\theta\cos\theta = 1}$.

If you use the trig identity $\sin(2\theta) = 2\sin\theta\cos\theta$ such that $\sin\theta\cos\theta = \frac{\sin(2\theta)}{2}$, this can be written as $\frac{r^2\sin(2\theta)}{2} = 1$ or $\boxed{r^2\sin(2\theta) = 2}$.

$y = \frac{1}{x}$ represents a hyperbola with the diagonal line $y = x$ as its axis of symmetry.

❿ Use $x = r\cos\theta$ and $y = r\sin\theta$ to get $r\sin\theta = r^2\cos^2\theta$.

Divide by r and by $\cos^2\theta$ on both sides: $\frac{\sin\theta}{\cos^2\theta} = r$.

If you use the trig identities $\tan\theta = \frac{\sin\theta}{\cos\theta}$ and $\sec\theta = \frac{1}{\cos\theta}$, this can be written as $\boxed{\tan\theta\sec\theta = r}$.

$y = x^2$ represents a parabola that is symmetric about the y-axis with its apex at the origin.

⓫ Use $x = r\cos\theta$ and $y = r\sin\theta$ to get $r\sin\theta = \frac{r\cos\theta}{2}$.

Divide by $r\cos\theta$ on both sides: $\boxed{\tan\theta = \frac{1}{2}}$.

$y = \frac{x}{2}$ represents a straight line with slope $\frac{1}{2}$ that passes through the origin.

⓬ Use $x = r\cos\theta$ and $y = r\sin\theta$ to get $\boxed{r^2\sin^2\theta + \frac{r^2\cos^2\theta}{4} = 1}$.

Multiply both sides by 4 and factor to get $\boxed{r^2(4\sin^2\theta + \cos^2\theta) = 4}$.

$y^2 + \frac{x^2}{4} = 1$ represents an ellipse centered about the origin with a semimajor axis of 2 and a semiminor axis of 1, which passes through $(\pm 2, 0)$ and $(0, \pm 1)$.

⓭ First use $\hat{\mathbf{r}} = \hat{\mathbf{i}}\cos\theta + \hat{\mathbf{j}}\sin\theta$ and $\hat{\boldsymbol{\theta}} = -\hat{\mathbf{i}}\sin\theta + \hat{\mathbf{j}}\cos\theta$.

$\vec{\mathbf{A}} = r^2(\hat{\mathbf{i}}\cos\theta + \hat{\mathbf{j}}\sin\theta)\sin\theta + r^2(-\hat{\mathbf{i}}\sin\theta + \hat{\mathbf{j}}\cos\theta)\cos\theta$

$\vec{\mathbf{A}} = \hat{\mathbf{i}}\,r^2\sin\theta\cos\theta + \hat{\mathbf{j}}\,r^2\sin^2\theta - \hat{\mathbf{i}}\,r^2\sin\theta\cos\theta + \hat{\mathbf{j}}\,r^2\cos^2\theta$

$\vec{\mathbf{A}} = \hat{\mathbf{j}}\,r^2(\sin^2\theta + \cos^2\theta) = \boxed{r^2\hat{\mathbf{j}}}$ because $\sin^2\theta + \cos^2\theta = 1$.

$\vec{\mathbf{A}} = \boxed{(x^2 + y^2)\hat{\mathbf{j}}}$ because $x^2 + y^2 = r^2$.

⓮ First use $\hat{\mathbf{r}} = \hat{\mathbf{i}}\cos\theta + \hat{\mathbf{j}}\sin\theta$ and $\hat{\boldsymbol{\theta}} = -\hat{\mathbf{i}}\sin\theta + \hat{\mathbf{j}}\cos\theta$.

$\vec{\mathbf{B}} = (\hat{\mathbf{i}}\cos\theta + \hat{\mathbf{j}}\sin\theta)\sec\theta - (-\hat{\mathbf{i}}\sin\theta + \hat{\mathbf{j}}\cos\theta)\csc\theta$

Recall the trig identities $\sec\theta = \frac{1}{\cos\theta}$ and $\csc\theta = \frac{1}{\sin\theta}$.

$\vec{\mathbf{B}} = \frac{\cos\theta}{\cos\theta}\hat{\mathbf{i}} + \frac{\sin\theta}{\cos\theta}\hat{\mathbf{j}} + \frac{\sin\theta}{\sin\theta}\hat{\mathbf{i}} - \frac{\cos\theta}{\sin\theta}\hat{\mathbf{j}} = \hat{\mathbf{i}} + \frac{\sin\theta}{\cos\theta}\hat{\mathbf{j}} + \hat{\mathbf{i}} - \frac{\cos\theta}{\sin\theta}\hat{\mathbf{j}} = 2\hat{\mathbf{i}} + \left(\frac{\sin\theta}{\cos\theta} - \frac{\cos\theta}{\sin\theta}\right)\hat{\mathbf{j}}$

Since $x = r\cos\theta$ and $y = r\sin\theta$, it follows that $\frac{y}{x} = \frac{\sin\theta}{\cos\theta}$ and $\frac{x}{y} = \frac{\cos\theta}{\sin\theta}$.

$\vec{\mathbf{B}} = \boxed{2\hat{\mathbf{i}} + \left(\frac{y}{x} - \frac{x}{y}\right)\hat{\mathbf{j}}}$

Chapter 7, Part A

❶ $x = r\cos\theta\sin\varphi = 8\cos\frac{2\pi}{3}\sin\frac{\pi}{4} = 8\left(-\frac{1}{2}\right)\left(\frac{\sqrt{2}}{2}\right) = \boxed{-2\sqrt{2}}$

$y = r\sin\theta\sin\varphi = 8\sin\frac{2\pi}{3}\sin\frac{\pi}{4} = 8\left(\frac{\sqrt{3}}{2}\right)\left(\frac{\sqrt{2}}{2}\right) = \boxed{2\sqrt{6}}$

$z = r\cos\varphi = 8\cos\frac{\pi}{4} = 8\left(\frac{\sqrt{2}}{2}\right) = \boxed{4\sqrt{2}}$

Note: φ is the polar (or zenith) angle and θ is the azimuthal angle in common math notation. For common physics notation, swap φ and θ. (The order may also differ.)

❷ $x = r\cos\theta\sin\varphi = \frac{1}{2}\cos\frac{3\pi}{2}\sin\frac{5\pi}{6} = \frac{1}{2}(0)\left(\frac{1}{2}\right) = \boxed{0}$

$y = r\sin\theta\sin\varphi = \frac{1}{2}\sin\frac{3\pi}{2}\sin\frac{5\pi}{6} = \frac{1}{2}(-1)\left(\frac{1}{2}\right) = \boxed{-\frac{1}{4}}$

$z = r\cos\varphi = \frac{1}{2}\cos\frac{5\pi}{6} = \frac{1}{2}\left(-\frac{\sqrt{3}}{2}\right) = \boxed{-\frac{\sqrt{3}}{4}}$

❸ $r = \sqrt{x^2 + y^2 + z^2} = \sqrt{\left(\sqrt{3}\right)^2 + (-3)^2 + (-2)^2} = \sqrt{3 + 9 + 4} = \sqrt{16} = \boxed{4}$

$\theta = \tan^{-1}\left(\frac{y}{x}\right) = \tan^{-1}\left(\frac{-3}{\sqrt{3}}\right) = \tan^{-1}(-\sqrt{3}) = \boxed{-\frac{\pi}{3}} = \boxed{-60°}$ or $\boxed{\frac{5\pi}{3}} = \boxed{300°}$

$\varphi = \cos^{-1}\left(\frac{z}{r}\right) = \cos^{-1}\left(\frac{-2}{4}\right) = \cos^{-1}\left(-\frac{1}{2}\right) = \boxed{\frac{2\pi}{3}} = \boxed{120°}$

Notes: θ lies in Quadrant IV because $x > 0$ and $y < 0$ and $\varphi > \frac{\pi}{2}$ because $z < 0$.

Recall that $0 \le \varphi \le \pi$ whereas $0 \le \theta \le 2\pi$.

❹ $r = \sqrt{x^2 + y^2 + z^2} = \sqrt{\left(-\frac{3}{2}\right)^2 + \left(\frac{3}{2}\right)^2 + \left(\frac{\sqrt{6}}{2}\right)^2} = \sqrt{\frac{9}{4} + \frac{9}{4} + \frac{6}{4}} = \sqrt{\frac{24}{4}} = \boxed{\sqrt{6}}$

$\theta = \tan^{-1}\left(\frac{y}{x}\right) = \tan^{-1}\left(\frac{3/2}{-3/2}\right) = \tan^{-1}(-1) = \boxed{\frac{3\pi}{4}} = \boxed{135°}$

$\varphi = \cos^{-1}\left(\frac{z}{r}\right) = \cos^{-1}\left(\frac{\sqrt{6}/2}{\sqrt{6}}\right) = \cos^{-1}\left(\frac{1}{2}\right) = \boxed{\frac{\pi}{3}} = \boxed{60°}$

Note: θ lies in Quadrant II because $x < 0$ and $y > 0$.

❺ Note that $\frac{y}{x} = \tan\theta$ and $\frac{r}{z} = \frac{1}{\cos\varphi} = \sec\varphi$.

$\frac{y}{x} = \frac{r}{z}$ such that $\frac{y}{x} = \frac{\sqrt{x^2+y^2+z^2}}{z}$. Square both sides: $\frac{y^2}{x^2} = \frac{x^2+y^2+z^2}{z^2}$.

Cross multiply: $\boxed{y^2z^2 = x^4 + x^2y^2 + x^2z^2}$.

❻ Multiply by r^2 on both sides: $r^2\cos^2\theta\sin^2\varphi + r^2\cos^2\varphi = 1$.

$\boxed{x^2 + z^2 = 1}$.

Chapter 7, Part B

❼ Add z^2 to both sides to get $x^2 + y^2 + z^2 = 2z^2$. Use $r^2 = x^2 + y^2 + z^2$ and $z = r\cos\varphi$ to write this as $r^2 = 2r^2\cos^2\varphi$. Divide by r^2 on both sides: $1 = 2\cos^2\varphi$, which may be expressed as $\boxed{\frac{1}{2} = \cos^2\varphi}$. **Note**: Recall that φ is the polar angle and θ is the azimuthal angle in this book.

❽ Use $x = r\cos\theta\sin\varphi$ and $z = r\cos\varphi$ to get $\boxed{r^2(\cos^2\theta\sin^2\varphi + \cos^2\varphi) = 25}$.

❾ Use $x = r\cos\theta\sin\varphi$ and $z = r\cos\varphi$ to get $r\cos\varphi = r^2\cos^2\theta\sin^2\varphi$.
Divide by r on both sides: $\boxed{\cos\varphi = r\cos^2\theta\sin^2\varphi}$.

❿ Divide by x and multiply by z on both sides to get $\frac{yz}{x} = 1$.
Use $\frac{y}{x} = \tan\theta$ and $z = r\cos\varphi$ to get $\boxed{r\tan\theta\cos\varphi = 1}$.
Note: The answer is equivalent to $\boxed{r = \cot\theta\sec\varphi}$.

⓫ Use $\hat{\mathbf{r}} = \hat{\mathbf{i}}\cos\theta\sin\varphi + \hat{\mathbf{j}}\sin\theta\sin\varphi + \hat{\mathbf{k}}\cos\varphi$, $\hat{\boldsymbol{\theta}} = -\hat{\mathbf{i}}\sin\theta + \hat{\mathbf{j}}\cos\theta$, and $\hat{\boldsymbol{\varphi}} = \hat{\mathbf{i}}\cos\theta\cos\varphi + \hat{\mathbf{j}}\sin\theta\cos\varphi - \hat{\mathbf{k}}\sin\varphi$.

$\vec{\mathbf{A}} = r^2(\hat{\mathbf{i}}\cos\theta\sin\varphi + \hat{\mathbf{j}}\sin\theta\sin\varphi + \hat{\mathbf{k}}\cos\varphi)\cos\theta\sin\varphi + r^2(-\hat{\mathbf{i}}\sin\theta + \hat{\mathbf{j}}\cos\theta)\sin\theta\sin^2\varphi + r^2(\hat{\mathbf{i}}\cos\theta\cos\varphi + \hat{\mathbf{j}}\sin\theta\cos\varphi - \hat{\mathbf{k}}\sin\varphi)\sin\varphi$

$\vec{\mathbf{A}} = \hat{\mathbf{i}}\,r^2\cos^2\theta\sin^2\varphi + \hat{\mathbf{j}}\,r^2\cos\theta\sin\theta\sin^2\varphi + \hat{\mathbf{k}}\,r^2\cos\theta\sin\varphi\cos\varphi - \hat{\mathbf{i}}\,r^2\sin^2\theta\sin^2\varphi + \hat{\mathbf{j}}\,r^2\cos\theta\sin\theta\sin^2\varphi + \hat{\mathbf{i}}\,r^2\cos\theta\cos\varphi\sin\varphi + \hat{\mathbf{j}}\,r^2\sin\theta\cos\varphi\sin\varphi - \hat{\mathbf{k}}\,r^2\sin^2\varphi$

Now use $x = r\cos\theta\sin\varphi$, $y = r\sin\theta\sin\varphi$, and $z = r\cos\varphi$.

$\vec{\mathbf{A}} = x^2\hat{\mathbf{i}} + xy\hat{\mathbf{j}} + xz\hat{\mathbf{k}} - y^2\hat{\mathbf{i}} + xy\hat{\mathbf{j}} + xz\hat{\mathbf{i}} + yz\hat{\mathbf{j}} - \hat{\mathbf{k}}\,r^2\sin^2\varphi$

Since $\sin^2\varphi + \cos^2\varphi = 1$, it follows that $\sin^2\varphi = 1 - \cos^2\varphi$, which shows that $r^2\sin^2\varphi = r^2 - r^2\cos^2\varphi = r^2 - z^2 = x^2 + y^2 + z^2 - z^2 = x^2 + y^2$ (since $r^2 = x^2 + y^2 + z^2$).

$\vec{\mathbf{A}} = x^2\hat{\mathbf{i}} + xy\hat{\mathbf{j}} + xz\hat{\mathbf{k}} - y^2\hat{\mathbf{i}} + xy\hat{\mathbf{j}} + xz\hat{\mathbf{i}} + yz\hat{\mathbf{j}} - x^2\hat{\mathbf{k}} - y^2\hat{\mathbf{k}}$

$\vec{\mathbf{A}} = \boxed{(x^2 - y^2 + xz)\hat{\mathbf{i}} + (2xy + yz)\hat{\mathbf{j}} + (xz - x^2 - y^2)\hat{\mathbf{k}}}$

Chapter 8, Part A

❶ $x = r_c \cos\theta = 4\cos\left(-\frac{\pi}{6}\right) = 4\left(\frac{\sqrt{3}}{2}\right) = \boxed{2\sqrt{3}}$

$y = r_c \sin\theta = 4\sin\left(-\frac{\pi}{6}\right) = 4\left(-\frac{1}{2}\right) = \boxed{-2}$, $\boxed{z = 6}$

❷ $x = r_c \cos\theta = \frac{2}{3}\cos\frac{2\pi}{3} = \frac{2}{3}\left(-\frac{1}{2}\right) = \boxed{-\frac{1}{3}}$

$y = r_c \sin\theta = \frac{2}{3}\sin\frac{2\pi}{3} = \frac{2}{3}\left(\frac{\sqrt{3}}{2}\right) = \boxed{\frac{\sqrt{3}}{3}}$, $\boxed{z = -\frac{1}{3}}$

❸ $r_c = \sqrt{x^2 + y^2} = \sqrt{(-2)^2 + 0^2} = \sqrt{4+0} = \sqrt{4} = \boxed{2}$

$\theta = \tan^{-1}\left(\frac{y}{x}\right) = \tan^{-1}\left(\frac{0}{-2}\right) = \tan^{-1}(0) = \boxed{\pi} = \boxed{180°}$, $\boxed{z = 2}$

Notes: $\theta = 180°$ because $x < 0$ and $y = 0$.

❹ $r = \sqrt{x^2 + y^2} = \sqrt{\left(-\sqrt{6}\right)^2 + \sqrt{2}^2} = \sqrt{6+2} = \sqrt{8} = \sqrt{(4)(2)} = \boxed{2\sqrt{2}}$

$\theta = \tan^{-1}\left(\frac{y}{x}\right) = \tan^{-1}\left(\frac{\sqrt{2}}{-\sqrt{6}}\right) = \tan^{-1}\left(-\frac{1}{\sqrt{3}}\right) = \boxed{\frac{5\pi}{6}} = \boxed{150°}$, $\boxed{z = \sqrt{3}}$

Notes: θ lies in Quadrant II because $x < 0$ and $y > 0$.

❺ Use $r_c = \sqrt{x^2 + y^2}$ to get $\boxed{z = x^2 + y^2}$.

❻ Use $\frac{y}{x} = \frac{\sin\theta}{\cos\theta} = \tan\theta$ to get $\frac{zy}{x} = 1$. Multiply by x on both sides: $\boxed{zy = x}$.

Chapter 8, Part B

❼ Use $r_c = \sqrt{x^2 + y^2}$ to get $\boxed{r_c^2 + z^2 = 9}$.

❽ Use $r_c = \sqrt{x^2 + y^2}$ to get $\boxed{r_c = 2z}$.

❾ Use $x = r_c \cos\theta$ and $y = r_c \sin\theta$ to get $\boxed{z = 2r_c^2 \sin\theta\cos\theta}$ or $\boxed{z = r_c^2 \sin(2\theta)}$.

Recall the trig identity $\sin(2\theta) = 2\sin\theta\cos\theta$.

❿ Factor: $y^2(x^2 + y^2) = x^2z^2$. Use $r_c = \sqrt{x^2 + y^2}$ to get $y^2r_c^2 = x^2z^2$.

Square root both sides: $yr_c = \pm xz$. Divide by x on both sides: $z = \pm\frac{yr_c}{x}$.

Use $\frac{y}{x} = \frac{\sin\theta}{\cos\theta} = \tan\theta$ to get $\boxed{z = \pm r_c \tan\theta}$.

⓫ First use $\hat{\mathbf{r}} = \hat{\mathbf{i}}\cos\theta + \hat{\mathbf{j}}\sin\theta$ and $\hat{\boldsymbol{\theta}} = -\hat{\mathbf{i}}\sin\theta + \hat{\mathbf{j}}\cos\theta$.

$\vec{\mathbf{A}} = r_c^2\left(\hat{\mathbf{i}}\cos\theta + \hat{\mathbf{j}}\sin\theta\right)\cos\theta - r_c^2\left(-\hat{\mathbf{i}}\sin\theta + \hat{\mathbf{j}}\cos\theta\right)\sin\theta + z^2\hat{\mathbf{k}}$

$\vec{\mathbf{A}} = \hat{\mathbf{i}}\,r_c^2\cos^2\theta + \hat{\mathbf{j}}\,r_c^2\sin\theta\cos\theta + \hat{\mathbf{i}}\,r_c^2\sin^2\theta - \hat{\mathbf{j}}r_c^2\sin\theta\cos\theta + z^2\hat{\mathbf{k}}$

$\vec{\mathbf{A}} = \hat{\mathbf{i}}\,r_c^2(\cos^2\theta + \sin^2\theta) + z^2\hat{\mathbf{k}} = r_c^2\hat{\mathbf{i}} + z^2\hat{\mathbf{k}}$ because $\sin^2\theta + \cos^2\theta = 1$.

$\vec{\mathbf{A}} = \boxed{(x^2 + y^2)\hat{\mathbf{i}} + z^2\hat{\mathbf{k}}}$ because $x^2 + y^2 = r_c^2$.

Chapter 9, Part A

❶ $\vec{\nabla} f = \hat{\mathbf{i}}\frac{\partial f}{\partial x} + \hat{\mathbf{j}}\frac{\partial f}{\partial y} + \hat{\mathbf{k}}\frac{\partial f}{\partial z} = \hat{\mathbf{i}}\frac{\partial}{\partial x}x^5y^3 + \hat{\mathbf{j}}\frac{\partial}{\partial y}x^5y^3 + \hat{\mathbf{k}}\frac{\partial}{\partial z}x^5y^3$

$\vec{\nabla} f = 5x^4y^3\hat{\mathbf{i}} + 3x^5y^2\hat{\mathbf{j}} + 0\hat{\mathbf{k}} = \boxed{5x^4y^3\hat{\mathbf{i}} + 3x^5y^2\hat{\mathbf{j}}}$

❷ $\vec{\nabla} f = \hat{\mathbf{i}}\frac{\partial f}{\partial x} + \hat{\mathbf{j}}\frac{\partial f}{\partial y} + \hat{\mathbf{k}}\frac{\partial f}{\partial z} = \hat{\mathbf{i}}\frac{\partial}{\partial x}\frac{x^3y^2}{z} + \hat{\mathbf{j}}\frac{\partial}{\partial y}\frac{x^3y^2}{z} + \hat{\mathbf{k}}\frac{\partial}{\partial z}\frac{x^3y^2}{z}$

$\vec{\nabla} f = \boxed{\frac{3x^2y^2}{z}\hat{\mathbf{i}} + \frac{2x^3y}{z}\hat{\mathbf{j}} - \frac{x^3y^2}{z^2}\hat{\mathbf{k}}}$

Note: $\frac{d}{dz}\frac{1}{z} = \frac{d}{dz}z^{-1} = -z^{-2} = -\frac{1}{z^2}$.

❸ $\vec{\nabla} f = \hat{\mathbf{i}}\frac{\partial f}{\partial x} + \hat{\mathbf{j}}\frac{\partial f}{\partial y} + \hat{\mathbf{k}}\frac{\partial f}{\partial z} = \hat{\mathbf{i}}\frac{\partial}{\partial x}y\sqrt{x} + \hat{\mathbf{j}}\frac{\partial}{\partial y}y\sqrt{x} + \hat{\mathbf{k}}\frac{\partial}{\partial z}y\sqrt{x}$

$\vec{\nabla} f = \frac{y}{2\sqrt{x}}\hat{\mathbf{i}} + \sqrt{x}\,\hat{\mathbf{j}} + 0\hat{\mathbf{k}} = \boxed{\frac{y}{2\sqrt{x}}\hat{\mathbf{i}} + \sqrt{x}\,\hat{\mathbf{j}}} = \boxed{\frac{y\sqrt{x}}{2x}\hat{\mathbf{i}} + \sqrt{x}\,\hat{\mathbf{j}}}$

Note: $\frac{d}{dx}\sqrt{x} = \frac{d}{dx}x^{1/2} = \frac{1}{2}x^{-1/2} = \frac{1}{2x^{1/2}} = \frac{1}{2\sqrt{x}}$.

❹ Note: φ is the polar angle (measured from the zenith) of spherical coordinates.

$\vec{\nabla} f = \hat{\mathbf{r}}\frac{\partial f}{\partial r} + \hat{\boldsymbol{\theta}}\frac{1}{r\sin\varphi}\frac{\partial f}{\partial \theta} + \hat{\boldsymbol{\varphi}}\frac{1}{r}\frac{\partial f}{\partial \varphi} = \hat{\mathbf{r}}\frac{\partial}{\partial r}r^3\cos^2\varphi + \hat{\boldsymbol{\theta}}\frac{1}{r\sin\varphi}\frac{\partial}{\partial \theta}r^3\cos^2\varphi + \hat{\boldsymbol{\varphi}}\frac{1}{r}\frac{\partial}{\partial \varphi}r^3\cos^2\varphi$

$\vec{\nabla} f = 3r^2\hat{\mathbf{r}}\cos^2\varphi + (0)\hat{\boldsymbol{\theta}} + \frac{r^3}{r}\hat{\boldsymbol{\varphi}}2\cos\varphi\,(-\sin\varphi) = \boxed{3r^2\hat{\mathbf{r}}\cos^2\varphi - 2r^2\hat{\boldsymbol{\varphi}}\sin\varphi\cos\varphi}$

$\vec{\nabla} f = \boxed{3r^2\hat{\mathbf{r}}\cos^2\varphi - r^2\hat{\boldsymbol{\varphi}}\sin(2\varphi)}$

Notes: We used the chain rule. Let $u = \cos\varphi$ and $g = u^2 = \cos^2\varphi$:

$\frac{d}{d\varphi}\cos^2\varphi = \frac{dg}{d\varphi} = \frac{dg}{du}\frac{du}{d\varphi} = \frac{d}{du}u^2\frac{d}{d\varphi}\cos\varphi = 2u(-\sin\varphi) = -2\cos\varphi\sin\varphi$.

Recall the trig identity $\sin(2\varphi) = 2\sin\varphi\cos\varphi$.

Note: Recall that φ is the polar angle and θ is the azimuthal angle in common math notation. For common physics notation, swap φ and θ in spherical coordinates.

❺ $\vec{\nabla} f = \hat{\mathbf{r}}\frac{\partial f}{\partial r} + \hat{\boldsymbol{\theta}}\frac{1}{r\sin\varphi}\frac{\partial f}{\partial \theta} + \hat{\boldsymbol{\varphi}}\frac{1}{r}\frac{\partial f}{\partial \varphi}$

$\vec{\nabla} f = \hat{\mathbf{r}}\frac{\partial}{\partial r}r^2\cos\theta\sin\varphi + \hat{\boldsymbol{\theta}}\frac{1}{r\sin\varphi}\frac{\partial}{\partial \theta}r^2\cos\theta\sin\varphi + \hat{\boldsymbol{\varphi}}\frac{1}{r}\frac{\partial}{\partial \varphi}r^2\cos\theta\sin\varphi$

$\vec{\nabla} f = 2r\hat{\mathbf{r}}\cos\theta\sin\varphi + \frac{r^2\sin\varphi}{r\sin\varphi}\hat{\boldsymbol{\theta}}(-\sin\theta) + \frac{r^2\cos\theta}{r}\hat{\boldsymbol{\varphi}}\cos\varphi$

$\vec{\nabla} f = \boxed{2r\hat{\mathbf{r}}\cos\theta\sin\varphi - r\hat{\boldsymbol{\theta}}\sin\theta + r\hat{\boldsymbol{\varphi}}\cos\theta\cos\varphi}$

❻ $\vec{\nabla} f = \hat{\mathbf{r}}_c \frac{\partial f}{\partial r_c} + \hat{\boldsymbol{\theta}} \frac{1}{r_c} \frac{\partial f}{\partial \theta} + \hat{\mathbf{k}} \frac{\partial f}{\partial z}$

$\vec{\nabla} f = \hat{\mathbf{r}}_c \frac{\partial}{\partial r_c}(r_c^2 - r_c z \cos\theta + z^2) + \hat{\boldsymbol{\theta}} \frac{1}{r_c} \frac{\partial}{\partial \theta}(r_c^2 - r_c z \cos\theta + z^2) + \hat{\mathbf{k}} \frac{\partial}{\partial z}(r_c^2 - r_c z \cos\theta + z^2)$

$\vec{\nabla} f = \hat{\mathbf{r}}_c(2r_c - z\cos\theta) + \hat{\boldsymbol{\theta}} \frac{1}{r_c}(r_c z \sin\theta) + \hat{\mathbf{k}}(-r_c \cos\theta + 2z)$

$\vec{\nabla} f = \boxed{\hat{\mathbf{r}}_c(2r_c - z\cos\theta) + z\hat{\boldsymbol{\theta}} \sin\theta + \hat{\mathbf{k}}(-r_c\cos\theta + 2z)}$

❼ The magnitude of $\vec{\mathbf{A}} = \hat{\mathbf{i}} + \hat{\mathbf{j}}$ is $\|\vec{\mathbf{A}}\| = \sqrt{A_x^2 + A_y^2 + A_z^2} = \sqrt{1^2 + 1^2 + 0^2} = \sqrt{1+1} = \sqrt{2}$. A unit vector along $\vec{\mathbf{A}}$ is $\hat{\mathbf{A}} = \frac{\vec{\mathbf{A}}}{\|\vec{\mathbf{A}}\|} = \frac{\hat{\mathbf{i}}+\hat{\mathbf{j}}}{\sqrt{2}}$.

$D_{\vec{\mathbf{A}}} f = \vec{\nabla} f \cdot \hat{\mathbf{A}} = \left(\hat{\mathbf{i}} \frac{\partial f}{\partial x} + \hat{\mathbf{j}} \frac{\partial f}{\partial y} + \hat{\mathbf{k}} \frac{\partial f}{\partial z}\right) \cdot \left(\frac{\hat{\mathbf{i}}+\hat{\mathbf{j}}}{\sqrt{2}}\right)$

$D_{\vec{\mathbf{A}}} f = \frac{1}{\sqrt{2}} \frac{\partial}{\partial x}(x^2 - y^2) + \frac{1}{\sqrt{2}} \frac{\partial}{\partial y}(x^2 - y^2) + 0 = \boxed{\frac{2x-2y}{\sqrt{2}}} = \boxed{\sqrt{2}(x-y)}$

Note: $\frac{2}{\sqrt{2}} = \sqrt{2}$ because $\sqrt{2}\sqrt{2} = 2$.

Chapter 9, Part B

❽ $\vec{\nabla} f = \hat{\mathbf{i}} \frac{\partial f}{\partial x} + \hat{\mathbf{j}} \frac{\partial f}{\partial y} + \hat{\mathbf{k}} \frac{\partial f}{\partial z} = \hat{\mathbf{i}} \frac{\partial}{\partial x} \frac{x}{y} + \hat{\mathbf{j}} \frac{\partial}{\partial y} \frac{x}{y} + \hat{\mathbf{k}} \frac{\partial}{\partial z} \frac{x}{y} = \frac{1}{y}\hat{\mathbf{i}} - \frac{x}{y^2}\hat{\mathbf{j}} + 0\hat{\mathbf{k}} = \frac{1}{y}\hat{\mathbf{i}} - \frac{x}{y^2}\hat{\mathbf{j}}$

$\vec{\nabla} f(2,4) = \frac{1}{4}\hat{\mathbf{i}} - \frac{2}{4^2}\hat{\mathbf{j}} = \frac{1}{4}\hat{\mathbf{i}} - \frac{2}{16}\hat{\mathbf{j}} = \boxed{\frac{1}{4}\hat{\mathbf{i}} - \frac{1}{8}\hat{\mathbf{j}}}$

Note: $\frac{d}{dy}\frac{1}{y} = \frac{d}{dy} y^{-1} = -y^{-2} = -\frac{1}{y^2}$.

❾ $\vec{\nabla} f = \hat{\mathbf{i}} \frac{\partial f}{\partial x} + \hat{\mathbf{j}} \frac{\partial f}{\partial y} + \hat{\mathbf{k}} \frac{\partial f}{\partial z} = \hat{\mathbf{i}} \frac{\partial}{\partial x} x^2y^2z^4 + \hat{\mathbf{j}} \frac{\partial}{\partial y} x^2y^2z^4 + \hat{\mathbf{k}} \frac{\partial}{\partial z} x^2y^2z^4$

$\vec{\nabla} f = 2xy^2z^4\hat{\mathbf{i}} + 2x^2yz^4\hat{\mathbf{j}} + 4x^2y^2z^3\hat{\mathbf{k}}$

$\vec{\nabla} f(3,3,2) = 2(3)(3)^2(2)^4\hat{\mathbf{i}} + 2(3)^2(3)(2)^4\hat{\mathbf{j}} + 4(3)^2(3)^2(2)^3\hat{\mathbf{k}}$

$\vec{\nabla} f(3,3,2) = (6)(9)(16)\hat{\mathbf{i}} + (6)(9)(16)\hat{\mathbf{j}} + (4)(9)(9)(8)\hat{\mathbf{k}} = \boxed{864\hat{\mathbf{i}} + 864\hat{\mathbf{j}} + 2592\hat{\mathbf{k}}}$

❿ In physics texts, not only may θ and φ be swapped, but the order may differ.

$\vec{\nabla} f = \hat{\mathbf{r}} \frac{\partial f}{\partial r} + \hat{\boldsymbol{\theta}} \frac{1}{r\sin\varphi} \frac{\partial f}{\partial \theta} + \hat{\boldsymbol{\varphi}} \frac{1}{r} \frac{\partial f}{\partial \varphi} = \hat{\mathbf{r}} \frac{\partial}{\partial r} r\tan\theta + \hat{\boldsymbol{\theta}} \frac{1}{r\sin\varphi} \frac{\partial}{\partial \theta} r\tan\theta + \hat{\boldsymbol{\varphi}} \frac{1}{r} \frac{\partial}{\partial \varphi} r\tan\theta$

$\vec{\nabla} f = \hat{\mathbf{r}}\tan\theta + \frac{r\sec^2\theta}{r\sin\varphi}\hat{\boldsymbol{\theta}} + \frac{r}{r}\hat{\boldsymbol{\varphi}}(0) = \hat{\mathbf{r}}\tan\theta + \frac{\sec^2\theta}{\sin\varphi}\hat{\boldsymbol{\theta}} = \hat{\mathbf{r}}\tan\theta + \hat{\boldsymbol{\theta}}\sec^2\theta\csc\varphi$

$\vec{\nabla} f\left(2, \frac{\pi}{3}, \frac{\pi}{2}\right) = \hat{\mathbf{r}}\tan\left(\frac{\pi}{3}\right) + \hat{\boldsymbol{\theta}}\sec^2\left(\frac{\pi}{3}\right)\csc\left(\frac{\pi}{2}\right) = \hat{\mathbf{r}}\sqrt{3} + \hat{\boldsymbol{\theta}}(2)^2(1) = \boxed{\hat{\mathbf{r}}\sqrt{3} + 4\hat{\boldsymbol{\theta}}}$

⓫ $\vec{\nabla}f = \hat{\mathbf{i}}\frac{\partial f}{\partial x} + \hat{\mathbf{j}}\frac{\partial f}{\partial y} + \hat{\mathbf{k}}\frac{\partial f}{\partial z} = \hat{\mathbf{i}}\frac{\partial}{\partial x}\frac{\sqrt{z}}{xy} + \hat{\mathbf{j}}\frac{\partial}{\partial y}\frac{\sqrt{z}}{xy} + \hat{\mathbf{k}}\frac{\partial}{\partial z}\frac{\sqrt{z}}{xy} = -\frac{\sqrt{z}}{x^2 y}\hat{\mathbf{i}} - \frac{\sqrt{z}}{xy^2}\hat{\mathbf{j}} + \frac{1}{2xy\sqrt{z}}\hat{\mathbf{k}}$

$\vec{\nabla}f(-2,-2,9) = -\frac{\sqrt{9}}{(-2)^2(-2)}\hat{\mathbf{i}} - \frac{\sqrt{9}}{(-2)(-2)^2}\hat{\mathbf{j}} + \frac{1}{2(-2)(-2)\sqrt{9}}\hat{\mathbf{k}} = -\frac{3}{(4)(-2)}\hat{\mathbf{i}} - \frac{3}{(-2)(4)}\hat{\mathbf{j}} + \frac{1}{(8)(3)}\hat{\mathbf{k}}$

$\vec{\nabla}f(-2,-2,9) = \boxed{\frac{3}{8}\hat{\mathbf{i}} + \frac{3}{8}\hat{\mathbf{j}} + \frac{1}{24}\hat{\mathbf{k}}}$

Notes: $\frac{d}{dx}\frac{1}{x} = \frac{d}{dx}x^{-1} = -x^{-2} = -\frac{1}{x^2}$ and $\frac{d}{dz}\sqrt{z} = \frac{d}{dz}z^{1/2} = \frac{1}{2}z^{-1/2} = \frac{1}{2z^{1/2}} = \frac{1}{2\sqrt{z}}$.

⓬ $\vec{\nabla}f = \hat{\mathbf{r}}_{\mathbf{c}}\frac{\partial f}{\partial r_c} + \hat{\boldsymbol{\theta}}\frac{1}{r_c}\frac{\partial f}{\partial \theta} + \hat{\mathbf{k}}\frac{\partial f}{\partial z} = \hat{\mathbf{r}}_{\mathbf{c}}\frac{\partial}{\partial r_c}r_c^2 z^3 + \hat{\boldsymbol{\theta}}\frac{1}{r_c}\frac{\partial}{\partial \theta}r_c^2 z^3 + \hat{\mathbf{k}}\frac{\partial}{\partial z}r_c^2 z^3$

$\vec{\nabla}f = 2r_c z^3\hat{\mathbf{r}}_{\mathbf{c}} + \frac{r_c^2 z^3}{r_c}\hat{\boldsymbol{\theta}}(0) + 3r_c^2 z^2\hat{\mathbf{k}} = 2r_c z^3\hat{\mathbf{r}}_{\mathbf{c}} + 3r_c^2 z^2\hat{\mathbf{k}}$

$\vec{\nabla}f\left(3,\frac{\pi}{4},4\right) = 2(3)(4)^3\hat{\mathbf{r}}_{\mathbf{c}} + 3(3)^2(4)^2\hat{\mathbf{k}} = \boxed{384\hat{\mathbf{r}}_{\mathbf{c}} + 432\hat{\mathbf{k}}}$

⓭ $\hat{\mathbf{r}}\frac{\partial f}{\partial r} + \hat{\boldsymbol{\theta}}\frac{1}{r\sin\varphi}\frac{\partial f}{\partial \theta} + \hat{\boldsymbol{\varphi}}\frac{1}{r}\frac{\partial f}{\partial \varphi} = \hat{\mathbf{r}}\frac{\partial}{\partial r}\frac{\sin\varphi}{r\cos\theta} + \hat{\boldsymbol{\theta}}\frac{1}{r\sin\varphi}\frac{\partial}{\partial \theta}\frac{\sin\varphi}{r\cos\theta} + \hat{\boldsymbol{\varphi}}\frac{1}{r}\frac{\partial}{\partial \varphi}\frac{\sin\varphi}{r\cos\theta}$

$\vec{\nabla}f = -\frac{\sin\varphi}{r^2\cos\theta}\hat{\mathbf{r}} + \frac{\sin\varphi}{r^2\sin\varphi}\hat{\boldsymbol{\theta}}\sec\theta\tan\theta + \frac{1}{r^2\cos\theta}\hat{\boldsymbol{\varphi}}\cos\varphi$

$\vec{\nabla}f = -\frac{\sin\varphi}{r^2\cos\theta}\hat{\mathbf{r}} + \frac{\sin\theta}{r^2\cos^2\theta}\hat{\boldsymbol{\theta}} + \frac{\cos\varphi}{r^2\cos\theta}\hat{\boldsymbol{\varphi}}$

$\vec{\nabla}f\left(4,\frac{4\pi}{3},\frac{3\pi}{4}\right) = -\frac{\sin\left(\frac{3\pi}{4}\right)}{4^2\cos\left(\frac{4\pi}{3}\right)}\hat{\mathbf{r}} + \frac{\sin\left(\frac{4\pi}{3}\right)}{4^2\cos^2\left(\frac{4\pi}{3}\right)}\hat{\boldsymbol{\theta}} + \frac{\cos\left(\frac{3\pi}{4}\right)}{4^2\cos\left(\frac{4\pi}{3}\right)}\hat{\boldsymbol{\varphi}} = -\frac{\sqrt{2}/2}{16\left(-\frac{1}{2}\right)}\hat{\mathbf{r}} + \frac{-\sqrt{3}/2}{16\left(-\frac{1}{2}\right)^2}\hat{\boldsymbol{\theta}} + \frac{-\sqrt{2}/2}{16\left(-\frac{1}{2}\right)}\hat{\boldsymbol{\varphi}}$

$\vec{\nabla}f\left(4,\frac{4\pi}{3},\frac{3\pi}{4}\right) = -\frac{\sqrt{2}/2}{-8}\hat{\mathbf{r}} - \frac{\sqrt{3}/2}{16\left(\frac{1}{4}\right)}\hat{\boldsymbol{\theta}} + \frac{-\sqrt{2}/2}{-8}\hat{\boldsymbol{\varphi}} = \frac{\sqrt{2}}{16}\hat{\mathbf{r}} - \frac{\sqrt{3}/2}{4}\hat{\boldsymbol{\theta}} + \frac{\sqrt{2}}{16}\hat{\boldsymbol{\varphi}} = \boxed{\frac{\sqrt{2}}{16}\hat{\mathbf{r}} - \frac{\sqrt{3}}{8}\hat{\boldsymbol{\theta}} + \frac{\sqrt{2}}{16}\hat{\boldsymbol{\varphi}}}$

Notes: $\frac{d}{d\theta}\frac{1}{\cos\theta} = \frac{d}{d\theta}\sec\theta = \sec\theta\tan\theta$, $\frac{\frac{\sqrt{2}}{2}}{8} = \frac{\sqrt{2}}{2} \div \frac{8}{1} = \frac{\sqrt{2}}{2} \times \frac{1}{8} = \frac{\sqrt{2}}{16}$, and $\frac{\frac{\sqrt{3}}{2}}{4} = \frac{\sqrt{3}}{2} \div \frac{4}{1}$ $= \frac{\sqrt{3}}{2} \times \frac{1}{4} = \frac{\sqrt{3}}{8}$.

⓮ The magnitude of $\vec{\mathbf{A}} = 10\hat{\mathbf{i}} - 5\hat{\mathbf{j}} + 10\hat{\mathbf{k}}$ is $\|\vec{\mathbf{A}}\| = \sqrt{A_x^2 + A_y^2 + A_z^2} = \sqrt{10^2 + (-5)^2 + 10^2} = \sqrt{100 + 25 + 100} = \sqrt{225} = 15$. A unit vector along $\vec{\mathbf{A}}$ is $\hat{\mathbf{A}} = \frac{\vec{\mathbf{A}}}{\|\vec{\mathbf{A}}\|} = \frac{10\hat{\mathbf{i}} - 5\hat{\mathbf{j}} + 10\hat{\mathbf{k}}}{15} = \frac{2}{3}\hat{\mathbf{i}} - \frac{1}{3}\hat{\mathbf{j}} + \frac{2}{3}\hat{\mathbf{k}}$.

$D_{\vec{\mathbf{A}}}f = \vec{\nabla}f \cdot \hat{\mathbf{A}} = \left(\hat{\mathbf{i}}\frac{\partial f}{\partial x} + \hat{\mathbf{j}}\frac{\partial f}{\partial y} + \hat{\mathbf{k}}\frac{\partial f}{\partial z}\right) \cdot \left(\frac{2}{3}\hat{\mathbf{i}} - \frac{1}{3}\hat{\mathbf{j}} + \frac{2}{3}\hat{\mathbf{k}}\right)$

$D_{\vec{\mathbf{A}}}f = \frac{2}{3}\frac{\partial}{\partial x}(x^3 + xyz + z^3) - \frac{1}{3}\frac{\partial}{\partial y}(x^3 + xyz + z^3) + \frac{2}{3}\frac{\partial}{\partial z}(x^3 + xyz + z^3)$

$= \frac{2}{3}3x^2 + \frac{2}{3}yz - \frac{1}{3}xz + \frac{2}{3}xy + \frac{2}{3}3z^2 = \frac{6x^2 + 2yz - xz + 2xy + 6z^2}{3}$

$D_{\vec{\mathbf{A}}}f(2,-1,2) = \frac{6(2)^2 + 2(-1)(2) - (2)(2) + 2(2)(-1) + 6(2)^2}{3} = \frac{24 - 4 - 4 - 4 + 24}{3} = \frac{36}{3} = \boxed{12}$

Chapter 10, Part A

❶ $\vec{\nabla} \cdot \vec{A} = \frac{\partial A_x}{\partial x} + \frac{\partial A_y}{\partial y} + \frac{\partial A_z}{\partial z} = \frac{\partial}{\partial x} x^3 + \frac{\partial}{\partial y} x^2 y + \frac{\partial}{\partial z} xy^2 = 3x^2 + x^2 + 0 = \boxed{4x^2}$

❷ $\vec{\nabla} \cdot \vec{B} = \frac{\partial B_x}{\partial x} + \frac{\partial B_y}{\partial y} + \frac{\partial B_z}{\partial z} = \frac{\partial}{\partial x} x^4 y^3 - \frac{\partial}{\partial y} x^3 y^4 + \frac{\partial}{\partial z} x^2 y^2 z^3$

$\vec{\nabla} \cdot \vec{B} = 4x^3 y^3 - 4x^3 y^3 + 3x^2 y^2 z^2 = \boxed{3x^2 y^2 z^2}$

❸ $\vec{\nabla} \cdot \vec{C} = \frac{\partial C_x}{\partial x} + \frac{\partial C_y}{\partial y} + \frac{\partial C_z}{\partial z} = \frac{\partial}{\partial x} e^{xy} + \frac{\partial}{\partial y} e^{xy} - \frac{\partial}{\partial z} xze^{xy} = ye^{xy} + xe^{xy} - xe^{xy} = \boxed{ye^{xy}}$

❹ $\vec{\nabla} \cdot \vec{D} = \frac{\partial D_x}{\partial x} + \frac{\partial D_y}{\partial y} + \frac{\partial D_z}{\partial z} = \frac{\partial}{\partial x} y \ln x + \frac{\partial}{\partial y} \frac{y^2}{x} + \frac{\partial}{\partial z} \frac{\ln y}{x} = \frac{y}{x} + \frac{2y}{x} + 0 = \boxed{\frac{3y}{x}}$

❺ $\vec{\nabla} \cdot \vec{E} = \frac{\partial E_x}{\partial x} + \frac{\partial E_y}{\partial y} + \frac{\partial E_z}{\partial z} = \frac{\partial}{\partial x}(x^2 + yz) + \frac{\partial}{\partial y}(xy - z^2) + \frac{\partial}{\partial z}(y^2 + xz) = 2x + x + x = \boxed{4x}$

❻ $\vec{\nabla} \cdot \vec{F} = \frac{1}{r_c} \frac{\partial}{\partial r_c}(r_c F_{r_c}) + \frac{1}{r_c} \frac{\partial F_\theta}{\partial \theta} + \frac{\partial F_z}{\partial z} = \frac{1}{r_c} \frac{\partial}{\partial r_c}(r_c r_c^2 \cos\theta) + \frac{1}{r_c} \frac{\partial}{\partial \theta} r_c^2 \sin\theta + \frac{\partial}{\partial z} 0$

$\vec{\nabla} \cdot \vec{F} = \frac{1}{r_c} \frac{\partial}{\partial r_c}(r_c^3 \cos\theta) + \frac{r_c^2}{r_c} \frac{\partial}{\partial \theta} \sin\theta + 0 = \frac{\cos\theta}{r_c} 3r_c^2 + r_c \cos\theta = \boxed{4r_c \cos\theta}$

Note: Recall that φ is the polar angle and θ is the azimuthal angle in common math notation. For common physics notation, swap φ and θ in spherical coordinates.

❼ $\vec{\nabla} \cdot \vec{G} = \frac{1}{r^2} \frac{\partial}{\partial r}(r^2 G_r) + \frac{1}{r \sin\varphi} \frac{\partial G_\theta}{\partial \theta} + \frac{1}{r \sin\varphi} \frac{\partial}{\partial \varphi}(G_\varphi \sin\varphi)$

$\vec{\nabla} \cdot \vec{G} = \frac{1}{r^2} \frac{\partial}{\partial r}(r^2 r) + \frac{1}{r \sin\varphi} \frac{\partial}{\partial \theta}(r \tan\theta) + \frac{1}{r \sin\varphi} \frac{\partial}{\partial \varphi}(r \cos\theta \cot\varphi \sin\varphi)$

$\vec{\nabla} \cdot \vec{G} = \frac{1}{r^2} \frac{\partial}{\partial r} r^3 + \frac{r}{r \sin\varphi} \frac{\partial}{\partial \theta} \tan\theta + \frac{r \cos\theta}{r \sin\varphi} \frac{\partial}{\partial \varphi} \cos\varphi$

$\vec{\nabla} \cdot \vec{G} = \frac{1}{r^2} 3r^2 + \frac{\sec^2\theta}{\sin\varphi} + \frac{\cos\theta}{\sin\varphi}(-\sin\varphi) = \boxed{3 + \csc\varphi \sec^2\theta - \cos\theta}$

Notes: $\cot\varphi \sin\varphi = \frac{\cos\varphi}{\sin\varphi} \sin\varphi = \cos\varphi$ and $\frac{\sec^2\theta}{\sin\varphi} = \csc\varphi \sec^2\theta = \frac{1}{\sin\varphi \cos^2\theta}$.

❽ $\vec{\nabla} \cdot \vec{H} = \frac{1}{r^2} \frac{\partial}{\partial r}(r^2 H_r) + \frac{1}{r \sin\varphi} \frac{\partial H_\theta}{\partial \theta} + \frac{1}{r \sin\varphi} \frac{\partial}{\partial \varphi}(H_\varphi \sin\varphi)$

$\vec{\nabla} \cdot \vec{H} = \frac{1}{r^2} \frac{\partial}{\partial r}(r^2 r^3) + \frac{1}{r \sin\varphi} \frac{\partial}{\partial \theta}(r^3 \cos\theta \cos\varphi) + \frac{1}{r \sin\varphi} \frac{\partial}{\partial \varphi}(r^3 \sin\theta \sin\varphi)$

$\vec{\nabla} \cdot \vec{H} = \frac{1}{r^2} \frac{\partial}{\partial r} r^5 + \frac{r^3 \cos\varphi}{r \sin\varphi} \frac{\partial}{\partial \theta} \cos\theta + \frac{r^3 \sin\theta}{r \sin\varphi} \frac{\partial}{\partial \varphi} \sin\varphi$

$\vec{\nabla} \cdot \vec{H} = \frac{1}{r^2} 5r^4 + r^2 \cot\varphi\,(-\sin\theta) + \frac{r^2 \sin\theta}{\sin\varphi} \cos\varphi$

$\vec{\nabla} \cdot \vec{H} = 5r^2 - r^2 \sin\theta \cot\varphi + r^2 \sin\theta \cot\varphi = \boxed{5r^2}$

Chapter 10, Part B

9 $\nabla^2 f = \frac{\partial^2 f}{\partial x^2} + \frac{\partial^2 f}{\partial y^2} + \frac{\partial^2 f}{\partial z^2} = \frac{\partial^2}{\partial x^2} x^5 y^3 z + \frac{\partial^2}{\partial y^2} x^5 y^3 z + \frac{\partial^2}{\partial z^2} x^5 y^3 z$

$$\nabla^2 f = \frac{\partial}{\partial x}\left(\frac{\partial}{\partial x} x^5 y^3 z\right) + \frac{\partial}{\partial y}\left(\frac{\partial}{\partial y} x^5 y^3 z\right) + \frac{\partial}{\partial z}\left(\frac{\partial}{\partial z} x^5 y^3 z\right)$$

$$\nabla^2 f = \frac{\partial}{\partial x}(5x^4 y^3 z) + \frac{\partial}{\partial y}(3x^5 y^2 z) + \frac{\partial}{\partial z}(x^5 y^3)$$

$$\nabla^2 f = 20x^3 y^3 z + 6x^5 yz + 0 = \boxed{20x^3 y^3 z + 6x^5 yz} = \boxed{2x^3 yz(10y^2 + 3x^2)}$$

10 $\nabla^2 g = \frac{\partial^2 g}{\partial x^2} + \frac{\partial^2 g}{\partial y^2} + \frac{\partial^2 g}{\partial z^2} = \frac{\partial^2}{\partial x^2}\frac{z^2}{xy} + \frac{\partial^2}{\partial y^2}\frac{z^2}{xy} + \frac{\partial^2}{\partial z^2}\frac{z^2}{xy}$

$$\nabla^2 g = \frac{\partial}{\partial x}\left(\frac{\partial}{\partial x}\frac{z^2}{xy}\right) + \frac{\partial}{\partial y}\left(\frac{\partial}{\partial y}\frac{z^2}{xy}\right) + \frac{\partial}{\partial z}\left(\frac{\partial}{\partial z}\frac{z^2}{xy}\right) = \frac{\partial}{\partial x}\left(-\frac{z^2}{x^2 y}\right) + \frac{\partial}{\partial y}\left(-\frac{z^2}{xy^2}\right) + \frac{\partial}{\partial z}\left(\frac{2z}{xy}\right)$$

$$\nabla^2 g = \boxed{\frac{2z^2}{x^3 y} + \frac{2z^2}{xy^3} + \frac{2}{xy}} = \boxed{\frac{2}{xy}\left(\frac{z^2}{x^2} + \frac{z^2}{y^2} + 1\right)} = \boxed{\frac{2z^2}{xy}\left(\frac{1}{x^2} + \frac{1}{y^2} + \frac{1}{z^2}\right)}$$

Notes: $\frac{d}{dx}\frac{1}{x} = \frac{d}{dx}x^{-1} = -x^{-2} = -\frac{1}{x^2}$ and $\frac{d}{dx}\frac{-1}{x^2} = \frac{d}{dx}(-x^{-2}) = 2x^{-3} = \frac{2}{x^3}$.

11 $\nabla^2 h = \frac{\partial^2 h}{\partial x^2} + \frac{\partial^2 h}{\partial y^2} + \frac{\partial^2 h}{\partial z^2} = \frac{\partial^2}{\partial x^2}(x^2 + y^2 + z^2) + \frac{\partial^2}{\partial y^2}(x^2 + y^2 + z^2) + \frac{\partial^2}{\partial z^2}(x^2 + y^2 + z^2)$

$$\nabla^2 h = \frac{\partial}{\partial x}\left[\frac{\partial}{\partial x}(x^2 + y^2 + z^2)\right] + \frac{\partial}{\partial y}\left[\frac{\partial}{\partial y}(x^2 + y^2 + z^2)\right] + \frac{\partial}{\partial z}\left[\frac{\partial}{\partial z}(x^2 + y^2 + z^2)\right]$$

$$\nabla^2 h = \frac{\partial}{\partial x}(2x) + \frac{\partial}{\partial y}(2y) + \frac{\partial}{\partial z}(2z) = 2 + 2 + 2 = \boxed{6}$$

12 $\nabla^2 p = \frac{1}{r_c}\frac{\partial}{\partial r_c}\left(r_c \frac{\partial p}{\partial r_c}\right) + \frac{1}{r_c^2}\frac{\partial^2 p}{\partial \theta^2} + \frac{\partial^2 p}{\partial z^2}$

$$\nabla^2 p = \frac{1}{r_c}\frac{\partial}{\partial r_c}\left(r_c \frac{\partial}{\partial r_c} r_c^2 z^2 \sin\theta\right) + \frac{1}{r_c^2}\frac{\partial}{\partial \theta}\left(\frac{\partial}{\partial \theta} r_c^2 z^2 \sin\theta\right) + \frac{\partial}{\partial z}\left(\frac{\partial}{\partial z} r_c^2 z^2 \sin\theta\right)$$

$$\nabla^2 p = \frac{1}{r_c}\frac{\partial}{\partial r_c}(r_c 2r_c z^2 \sin\theta) + \frac{1}{r_c^2}\frac{\partial}{\partial \theta}(r_c^2 z^2 \cos\theta) + \frac{\partial}{\partial z}(r_c^2 2z \sin\theta)$$

$$\nabla^2 p = \frac{z^2 \sin\theta}{r_c}\frac{\partial}{\partial r_c}(2r_c^2) + \frac{r_c^2 z^2}{r_c^2}\frac{\partial}{\partial \theta}(\cos\theta) + 2r_c^2 \sin\theta \frac{\partial}{\partial z}(z)$$

$$\nabla^2 p = \frac{z^2 \sin\theta}{r_c}(4r_c) + z^2(-\sin\theta) + 2r_c^2 \sin\theta\,(1)$$

$$\nabla^2 p = 4z^2 \sin\theta - z^2 \sin\theta + 2r_c^2 \sin\theta = \boxed{3z^2 \sin\theta + 2r_c^2 \sin\theta} = \boxed{(3z^2 + 2r_c^2)\sin\theta}$$

13 $\nabla^2 q = \frac{1}{r^2}\frac{\partial}{\partial r}\left(r^2 \frac{\partial q}{\partial r}\right) + \frac{1}{r^2 \sin^2\varphi}\frac{\partial^2 q}{\partial \theta^2} + \frac{1}{r^2 \sin\varphi}\frac{\partial}{\partial \varphi}\left(\sin\varphi \frac{\partial q}{\partial \varphi}\right)$

$$\nabla^2 q = \frac{1}{r^2}\frac{\partial}{\partial r}\left(r^2 \frac{\partial}{\partial r} r^2 \cos\theta \sin\varphi\right) + \frac{1}{r^2 \sin^2\varphi}\frac{\partial}{\partial \theta}\left(\frac{\partial}{\partial \theta} r^2 \cos\theta \sin\varphi\right) + \frac{1}{r^2 \sin\varphi}\frac{\partial}{\partial \varphi}\left(\sin\varphi \frac{\partial}{\partial \varphi} r^2 \cos\theta \sin\varphi$$

$$\nabla^2 q = \frac{1}{r^2}\frac{\partial}{\partial r}(r^2 2r\cos\theta\sin\varphi) + \frac{1}{r^2\sin^2\varphi}\frac{\partial}{\partial\theta}(-r^2\sin\theta\sin\varphi) + \frac{1}{r^2\sin\varphi}\frac{\partial}{\partial\varphi}(\sin\varphi\, r^2\cos\theta\cos\varphi)$$

$$\nabla^2 q = \frac{\cos\theta\sin\varphi}{r^2}\frac{\partial}{\partial r}(2r^3) - \frac{r^2\sin\varphi}{r^2\sin^2\varphi}\frac{\partial}{\partial\theta}(\sin\theta) + \frac{r^2\cos\theta}{r^2\sin\varphi}\frac{\partial}{\partial\varphi}(\sin\varphi\cos\varphi)$$

$$\nabla^2 q = \frac{\cos\theta\sin\varphi}{r^2}6r^2 - \frac{1}{\sin\varphi}\cos\theta + \frac{\cos\theta}{\sin\varphi}(\cos^2\varphi - \sin^2\varphi)$$

$$\nabla^2 q = 6\cos\theta\sin\varphi - \frac{\cos\theta}{\sin\varphi} + \frac{\cos\theta\cos^2\varphi}{\sin\varphi} - \cos\theta\sin\varphi = 5\cos\theta\sin\varphi - \frac{\cos\theta}{\sin\varphi} + \frac{\cos\theta\cos^2\varphi}{\sin\varphi}$$

$$\nabla^2 q = \cos\theta\left(5\sin\varphi - \frac{1}{\sin\varphi} + \frac{\cos^2\varphi}{\sin\varphi}\right) = \frac{\cos\theta}{\sin\varphi}(5\sin^2\varphi - 1 + \cos^2\varphi)$$

$$\nabla^2 q = \frac{\cos\theta}{\sin\varphi}(5\sin^2\varphi - \sin^2\varphi) = \frac{\cos\theta}{\sin\varphi}(4\sin^2\varphi) = \boxed{4\cos\theta\sin\varphi}$$

Note: $\sin^2\varphi + \cos^2\varphi = 1$ leads to $\cos^2\varphi - 1 = -\sin^2\varphi$ or $-1 + \cos^2\varphi = -\sin^2\varphi$.

14 $$\nabla^2 w = \frac{1}{r^2}\frac{\partial}{\partial r}\left(r^2\frac{\partial w}{\partial r}\right) + \frac{1}{r^2\sin^2\varphi}\frac{\partial^2 w}{\partial\theta^2} + \frac{1}{r^2\sin\varphi}\frac{\partial}{\partial\varphi}\left(\sin\varphi\frac{\partial w}{\partial\varphi}\right)$$

$$\nabla^2 w = \frac{1}{r^2}\frac{\partial}{\partial r}\left(r^2\frac{\partial}{\partial r}r^4\tan\theta\cot\varphi\right) + \frac{1}{r^2\sin^2\varphi}\frac{\partial}{\partial\theta}\left(\frac{\partial}{\partial\theta}r^4\tan\theta\cot\varphi\right) + \frac{1}{r^2\sin\varphi}\frac{\partial}{\partial\varphi}\left(\sin\varphi\frac{\partial}{\partial\varphi}r^4\tan\theta\cot\varphi\right)$$

$$\nabla^2 w = \frac{1}{r^2}\frac{\partial}{\partial r}(r^2 4r^3\tan\theta\cot\varphi) + \frac{1}{r^2\sin^2\varphi}\frac{\partial}{\partial\theta}(r^4\sec^2\theta\cot\varphi) + \frac{1}{r^2\sin\varphi}\frac{\partial}{\partial\varphi}(-r^4\sin\varphi\tan\theta\csc^2\varphi)$$

$$\nabla^2 w = \frac{\tan\theta\cot\varphi}{r^2}\frac{\partial}{\partial r}(4r^5) + \frac{r^4\cot\varphi}{r^2\sin^2\varphi}\frac{\partial}{\partial\theta}(\sec^2\theta) - \frac{r^4\tan\theta}{r^2\sin\varphi}\frac{\partial}{\partial\varphi}(\csc\varphi)$$

$$\nabla^2 w = \frac{\tan\theta\cot\varphi}{r^2}20r^4 + \frac{r^2\cot\varphi}{\sin^2\varphi}2\sec^2\theta\tan\theta - \frac{r^2\tan\theta}{\sin\varphi}(-2\csc\varphi\cot\varphi)$$

$$\nabla^2 w = 20r^2\tan\theta\cot\varphi + 2r^2\sec^2\theta\tan\theta\csc^2\varphi\cot\varphi + 2r^2\tan\theta\csc^2\varphi\cot\varphi$$

$$\nabla^2 w = \boxed{2r^2\tan\theta\cot\varphi\,(10 + \sec^2\theta\csc^2\varphi + \csc^2\varphi)}$$

Notes: Use the chain rule $\frac{df}{d\theta} = \frac{df}{du}\frac{du}{d\theta}$ with $u = \sec\theta$ and $f = u^2 = \sec^2\theta$ to see that

$\frac{d}{d\theta}\sec^2\theta = \frac{df}{d\theta} = \frac{d}{du}u^2\frac{d}{d\theta}\sec\theta = 2u\sec\theta\tan\theta = 2\sec^2\theta\tan\theta.$

Chapter 10, Part C

15 $$\vec{\nabla} r = \hat{\mathbf{r}}\frac{\partial f}{\partial r} + \hat{\boldsymbol{\theta}}\frac{1}{r\sin\varphi}\frac{\partial f}{\partial\theta} + \hat{\boldsymbol{\varphi}}\frac{1}{r}\frac{\partial f}{\partial\varphi} = \hat{\mathbf{r}}\frac{\partial}{\partial r}r + 0 + 0 = \hat{\mathbf{r}}(1) + 0 + 0 = \boxed{\hat{\mathbf{r}}} = \boxed{\frac{\vec{\mathbf{r}}}{r}}$$

$$\vec{\nabla} r = \left(\hat{\mathbf{i}}\frac{\partial}{\partial x} + \hat{\mathbf{j}}\frac{\partial}{\partial y} + \hat{\mathbf{k}}\frac{\partial}{\partial z}\right)\sqrt{x^2+y^2+z^2}$$

$$\vec{\nabla} r = \hat{\mathbf{i}}\frac{\partial}{\partial x}\sqrt{x^2+y^2+z^2} + \hat{\mathbf{j}}\frac{\partial}{\partial y}\sqrt{x^2+y^2+z^2} + \hat{\mathbf{k}}\frac{\partial}{\partial z}\sqrt{x^2+y^2+z^2}$$

$$\vec{\nabla} r = \frac{x\hat{\mathbf{i}}}{\sqrt{x^2+y^2+z^2}} + \frac{y\hat{\mathbf{j}}}{\sqrt{x^2+y^2+z^2}} + \frac{z\hat{\mathbf{k}}}{\sqrt{x^2+y^2+z^2}} = \boxed{\frac{x\hat{\mathbf{i}}+y\hat{\mathbf{j}}+z\hat{\mathbf{k}}}{\sqrt{x^2+y^2+z^2}}} = \boxed{\frac{\vec{\mathbf{r}}}{r}} = \boxed{\hat{\mathbf{r}}}$$

Notes: $\vec{\mathbf{r}} = \|\vec{\mathbf{r}}\|\hat{\mathbf{r}} = r\hat{\mathbf{r}}$ (see Chapters 4 and 7) such that $\hat{\mathbf{r}} = \frac{\vec{\mathbf{r}}}{r}$. Use the chain rule $\frac{\partial f}{\partial x} = \frac{\partial f}{\partial u}\frac{\partial u}{\partial x}$ with $u = x^2 + y^2 + z^2$ and $f = \sqrt{u} = \sqrt{x^2 + y^2 + z^2}$ to see that $\frac{\partial}{\partial x}\sqrt{x^2 + y^2 + z^2} = \frac{\partial f}{\partial x} = \frac{\partial}{\partial u}\sqrt{u}\frac{\partial}{\partial x}(x^2 + y^2 + z^2) = \frac{1}{2\sqrt{u}}(2x) = \frac{x}{\sqrt{u}} = \frac{x}{\sqrt{x^2+y^2+z^2}}$.

16 $\vec{\nabla} \cdot \vec{\mathbf{r}} = \vec{\nabla} \cdot r\hat{\mathbf{r}} = \frac{1}{r^2}\frac{\partial}{\partial r}(r^2 r) + 0 + 0 = \frac{1}{r^2}\frac{\partial}{\partial r}(r^3) = \frac{1}{r^2}3r^2 = \boxed{3}$

$\vec{\nabla} \cdot \vec{\mathbf{r}} = \vec{\nabla} \cdot (x\hat{\mathbf{i}} + y\hat{\mathbf{j}} + z\hat{\mathbf{k}}) = \frac{\partial}{\partial x}x + \frac{\partial}{\partial y}y + \frac{\partial}{\partial z}z = 1 + 1 + 1 = \boxed{3}$

17 $\nabla^2 r^2 = \frac{1}{r^2}\frac{\partial}{\partial r}\left(r^2\frac{\partial}{\partial r}r^2\right) + 0 + 0 = \frac{1}{r^2}\frac{\partial}{\partial r}(r^2 2r) = \frac{1}{r^2}\frac{\partial}{\partial r}2r^3 = \frac{1}{r^2}6r^2 = \boxed{6}$

$\nabla^2 r^2 = \nabla^2\left(\sqrt{x^2 + y^2 + z^2}\right)^2 = \nabla^2(x^2 + y^2 + z^2)$

$\nabla^2 r^2 = \frac{\partial^2}{\partial x^2}(x^2 + y^2 + z^2) + \frac{\partial^2}{\partial y^2}(x^2 + y^2 + z^2) + \frac{\partial^2}{\partial z^2}(x^2 + y^2 + z^2)$

$\nabla^2 r^2 = \frac{\partial}{\partial x}\left[\frac{\partial}{\partial x}(x^2 + y^2 + z^2)\right] + \frac{\partial}{\partial y}\left[\frac{\partial}{\partial y}(x^2 + y^2 + z^2)\right] + \frac{\partial}{\partial z}\left[\frac{\partial}{\partial z}(x^2 + y^2 + z^2)\right]$

$\nabla^2 r^2 = \frac{\partial}{\partial x}2x + \frac{\partial}{\partial y}2y + \frac{\partial}{\partial z}2z = 2 + 2 + 2 = \boxed{6}$

18 $\vec{\nabla} \cdot (r\vec{\mathbf{r}}) = \vec{\nabla} \cdot r(r\hat{\mathbf{r}}) = \vec{\nabla} \cdot r^2\hat{\mathbf{r}} = \frac{1}{r^2}\frac{\partial}{\partial r}(r^2 r^2) + 0 + 0 = \frac{1}{r^2}\frac{\partial}{\partial r}(r^4) = \frac{1}{r^2}4r^3 = \boxed{4r}$

$\vec{\nabla} \cdot (r\vec{\mathbf{r}}) = \vec{\nabla} \cdot \left[\sqrt{x^2 + y^2 + z^2}(x\hat{\mathbf{i}} + y\hat{\mathbf{j}} + z\hat{\mathbf{k}})\right]$

$\vec{\nabla} \cdot (r\vec{\mathbf{r}}) = \vec{\nabla} \cdot \left(x\hat{\mathbf{i}}\sqrt{x^2 + y^2 + z^2} + y\hat{\mathbf{j}}\sqrt{x^2 + y^2 + z^2} + z\hat{\mathbf{k}}\sqrt{x^2 + y^2 + z^2}\right)$

$\vec{\nabla} \cdot (r\vec{\mathbf{r}}) = \frac{\partial}{\partial x}x\sqrt{x^2 + y^2 + z^2} + \frac{\partial}{\partial y}y\sqrt{x^2 + y^2 + z^2} + \frac{\partial}{\partial z}z\sqrt{x^2 + y^2 + z^2}$

$\vec{\nabla} \cdot (r\vec{\mathbf{r}}) = \sqrt{x^2 + y^2 + z^2} + \frac{x^2}{\sqrt{x^2+y^2+z^2}} + \sqrt{x^2 + y^2 + z^2} + \frac{y^2}{\sqrt{x^2+y^2+z^2}} + \sqrt{x^2 + y^2 + z^2} + \frac{z^2}{\sqrt{x^2+y^2+z^2}}$

$\vec{\nabla} \cdot (r\vec{\mathbf{r}}) = 3\sqrt{x^2 + y^2 + z^2} + \frac{x^2+y^2+z^2}{\sqrt{x^2+y^2+z^2}} = 3\sqrt{x^2 + y^2 + z^2} + \sqrt{x^2 + y^2 + z^2}$

$\vec{\nabla} \cdot (r\vec{\mathbf{r}}) = \boxed{4\sqrt{x^2 + y^2 + z^2}} = \boxed{4r}$

19 $\nabla^2 r^3 = \frac{1}{r^2}\frac{\partial}{\partial r}\left(r^2\frac{\partial}{\partial r}r^3\right) + 0 + 0 = \frac{1}{r^2}\frac{\partial}{\partial r}(r^2 3r^2) = \frac{1}{r^2}\frac{\partial}{\partial r}3r^4 = \frac{1}{r^2}12r^3 = \boxed{12r}$

$\nabla^2\left(\sqrt{x^2 + y^2 + z^2}\right)^3 = \nabla^2(x^2 + y^2 + z^2)^{3/2}$

$\nabla^2 r^3 = \frac{\partial^2}{\partial x^2}(x^2 + y^2 + z^2)^{3/2} + \frac{\partial^2}{\partial y^2}(x^2 + y^2 + z^2)^{3/2} + \frac{\partial^2}{\partial z^2}(x^2 + y^2 + z^2)^{3/2}$

$\nabla^2 r^3 = \frac{\partial}{\partial x}\left[\frac{\partial}{\partial x}(x^2 + y^2 + z^2)^{3/2}\right] + \frac{\partial}{\partial y}\left[\frac{\partial}{\partial y}(x^2 + y^2 + z^2)^{3/2}\right] + \frac{\partial}{\partial z}\left[\frac{\partial}{\partial z}(x^2 + y^2 + z^2)^{3/2}\right]$

$$\nabla^2 r^3 = \frac{\partial}{\partial x}\frac{3}{2}(x^2+y^2+z^2)^{1/2}(2x) + \frac{\partial}{\partial y}\frac{3}{2}(x^2+y^2+z^2)^{1/2}(2y) + \frac{\partial}{\partial z}\frac{3}{2}(x^2+y^2+z^2)^{1/2}(2z)$$

$$\nabla^2 r^3 = \frac{\partial}{\partial x}3x(x^2+y^2+z^2)^{1/2} + \frac{\partial}{\partial y}3y(x^2+y^2+z^2)^{1/2} + \frac{\partial}{\partial z}3z(x^2+y^2+z^2)^{1/2}$$

$$\nabla^2 r^3 = 3(x^2+y^2+z^2)^{1/2} + \frac{3x^2}{(x^2+y^2+z^2)^{1/2}} + 3(x^2+y^2+z^2)^{1/2} + \frac{3y^2}{(x^2+y^2+z^2)^{1/2}} + 3(x^2+y^2+z^2)^{1/2} + \frac{3z^2}{(x^2+y^2+z^2)^{1/2}}$$

$$\nabla^2 r^3 = 9(x^2+y^2+z^2)^{1/2} + \frac{3x^2+3y^2+3z^2}{(x^2+y^2+z^2)^{1/2}} = 9(x^2+y^2+z^2)^{1/2} + \frac{3(x^2+y^2+z^2)}{(x^2+y^2+z^2)^{1/2}}$$

$$\nabla^2 r^3 = 9(x^2+y^2+z^2)^{1/2} + 3(x^2+y^2+z^2)^{1/2} = \boxed{12\sqrt{x^2+y^2+z^2}} = \boxed{12r}$$

Notes: Use the chain rule $\frac{\partial f}{\partial x} = \frac{\partial f}{\partial u}\frac{\partial u}{\partial x}$ with $u = x^2+y^2+z^2$ and $f = \sqrt{u} = \sqrt{x^2+y^2+z^2}$ to see that $\frac{\partial}{\partial x}\sqrt{x^2+y^2+z^2} = \frac{\partial f}{\partial x} = \frac{\partial}{\partial u}\sqrt{u}\frac{\partial}{\partial x}(x^2+y^2+z^2) = \frac{1}{2\sqrt{u}}(2x) = \frac{x}{\sqrt{u}} = \frac{x}{\sqrt{x^2+y^2+z^2}}$. Similarly, $\frac{\partial}{\partial x}(x^2+y^2+z^2)^{3/2} = 3x(x^2+y^2+z^2)^{1/2}$.

Use the product rule to see that $\frac{\partial}{\partial x}\left(x\sqrt{x^2+y^2+z^2}\right) = \sqrt{x^2+y^2+z^2} + \frac{x^2}{\sqrt{x^2+y^2+z^2}}$.

20 $\vec{\nabla}\left(\frac{1}{r}\right) = \hat{\mathbf{r}}\frac{\partial}{\partial r}\frac{1}{r} + \hat{\boldsymbol{\theta}}\frac{1}{r\sin\varphi}\frac{\partial}{\partial\theta}r + \hat{\boldsymbol{\varphi}}\frac{1}{r}\frac{\partial}{\partial\varphi}r = \hat{\mathbf{r}}\frac{\partial}{\partial r}r^{-1} + 0 + 0 = \boxed{\frac{-\hat{\mathbf{r}}}{r^2}} = \boxed{\frac{-\vec{\mathbf{r}}}{r^3}}$

$$\vec{\nabla}\left(\frac{1}{\sqrt{x^2+y^2+z^2}}\right) = \vec{\nabla}(x^2+y^2+z^2)^{-1/2}$$

$$\vec{\nabla}\left(\frac{1}{r}\right) = \hat{\mathbf{i}}\frac{\partial}{\partial x}(x^2+y^2+z^2)^{-1/2} + \hat{\mathbf{j}}\frac{\partial}{\partial y}(x^2+y^2+z^2)^{-1/2} + \hat{\mathbf{k}}\frac{\partial}{\partial z}(x^2+y^2+z^2)^{-1/2}$$

$$\vec{\nabla}\left(\frac{1}{r}\right) = -x\hat{\mathbf{i}}(x^2+y^2+z^2)^{-3/2} - y\hat{\mathbf{j}}(x^2+y^2+z^2)^{-3/2} - z\hat{\mathbf{k}}(x^2+y^2+z^2)^{-3/2}$$

$$\vec{\nabla}\left(\frac{1}{r}\right) = \boxed{-\frac{x\hat{\mathbf{i}}+y\hat{\mathbf{j}}+z\hat{\mathbf{k}}}{(x^2+y^2+z^2)^{3/2}}} = \boxed{\frac{-x\hat{\mathbf{i}}-y\hat{\mathbf{j}}-z\hat{\mathbf{k}}}{(x^2+y^2+z^2)^{3/2}}} = \boxed{\frac{-\vec{\mathbf{r}}}{r^3}} = \boxed{\frac{-\hat{\mathbf{r}}}{r^2}}$$

Notes: $\vec{\mathbf{r}} = \|\vec{\mathbf{r}}\|\hat{\mathbf{r}} = r\hat{\mathbf{r}}$ (see Chapters 4 and 7) such that $\hat{\mathbf{r}} = \frac{\vec{\mathbf{r}}}{r}$. It follows that $\frac{\vec{\mathbf{r}}}{r^3} = \frac{\hat{\mathbf{r}}}{r^2}$. Use the chain rule $\frac{\partial f}{\partial x} = \frac{\partial f}{\partial u}\frac{\partial u}{\partial x}$ with $u = x^2+y^2+z^2$ and $f = u^{-1/2} = (x^2+y^2+z^2)^{-1/2}$ to see that $\frac{\partial}{\partial x}(x^2+y^2+z^2)^{-1/2} = \frac{\partial f}{\partial x} = \frac{\partial}{\partial u}u^{-1/2}\frac{\partial}{\partial x}(x^2+y^2+z^2) = -\frac{u^{-3/2}}{2}(2x) = -xu^{-3/2} = -\frac{x}{u^{3/2}} = -\frac{x}{(x^2+y^2+z^2)^{3/2}}$.

Chapter 11, Part A

❶ $\vec{\nabla} \times \vec{A} = \left(\frac{\partial A_z}{\partial y} - \frac{\partial A_y}{\partial z}\right)\hat{\mathbf{i}} + \left(\frac{\partial A_x}{\partial z} - \frac{\partial A_z}{\partial x}\right)\hat{\mathbf{j}} + \left(\frac{\partial A_y}{\partial x} - \frac{\partial A_x}{\partial y}\right)\hat{\mathbf{k}}$

$\vec{\nabla} \times \vec{A} = \left(\frac{\partial}{\partial y}xy - \frac{\partial}{\partial z}xz\right)\hat{\mathbf{i}} + \left(\frac{\partial}{\partial z}yz - \frac{\partial}{\partial x}xy\right)\hat{\mathbf{j}} + \left(\frac{\partial}{\partial x}xz - \frac{\partial}{\partial y}yz\right)\hat{\mathbf{k}}$

$\vec{\nabla} \times \vec{A} = (x - x)\hat{\mathbf{i}} + (y - y)\hat{\mathbf{j}} + (z - z)\hat{\mathbf{k}} = \boxed{0}$

❷ $\vec{\nabla} \times \vec{B} = \left(\frac{\partial B_z}{\partial y} - \frac{\partial B_y}{\partial z}\right)\hat{\mathbf{i}} + \left(\frac{\partial B_x}{\partial z} - \frac{\partial B_z}{\partial x}\right)\hat{\mathbf{j}} + \left(\frac{\partial B_y}{\partial x} - \frac{\partial B_x}{\partial y}\right)\hat{\mathbf{k}}$

$\vec{\nabla} \times \vec{B} = \left[\frac{\partial}{\partial y}0 - \frac{\partial}{\partial z}(-x^2y^3)\right]\hat{\mathbf{i}} + \left(\frac{\partial}{\partial z}x^3y^2 - \frac{\partial}{\partial x}0\right)\hat{\mathbf{j}} + \left[\frac{\partial}{\partial x}(-x^2y^3) - \frac{\partial}{\partial y}x^3y^2\right]\hat{\mathbf{k}}$

$\vec{\nabla} \times \vec{B} = (0 + 0)\hat{\mathbf{i}} + (0 - 0)\hat{\mathbf{j}} + (-2xy^3 - 2x^3y)\hat{\mathbf{k}} = \boxed{-2xy^3\hat{\mathbf{k}} - 2x^3y\hat{\mathbf{k}}} = \boxed{-2xy(x^2 + y^2)}$

❸ $\vec{\nabla} \times \vec{C} = \left(\frac{\partial C_z}{\partial y} - \frac{\partial C_y}{\partial z}\right)\hat{\mathbf{i}} + \left(\frac{\partial C_x}{\partial z} - \frac{\partial C_z}{\partial x}\right)\hat{\mathbf{j}} + \left(\frac{\partial C_y}{\partial x} - \frac{\partial C_x}{\partial y}\right)\hat{\mathbf{k}}$

$\vec{\nabla} \times \vec{C} = \left[\frac{\partial}{\partial y}(x^2 - y^2) - \frac{\partial}{\partial z}(z^2 - x^2)\right]\hat{\mathbf{i}} + \left[\frac{\partial}{\partial z}(y^2 - z^2) - \frac{\partial}{\partial x}(x^2 - y^2)\right]\hat{\mathbf{j}} +$
$\left[\frac{\partial}{\partial x}(z^2 - x^2) - \frac{\partial}{\partial y}(y^2 - z^2)\right]\hat{\mathbf{k}}$

$\vec{\nabla} \times \vec{C} = (-2y - 2z)\hat{\mathbf{i}} + (-2z - 2x)\hat{\mathbf{j}} + (-2x - 2y)\hat{\mathbf{k}}$

$\vec{\nabla} \times \vec{C} = \boxed{-2(y + z)\hat{\mathbf{i}} - 2(z + x)\hat{\mathbf{j}} - 2(x + y)\hat{\mathbf{k}}}$

❹ $\vec{\nabla} \times \vec{D} = \frac{1}{r\sin\varphi}\left(\frac{\partial}{\partial\varphi}D_\theta\sin\varphi - \frac{\partial}{\partial\theta}D_\varphi\right)\hat{\mathbf{r}} + \frac{1}{r}\left(\frac{1}{\sin\varphi}\frac{\partial D_r}{\partial\theta} - \frac{\partial}{\partial r}rD_\theta\right)\hat{\boldsymbol{\varphi}} + \frac{1}{r}\left(\frac{\partial}{\partial r}rD_\varphi - \frac{\partial D_r}{\partial\varphi}\right)\hat{\boldsymbol{\theta}}$

$\vec{\nabla} \times \vec{D} = \frac{1}{r\sin\varphi}\left[\frac{\partial}{\partial\varphi}r\sin\theta\sin\varphi\sin\varphi - \frac{\partial}{\partial\theta}(0)\right]\hat{\mathbf{r}} + \frac{1}{r}\left[\frac{1}{\sin\varphi}\frac{\partial}{\partial\theta}(0) - \frac{\partial}{\partial r}rr\sin\theta\sin\varphi\right]\hat{\boldsymbol{\varphi}} +$
$\frac{1}{r}\left[\frac{\partial}{\partial r}r(0) - \frac{\partial}{\partial\varphi}(0)\right]\hat{\boldsymbol{\theta}}$

$\vec{\nabla} \times \vec{D} = \frac{1}{r\sin\varphi}\left(\frac{\partial}{\partial\varphi}r\sin\theta\sin^2\varphi\right)\hat{\mathbf{r}} + \frac{1}{r}\left(-\frac{\partial}{\partial r}r^2\sin\theta\sin\varphi\right)\hat{\boldsymbol{\varphi}}$

$\vec{\nabla} \times \vec{D} = \frac{1}{r\sin\varphi}(2r\sin\theta\sin\varphi\cos\varphi)\hat{\mathbf{r}} - \frac{1}{r}(2r\sin\theta\sin\varphi)\hat{\boldsymbol{\varphi}}$

$\vec{\nabla} \times \vec{D} = \boxed{2\hat{\mathbf{r}}\sin\theta\cos\varphi - 2\hat{\boldsymbol{\varphi}}\sin\theta\sin\varphi} = \boxed{2\sin\theta\,(\hat{\mathbf{r}}\cos\varphi - \hat{\boldsymbol{\varphi}}\sin\varphi)}$

Note: Use the chain rule $\frac{df}{d\theta} = \frac{df}{du}\frac{du}{d\theta}$ with $u = \sin\varphi$ and $f = u^2 = \sin^2\varphi$ to see that $\frac{d}{d\varphi}\sin^2\varphi = \frac{df}{d\varphi} = \frac{d}{du}u^2\frac{d}{d\varphi}\sin\varphi = 2u\cos\varphi = 2\sin\varphi\cos\varphi$.

Note: Recall that φ is the polar angle and θ is the azimuthal angle in common math notation. For common physics notation, swap φ and θ in spherical coordinates.

Chapter 11, Part B

❺ $\vec{\nabla} \times \vec{A} = \left(\frac{\partial A_z}{\partial y} - \frac{\partial A_y}{\partial z}\right)\hat{\mathbf{i}} + \left(\frac{\partial A_x}{\partial z} - \frac{\partial A_z}{\partial x}\right)\hat{\mathbf{j}} + \left(\frac{\partial A_y}{\partial x} - \frac{\partial A_x}{\partial y}\right)\hat{\mathbf{k}}$

$\vec{\nabla} \times \vec{A} = \left(\frac{\partial}{\partial y}zx^2 - \frac{\partial}{\partial z}yz^2\right)\hat{\mathbf{i}} + \left(\frac{\partial}{\partial z}xy^2 - \frac{\partial}{\partial x}zx^2\right)\hat{\mathbf{j}} + \left(\frac{\partial}{\partial x}yz^2 - \frac{\partial}{\partial y}xy^2\right)\hat{\mathbf{k}}$

$\vec{\nabla} \times \vec{A} = (0 - 2yz)\hat{\mathbf{i}} + (0 - 2xz)\hat{\mathbf{j}} + (0 - 2xy)\hat{\mathbf{k}} = \boxed{-2yz\hat{\mathbf{i}} - 2xz\hat{\mathbf{j}} - 2xy\hat{\mathbf{k}}}$

❻ $\vec{\nabla} \times \vec{B} = \left(\frac{\partial B_z}{\partial y} - \frac{\partial B_y}{\partial z}\right)\hat{\mathbf{i}} + \left(\frac{\partial B_x}{\partial z} - \frac{\partial B_z}{\partial x}\right)\hat{\mathbf{j}} + \left(\frac{\partial B_y}{\partial x} - \frac{\partial B_x}{\partial y}\right)\hat{\mathbf{k}}$

$\vec{\nabla} \times \vec{B} = \left(\frac{\partial}{\partial y}x^2y^2z^3 - \frac{\partial}{\partial z}x^2y^3z^2\right)\hat{\mathbf{i}} + \left(\frac{\partial}{\partial z}x^3y^2z^2 - \frac{\partial}{\partial x}x^2y^2z^3\right)\hat{\mathbf{j}} + \left(\frac{\partial}{\partial x}x^2y^3z^2 - \frac{\partial}{\partial y}x^3y^2z^2\right)\hat{\mathbf{k}}$

$\vec{\nabla} \times \vec{B} = \boxed{(2x^2yz^3 - 2x^2y^3z)\hat{\mathbf{i}} + (2x^3y^2z - 2xy^2z^3)\hat{\mathbf{j}} + (2xy^3z^2 - 2x^3yz^2)\hat{\mathbf{k}}}$

$\vec{\nabla} \times \vec{B} = \boxed{2x^2yz(z^2 - y^2)\hat{\mathbf{i}} + 2xy^2z(x^2 - z^2)\hat{\mathbf{j}} + 2xyz^2(y^2 - x^2)\hat{\mathbf{k}}}$

❼ $\vec{\nabla} \times \vec{C} = \left(\frac{1}{r_c}\frac{\partial C_z}{\partial \theta} - \frac{\partial}{\partial z}C_\theta\right)\hat{\mathbf{r}}_c + \left(\frac{\partial C_{r_c}}{\partial z} - \frac{\partial C_z}{\partial r_c}\right)\hat{\boldsymbol{\theta}} + \frac{1}{r_c}\left(\frac{\partial}{\partial r_c}r_cC_\theta - \frac{\partial C_{r_c}}{\partial \theta}\right)\hat{\mathbf{k}}$

$\vec{\nabla} \times \vec{C} = \left(\frac{1}{r_c}\frac{\partial}{\partial \theta}0 - \frac{\partial}{\partial z}r_c\sin\theta\right)\hat{\mathbf{r}}_c + \left(\frac{\partial}{\partial z}r_c\cos\theta - \frac{\partial}{\partial r_c}0\right)\hat{\boldsymbol{\theta}} + \frac{1}{r_c}\left(\frac{\partial}{\partial r_c}r_cr_c\sin\theta - \frac{\partial}{\partial \theta}r_c\cos\theta\right)\hat{\mathbf{k}}$

$\vec{\nabla} \times \vec{C} = 0\hat{\mathbf{r}}_c + 0\hat{\boldsymbol{\theta}} + \frac{1}{r_c}\left(\frac{\partial}{\partial r_c}r_c^2\sin\theta - \frac{\partial}{\partial \theta}r_c\cos\theta\right)\hat{\mathbf{k}} = \frac{1}{r_c}(2r_c\sin\theta + r_c\sin\theta)\hat{\mathbf{k}} = \boxed{3\hat{\mathbf{k}}\sin\theta}$

❽ $\vec{\nabla} \times \vec{D} = \frac{1}{r\sin\varphi}\left(\frac{\partial}{\partial \varphi}D_\theta\sin\varphi - \frac{\partial}{\partial \theta}D_\varphi\right)\hat{\mathbf{r}} + \frac{1}{r}\left(\frac{1}{\sin\varphi}\frac{\partial D_r}{\partial \theta} - \frac{\partial}{\partial r}rD_\theta\right)\hat{\boldsymbol{\varphi}} + \frac{1}{r}\left(\frac{\partial}{\partial r}rD_\varphi - \frac{\partial D_r}{\partial \varphi}\right)\hat{\boldsymbol{\theta}}$

$\vec{\nabla} \times \vec{D} = \frac{1}{r\sin\varphi}\left[\frac{\partial}{\partial \varphi}(0)\sin\varphi - \frac{\partial}{\partial \theta}(0)\right]\hat{\mathbf{r}} + \frac{1}{r}\left[\frac{1}{\sin\varphi}\frac{\partial}{\partial \theta}r - \frac{\partial}{\partial r}r(0)\right]\hat{\boldsymbol{\varphi}} + \frac{1}{r}\left[\frac{\partial}{\partial r}r(0) - \frac{\partial}{\partial \varphi}r\right]\hat{\boldsymbol{\theta}}$

$\vec{\nabla} \times \vec{D} = 0\hat{\mathbf{r}} + \frac{1}{r}\left(\frac{1}{\sin\varphi}\frac{\partial}{\partial \theta}r\right)\hat{\boldsymbol{\varphi}} + \frac{1}{r}\left(-\frac{\partial}{\partial \varphi}r\right)\hat{\boldsymbol{\theta}} = 0\hat{\mathbf{r}} + 0\hat{\boldsymbol{\varphi}} + 0\hat{\boldsymbol{\theta}} = \boxed{0}$

Chapter 12, Part A

❶ $\vec{\mathbf{n}} = \vec{\mathbf{A}} \times \vec{\mathbf{B}} = (A_y B_z - A_z B_y)\hat{\mathbf{i}} + (A_z B_x - A_x B_z)\hat{\mathbf{j}} + (A_x B_y - A_y B_x)\hat{\mathbf{k}}$

$\vec{\mathbf{n}} = [(2)(-3) - (0)(0)]\hat{\mathbf{i}} + [(0)(4) - (5)(-3)]\hat{\mathbf{j}} + [(5)(0) - (2)(4)]\hat{\mathbf{k}}$

$\vec{\mathbf{n}} = (-6 - 0)\hat{\mathbf{i}} + (0 + 15)\hat{\mathbf{j}} + (0 - 8)\hat{\mathbf{k}} = -6\hat{\mathbf{i}} + 15\hat{\mathbf{j}} - 8\hat{\mathbf{k}}$

$\|\vec{\mathbf{n}}\| = \sqrt{(-6)^2 + 15^2 + (-8)^2} = \sqrt{36 + 225 + 64} = \sqrt{325} = \sqrt{(25)(13)} = 5\sqrt{13}$

$\hat{\mathbf{n}} = \frac{\vec{\mathbf{n}}}{\|\vec{\mathbf{n}}\|} = \frac{-6\hat{\mathbf{i}}+15\hat{\mathbf{j}}-8\hat{\mathbf{k}}}{5\sqrt{13}} = \boxed{-\frac{6\hat{\mathbf{i}}}{5\sqrt{13}} + \frac{3\hat{\mathbf{j}}}{\sqrt{13}} - \frac{8\hat{\mathbf{k}}}{5\sqrt{13}}} = \boxed{-\frac{6\hat{\mathbf{i}}\sqrt{13}}{65} + \frac{3\hat{\mathbf{j}}\sqrt{13}}{13} - \frac{8\hat{\mathbf{k}}\sqrt{13}}{65}}$

❷ $6x + 2y - 4z + d = 0 \to 6(5) + 2(-7) - 4(3) + d = 0 \to 30 - 14 - 12 + d = 0$

$4 + d = 0 \to d = -4 \to \boxed{6x + 2y - 4z - 4 = 0} \to \boxed{3x + y - 2z - 2 = 0}$

❸ $\vec{\mathbf{A}} = \langle 6 - 3, 4 - (-1), -2 - 2\rangle = \langle 3,5,-4\rangle$ is a vector from $(3,-1,2)$ to $(6,4,-2)$.

$\vec{\mathbf{B}} = \langle 0 - 3, 8 - (-1), 4 - 2\rangle = \langle -3,9,2\rangle$ is a vector from $(3,-1,2)$ to $(0,8,4)$.

$\vec{\mathbf{n}} = \vec{\mathbf{A}} \times \vec{\mathbf{B}} = (A_y B_z - A_z B_y)\hat{\mathbf{i}} + (A_z B_x - A_x B_z)\hat{\mathbf{j}} + (A_x B_y - A_y B_x)\hat{\mathbf{k}}$

$\vec{\mathbf{n}} = [(5)(2) - (-4)(9)]\hat{\mathbf{i}} + [(-4)(-3) - (3)(2)]\hat{\mathbf{j}} + [(3)(9) - (5)(-3)]\hat{\mathbf{k}}$

$\vec{\mathbf{n}} = (10 + 36)\hat{\mathbf{i}} + (12 - 6)\hat{\mathbf{j}} + (27 + 15)\hat{\mathbf{k}} = 46\hat{\mathbf{i}} + 6\hat{\mathbf{j}} + 42\hat{\mathbf{k}}$

$\|\vec{\mathbf{n}}\| = \sqrt{46^2 + 6^2 + 42^2} = \sqrt{3916} = 2\sqrt{979}$

$\hat{\mathbf{n}} = \frac{\vec{\mathbf{n}}}{\|\vec{\mathbf{n}}\|} = \frac{46\hat{\mathbf{i}}+6\hat{\mathbf{j}}+42\hat{\mathbf{k}}}{2\sqrt{979}} = \boxed{\frac{23\hat{\mathbf{i}}}{\sqrt{979}} + \frac{3\hat{\mathbf{j}}}{\sqrt{979}} + \frac{21\hat{\mathbf{k}}}{\sqrt{979}}} = \boxed{\frac{23\hat{\mathbf{i}}\sqrt{979}}{979} + \frac{3\hat{\mathbf{j}}\sqrt{979}}{979} + \frac{21\hat{\mathbf{k}}\sqrt{979}}{979}}$

❹ $\vec{\mathbf{n}}_1 = \langle\sqrt{2}, 0, -\sqrt{2}\rangle$ and $\vec{\mathbf{n}}_2 = \langle 0, \sqrt{2}, \sqrt{2}\rangle$

$\vec{\mathbf{n}}_1 \cdot \vec{\mathbf{n}}_2 = (\sqrt{2})(0) + (0)(\sqrt{2}) + (-\sqrt{2})(\sqrt{2}) = -2$

$\|\vec{\mathbf{n}}_1\| = \sqrt{(\sqrt{2})^2 + 0^2 + (-\sqrt{2})^2} = \sqrt{4} = 2$ and $\|\vec{\mathbf{n}}_2\| = \sqrt{0^2 + (\sqrt{2})^2 + (\sqrt{2})^2} = \sqrt{4} = 2$

$|\vec{\mathbf{n}}_1 \cdot \vec{\mathbf{n}}_2| = \|\vec{\mathbf{n}}_1\|\|\vec{\mathbf{n}}_2\| \cos\theta$ is $|-2| = (2)(2)\cos\theta$

$\theta = \cos^{-1}\left|\frac{-2}{4}\right| = \cos^{-1}\left(\frac{1}{2}\right) \Rightarrow$ acute angle $= \boxed{\frac{\pi}{3}} = \boxed{60°}$

Note: Since the angle between two planes is the **acute** angle between them, although $\cos^{-1}\left(-\frac{1}{2}\right)$ equals 120°, the absolute values on $\left|\frac{-2}{4}\right|$ yields the acute angle 60°.

❺ Standard form: $3x - 4y + 12 - 8 = 0 \Rightarrow a = 3, b = -4, c = 12,$ and $d = -8$.

$\frac{|ax_0+by_0+cz_0+d|}{\sqrt{a^2+b^2+c^2}} = \frac{|3(5)-4(9)+12(10)+(-8)|}{\sqrt{3^2+(-4)^2+12^2}} = \frac{|15-36+120-8|}{\sqrt{9+16+144}} = \frac{91}{\sqrt{169}} = \frac{91}{13} = \boxed{7}$

Chapter 12, Part B

❻ Find any point that lies on the first plane, such as (0,0,2). Now find the distance from this point to the second plane. Write the equation of the second plane in standard form: $6x + 3y - 6x - 9 = 0 \Rightarrow a = 6, b = 3, c = -6$, and $d = -9$.

$$\frac{|ax_0+by_0+cz_0+d|}{\sqrt{a^2+b^2+c^2}} = \frac{|6(0)+3(0)-6(2)+(-9)|}{\sqrt{6^2+3^2+(-6)^2}} = \frac{|0+0-12-9|}{\sqrt{36+9+36}} = \frac{21}{\sqrt{81}} = \frac{21}{9} = \boxed{\frac{7}{3}}$$

❼ $f(x,y,z) = 3x^2 + 3y^2 - 4z = 0, \frac{\partial f}{\partial x} = \frac{\partial}{\partial x}(3x^2 + 3y^2 - 4z) = 6x$

$$\frac{\partial f}{\partial y} = \frac{\partial}{\partial y}(3x^2 + 3y^2 - 4z) = 6y, \frac{\partial f}{\partial z} = \frac{\partial}{\partial z}(3x^2 + 3y^2 - 4z) = -4$$

$$(x - x_0)\left.\frac{\partial f}{\partial x}\right|_{x_0,y_0,z_0} + (y - y_0)\left.\frac{\partial f}{\partial y}\right|_{x_0,y_0,z_0} + (z - z_0)\left.\frac{\partial f}{\partial z}\right|_{x_0,y_0,z_0} = 0$$

$$(x - 2)6(2) + (y - 2)6(2) + (z - 6)(-4) = 0$$

$$12x - 24 + 12y - 24 - 4z + 24 = 0$$

$$12x + 12y - 4y - 24 = 0 \rightarrow \boxed{3x + 3y - y - 6 = 0}$$

$$\frac{x-x_0}{\left.\frac{\partial f}{\partial x}\right|_{x_0,y_0,z_0}} = \frac{y-y_0}{\left.\frac{\partial f}{\partial y}\right|_{x_0,y_0,z_0}} = \frac{z-z_0}{\left.\frac{\partial f}{\partial z}\right|_{x_0,y_0,z_0}}$$

$$\frac{x-2}{6(2)} = \frac{y-2}{6(2)} = \frac{z-6}{-4} \rightarrow \boxed{\frac{x-2}{12} = \frac{y-2}{12} = \frac{6-z}{4}} \rightarrow \boxed{\frac{x-2}{3} = \frac{y-2}{3} = 6 - z} \rightarrow \boxed{x - 2 = y - 2 = 18 - 3z}$$

Note: In the last steps, we multiplied each side of the equations first by 4 and then by 3.

❽ $\frac{dy}{dx} = \frac{d}{dx}x^2 = 2x, \frac{d^2y}{dx^2} = \frac{d}{dx}(2x) = 2, \kappa = \frac{\left|\frac{d^2y}{dx^2}\right|}{\left[1+\left(\frac{dy}{dx}\right)^2\right]^{3/2}} = \frac{|2|}{[1+(2x)^2]^{3/2}} = \frac{2}{(1+4x^2)^{3/2}}$

$$\kappa(0,0) = \frac{2}{[1+4(0)^2]^{3/2}} = \frac{2}{1^{3/2}} = \frac{2}{1} = \boxed{2}$$

$$\kappa(\sqrt{2},2) = \frac{2}{\left[1+4\left(\sqrt{2}\right)^2\right]^{3/2}} = \frac{2}{[1+4(2)]^{3/2}} = \frac{2}{9^{3/2}} = \frac{2}{3^3} = \boxed{\frac{2}{27}}$$

❾ $\frac{dy}{dx} = \frac{d}{dx}\cos x = -\sin x, \frac{d^2y}{dx^2} = \frac{d}{dx}(-\sin x) = -\cos x, \kappa = \frac{\left|\frac{d^2y}{dx^2}\right|}{\left[1+\left(\frac{dy}{dx}\right)^2\right]^{3/2}} = \frac{|-\cos x|}{(1+\sin^2 x)^{3/2}}$

$$\kappa(0,1) = \frac{\cos 0}{(1+\sin^2 0)^{3/2}} = \frac{1}{(1+0^2)^{3/2}} = \frac{1}{1^{3/2}} = \boxed{1}$$

$$\kappa\left(\frac{\pi}{2},0\right) = \frac{\cos\frac{\pi}{2}}{\left(1+\sin^2\frac{\pi}{2}\right)^{3/2}} = \frac{0}{(1+1^2)^{3/2}} = \boxed{0}$$

Chapter 12, Part C

⑩ $\vec{\mathbf{r}} = x\hat{\mathbf{i}} + y\hat{\mathbf{j}}$ (see Chapter 4): $x = 10t\sqrt{3}$ and $y = 10t - 5t^2$.

Isolate t in the x-equation: $t = \frac{x}{10\sqrt{3}} = \frac{x}{10\sqrt{3}}\frac{\sqrt{3}}{\sqrt{3}} = \frac{x\sqrt{3}}{10(3)} = \frac{x\sqrt{3}}{30}$. Plug this into the y-equation:

$y = 10\left(\frac{x\sqrt{3}}{30}\right) - 5\left(\frac{x\sqrt{3}}{30}\right)^2 = \frac{x\sqrt{3}}{3} - 5\left(\frac{x^2 3}{900}\right) = \boxed{\frac{x\sqrt{3}}{3} - \frac{x^2}{60}}$. This is an equation for a parabola.

$$\vec{\mathbf{v}} = \frac{d\vec{\mathbf{r}}}{dt} = \frac{d}{dt}\left[10t\hat{\mathbf{i}}\sqrt{3} + (10t - 5t^2)\hat{\mathbf{j}}\right] = \boxed{10\hat{\mathbf{i}}\sqrt{3} + (10 - 10t)\hat{\mathbf{j}}} = \boxed{10\hat{\mathbf{i}}\sqrt{3} + 10(1 - t)\hat{\mathbf{j}}}$$

$$\vec{\mathbf{a}} = \frac{d\vec{\mathbf{v}}}{dt} = \frac{d}{dt}\left[10\hat{\mathbf{i}}\sqrt{3} + (10 - 10t)\hat{\mathbf{j}}\right] = \boxed{-10\hat{\mathbf{j}}}$$

$$v = \|\vec{\mathbf{v}}\| = \sqrt{10^2(\sqrt{3})^2 + 10^2(1 - t)^2} = 10\sqrt{3 + (1 - t)^2} = 10\sqrt{3 + 1 - 2t + t^2} = 10\sqrt{t^2 - 2t +$$

$$\hat{\mathbf{T}} = \frac{\vec{\mathbf{v}}}{\|\vec{\mathbf{v}}\|} = \frac{10\hat{\mathbf{i}}\sqrt{3} + 10(1-t)\hat{\mathbf{j}}}{10\sqrt{t^2-2t+4}} = \boxed{\frac{\hat{\mathbf{i}}\sqrt{3} + (1-t)\hat{\mathbf{j}}}{\sqrt{t^2-2t+4}}}$$

$$\vec{\mathbf{v}} \times \vec{\mathbf{a}} = (v_y a_z - v_z a_y)\hat{\mathbf{i}} + (v_z a_x - v_x a_z)\hat{\mathbf{j}} + (v_x a_y - v_y a_x)\hat{\mathbf{k}}$$

$$\vec{\mathbf{v}} \times \vec{\mathbf{a}} = [(10 - 10t)(0) - (0)(-10)]\hat{\mathbf{i}} + [(0)(0) - (10\sqrt{3})(0)]\hat{\mathbf{j}} + [(10\sqrt{3})(-10) - (10 - 10t)(0)$$

$$\vec{\mathbf{v}} \times \vec{\mathbf{a}} = (0 + 0)\hat{\mathbf{i}} + (0 - 0)\hat{\mathbf{j}} + (-100\sqrt{3} - 0)\hat{\mathbf{k}} = -100\hat{\mathbf{k}}\sqrt{3}$$

$$\kappa = \frac{\left\|\frac{d\vec{\mathbf{r}}}{dt} \times \frac{d^2\vec{\mathbf{r}}}{dt^2}\right\|}{\left\|\frac{d\vec{\mathbf{r}}}{dt}\right\|^3} = \frac{\|\vec{\mathbf{v}} \times \vec{\mathbf{a}}\|}{v^3} = \frac{100\sqrt{3}}{\left(10\sqrt{t^2-2t+4}\right)^3} = \frac{100\sqrt{3}}{1000(t^2-2t+4)^{3/2}} = \boxed{\frac{\sqrt{3}}{10(t^2-2t+4)^{3/2}}}$$

$$\vec{\mathbf{v}} \cdot \vec{\mathbf{a}} = \left[10\hat{\mathbf{i}}\sqrt{3} + 10(1 - t)\hat{\mathbf{j}}\right] \cdot (-10\hat{\mathbf{j}}) = -100(1 - t) = 100(t - 1)$$

$$a_T = \frac{dv}{dt} = \frac{\vec{\mathbf{v}} \cdot \vec{\mathbf{a}}}{v} = \frac{100(t-1)}{10\sqrt{t^2-2t+4}} = \boxed{\frac{10(t-1)}{\sqrt{t^2-2t+4}}} \quad , \quad a_N = \kappa v^2 = \frac{100\sqrt{3}(t^2-2t+4)}{10(t^2-2t+4)^{3/2}} = \boxed{\frac{10\sqrt{3}}{\sqrt{t^2-2t+4}}}$$

$$\vec{\mathbf{v}}(2) = \boxed{10\hat{\mathbf{i}}\sqrt{3} - 10\hat{\mathbf{j}}} \quad , \quad \vec{\mathbf{a}}(2) = \boxed{-10\hat{\mathbf{j}}} \quad , \quad \hat{\mathbf{T}}(2) = \frac{\hat{\mathbf{i}}\sqrt{3} + (1-2)\hat{\mathbf{j}}}{\sqrt{2^2-2(2)+4}} = \frac{\hat{\mathbf{i}}\sqrt{3} - \hat{\mathbf{j}}}{\sqrt{4}} = \boxed{\frac{\hat{\mathbf{i}}\sqrt{3}}{2} - \frac{\hat{\mathbf{j}}}{2}}$$

$$\kappa(2) = \frac{\sqrt{3}}{10[2^2-2(2)+4]^{3/2}} = \frac{\sqrt{3}}{10(2)^3} = \boxed{\frac{\sqrt{3}}{80}} \quad , \quad a_T(2) = \frac{10(2-1)}{\sqrt{2^2-2(2)+4}} = \frac{10(1)}{\sqrt{4}} = \frac{10}{2} = \boxed{5}$$

$$a_N(2) = \frac{10\sqrt{3}}{\sqrt{2^2-2(2)+4}} = \frac{10\sqrt{3}}{\sqrt{4}} = \frac{10\sqrt{3}}{2} = \boxed{5\sqrt{3}}$$

Note: The equation $\vec{\mathbf{r}} = 10t\hat{\mathbf{i}}\sqrt{3} + (10t - 5t^2)\hat{\mathbf{j}}$ represents a projectile (in the absence of air resistance) near earth's surface (where 9.81 m/s^2 was rounded to 10) launched at angle of 30° above the horizontal from the ground with a speed of 20 m/s. Observe that $\sqrt{a_T^2 + a_N^2} = \sqrt{5^2 + (5\sqrt{3})^2} = \sqrt{25 + 75} = \sqrt{100} = 10 = \|\vec{\mathbf{a}}\|$ at $t = 2$.

⓫ Recall from Chapter 6 that $\hat{\mathbf{r}} = \hat{\mathbf{i}}\cos\theta + \hat{\mathbf{j}}\sin\theta$. Apply the chain rule:

$$\frac{d\hat{\mathbf{r}}}{dt} = \frac{d\hat{\mathbf{r}}}{d\theta}\frac{d\theta}{dt} = \frac{d\hat{\mathbf{r}}}{d\theta}\omega = \omega\frac{d}{d\theta}\left(\hat{\mathbf{i}}\cos\theta + \hat{\mathbf{j}}\sin\theta\right) = -\hat{\mathbf{i}}\omega\sin\theta + \hat{\mathbf{j}}\omega\cos\theta = \boxed{\omega\hat{\boldsymbol{\theta}}}$$

$$\frac{d\hat{\boldsymbol{\theta}}}{dt} = \frac{d\hat{\boldsymbol{\theta}}}{d\theta}\frac{d\theta}{dt} = \frac{d\hat{\boldsymbol{\theta}}}{d\theta}\omega = \omega\frac{d}{d\theta}\left(-\hat{\mathbf{i}}\sin\theta + \hat{\mathbf{j}}\cos\theta\right) = -\hat{\mathbf{i}}\omega\cos\theta - \hat{\mathbf{j}}\omega\sin\theta = \boxed{-\omega\hat{\mathbf{r}}}$$

Apply the product rule: $\vec{\mathbf{v}} = \frac{d\vec{\mathbf{r}}}{dt} = \frac{d}{dt}[t^2\hat{\mathbf{r}}] = t^2\frac{d}{dt}\hat{\mathbf{r}} + \hat{\mathbf{r}}\frac{d}{dt}t^2 = \boxed{\omega t^2\hat{\boldsymbol{\theta}} + 2t\hat{\mathbf{r}}}$

$$\vec{\mathbf{a}} = \frac{d\vec{\mathbf{v}}}{dt} = \frac{d}{dt}\left(\omega t^2\hat{\boldsymbol{\theta}} + 2t\hat{\mathbf{r}}\right) = \omega t^2\frac{d}{dt}\hat{\boldsymbol{\theta}} + \omega\hat{\boldsymbol{\theta}}\frac{d}{dt}t^2 + 2t\frac{d}{dr}\hat{\mathbf{r}} + 2\hat{\mathbf{r}}\frac{d}{dt}t$$

$$\vec{\mathbf{a}} = -\omega^2t^2\hat{\mathbf{r}} + 2\omega t\hat{\boldsymbol{\theta}} + 2\omega t\hat{\boldsymbol{\theta}} + 2\hat{\mathbf{r}} = \boxed{(2-\omega^2t^2)\hat{\mathbf{r}} + 4\omega t\hat{\boldsymbol{\theta}}}$$

$$v = \|\vec{\mathbf{v}}\| = \sqrt{(\omega t^2)^2 + (2t)^2} = \sqrt{\omega^2t^4 + 4t^2} = t\sqrt{\omega^2t^2+4}$$

$$\hat{\mathbf{T}} = \frac{\vec{\mathbf{v}}}{\|\vec{\mathbf{v}}\|} = \frac{\omega t^2\hat{\boldsymbol{\theta}}+2t\hat{\mathbf{r}}}{t\sqrt{\omega^2t^2+4}} = \boxed{\frac{\omega t\hat{\boldsymbol{\theta}}+2\hat{\mathbf{r}}}{\sqrt{\omega^2t^2+4}}}$$

$$\frac{d\hat{\mathbf{T}}}{dt} = \frac{d}{dt}\frac{\omega t\hat{\boldsymbol{\theta}}+2\hat{\mathbf{r}}}{\sqrt{\omega^2t^2+4}} = \frac{\sqrt{\omega^2t^2+4}\frac{d}{dt}(\omega t\hat{\boldsymbol{\theta}}+2\hat{\mathbf{r}}) - (\omega t\hat{\boldsymbol{\theta}}+2\hat{\mathbf{r}})\frac{d}{dt}\sqrt{\omega^2t^2+4}}{\left(\sqrt{\omega^2t^2+4}\right)^2}$$

$$\frac{d\hat{\mathbf{T}}}{dt} = \frac{\sqrt{\omega^2t^2+4}\left(\omega t\frac{d}{dt}\hat{\boldsymbol{\theta}}+\omega\hat{\boldsymbol{\theta}}\frac{d}{dt}t+2\frac{d}{dt}\hat{\mathbf{r}}\right)-(\omega t\hat{\boldsymbol{\theta}}+2\hat{\mathbf{r}})\frac{\omega^2t}{\sqrt{\omega^2t^2+4}}}{\omega^2t^2+4} = \frac{\sqrt{\omega^2t^2+4}(-\omega^2t\hat{\mathbf{r}}+\omega\hat{\boldsymbol{\theta}}+2\omega\hat{\boldsymbol{\theta}})-\frac{\omega^3t^2\hat{\boldsymbol{\theta}}+2\omega^2t\hat{\mathbf{r}}}{\sqrt{\omega^2t^2+4}}}{\omega^2t^2+4}$$

$$\frac{d\hat{\mathbf{T}}}{dt} = \frac{\frac{\omega^2t^2+4}{\sqrt{\omega^2t^2+4}}(-\omega^2t\hat{\mathbf{r}}+3\omega\hat{\boldsymbol{\theta}})-\frac{\omega^3t^2\hat{\boldsymbol{\theta}}+2\omega^2t\hat{\mathbf{r}}}{\sqrt{\omega^2t^2+4}}}{\omega^2t^2+4} = \frac{(\omega^2t^2+4)(-\omega^2t\hat{\mathbf{r}}+3\omega\hat{\boldsymbol{\theta}})-(\omega^3t^2\hat{\boldsymbol{\theta}}+2\omega^2t\hat{\mathbf{r}})}{(\omega^2t^2+4)^{3/2}}$$

$$\frac{d\hat{\mathbf{T}}}{dt} = \frac{-\omega^4t^3\hat{\mathbf{r}}+3\omega^3t^2\hat{\boldsymbol{\theta}}-4\omega^2t\hat{\mathbf{r}}+12\omega\hat{\boldsymbol{\theta}}-\omega^3t^2\hat{\boldsymbol{\theta}}-2\omega^2t\hat{\mathbf{r}}}{(\omega^2t^2+4)^{3/2}} = \frac{-\omega^4t^3\hat{\mathbf{r}}-6\omega^2t\hat{\mathbf{r}}+2\omega^3t^2\hat{\boldsymbol{\theta}}+12\omega\hat{\boldsymbol{\theta}}}{(\omega^2t^2+4)^{3/2}}$$

$$\frac{d\hat{\mathbf{T}}}{dt} = \frac{-\omega^2t(\omega^2t^2+6)\hat{\mathbf{r}}+2\omega(\omega^2t^2+6)\hat{\boldsymbol{\theta}}}{(\omega^2t^2+4)^{3/2}} = \frac{(\omega^2t^2+6)(-\omega^2t\hat{\mathbf{r}}+2\omega\hat{\boldsymbol{\theta}})}{(\omega^2t^2+4)^{3/2}}$$

$$\left\|\frac{d\hat{\mathbf{T}}}{dt}\right\| = \frac{\omega^2t^2+6}{(\omega^2t^2+4)^{3/2}}\sqrt{(-\omega^2t)^2+(2\omega)^2} = \frac{\omega^2t^2+6}{(\omega^2t^2+4)^{3/2}}\sqrt{\omega^4t^2+4\omega^2}$$

$$\left\|\frac{d\hat{\mathbf{T}}}{dt}\right\| = \frac{(\omega^2t^2+6)\omega}{(\omega^2t^2+4)^{3/2}}\sqrt{\omega^2t^2+4} = \frac{(\omega^2t^2+6)\omega}{\omega^2t^2+4}$$

$$\hat{\mathbf{N}} = \frac{d\hat{\mathbf{T}}/dt}{\|d\hat{\mathbf{T}}/dt\|} = \frac{(\omega^2t^2+6)(-\omega^2t\hat{\mathbf{r}}+2\omega\hat{\boldsymbol{\theta}})}{(\omega^2t^2+4)^{3/2}} \div \frac{(\omega^2t^2+6)\omega}{\omega^2t^2+4} = \frac{-\omega^2t\hat{\mathbf{r}}+2\omega\hat{\boldsymbol{\theta}}}{\omega\sqrt{\omega^2t^2+4}} = \boxed{\frac{-\omega t\hat{\mathbf{r}}+2\hat{\boldsymbol{\theta}}}{\sqrt{\omega^2t^2+4}}}$$

$$\kappa = \frac{\left\|\frac{d\hat{\mathbf{T}}}{dt}\right\|}{\left\|\frac{d\vec{\mathbf{r}}}{dt}\right\|} = \frac{\|d\hat{\mathbf{T}}/dt\|}{v} = \frac{(\omega^2t^2+6)\omega}{\omega^2t^2+4} \div t\sqrt{\omega^2t^2+4} = \boxed{\frac{\omega(\omega^2t^2+6)}{t(\omega^2t^2+4)^{3/2}}}$$

$$a_T = \frac{dv}{dt} = \frac{d}{dt}t\sqrt{\omega^2t^2+4} = \sqrt{\omega^2t^2+4}\frac{d}{dt}t + t\frac{d}{dt}\sqrt{\omega^2t^2+4}$$

$$a_T = \sqrt{\omega^2t^2+4} + \frac{\omega^2t^2}{\sqrt{\omega^2t^2+4}} = \frac{\omega^2t^2+4}{\sqrt{\omega^2t^2+4}} + \frac{\omega^2t^2}{\sqrt{\omega^2t^2+4}} = \boxed{\frac{2\omega^2t^2+4}{\sqrt{\omega^2t^2+4}}}$$

$$a_N = \kappa v^2 = \frac{\omega(\omega^2t^2+6)}{t(\omega^2t^2+4)^{3/2}}\left(t\sqrt{\omega^2t^2+4}\right)^2 = \frac{\omega(\omega^2t^2+6)}{t(\omega^2t^2+4)^{3/2}}t^2(\omega^2t^2+4) = \boxed{\frac{\omega t(\omega^2t^2+6)}{\sqrt{\omega^2t^2+4}}}$$

Chapter 13, Part A

❶ $s = \int_C ds = \int_C \sqrt{dx^2 + dy^2} = \int_C \sqrt{dx^2 \left[1 + \left(\frac{dy}{dx}\right)^2\right]} = \int_{x=0}^{1} \sqrt{1 + \left(\frac{dy}{dx}\right)^2}\, dx$

$$s = \int_{x=0}^{1} \sqrt{1 + \left(\frac{d}{dx}\sqrt{1-x^2}\right)^2}\, dx = \int_{x=0}^{1} \sqrt{1 + \left(\frac{-x}{\sqrt{1-x^2}}\right)^2}\, dx = \int_{x=0}^{1} \sqrt{1 + \frac{x^2}{1-x^2}}\, dx$$

$$s = \int_{x=0}^{1} \sqrt{\frac{1-x^2}{1-x^2} + \frac{x^2}{1-x^2}}\, dx = \int_{x=0}^{1} \sqrt{\frac{1}{1-x^2}}\, dx = \int_{x=0}^{1} \frac{dx}{\sqrt{1-x^2}}$$

Let $x = \sin\theta$ such that $dx = \cos\theta\, d\theta$. When $x = 0, \theta = 0$. When $x = 1, \theta = \frac{\pi}{2}$.

$$s = \int_{\theta=0}^{\pi/2} \frac{\cos\theta d\theta}{\sqrt{1-\sin^2\theta}} = \int_{\theta=0}^{\pi/2} \frac{\cos\theta d\theta}{\sqrt{\cos^2\theta}} = \int_{\theta=0}^{\pi/2} \frac{\cos\theta d\theta}{\cos\theta} = \int_{\theta=0}^{\pi/2} d\theta = \frac{\pi}{2} - 0 = \boxed{\frac{\pi}{2}}$$

Notes: $\frac{dy}{dx} = \frac{d}{dx}\sqrt{1-x^2} = \frac{d}{dx}(1-x^2)^{1/2} = \frac{1}{2}(1-x^2)^{-1/2}(-2x) = \frac{-x}{\sqrt{1-x^2}}$. We used the trig identity $\sin^2\theta + \cos^2\theta = 1$ to replace $1 - \sin^2\theta$ with $\cos^2\theta$. The equation $y = \sqrt{1-x^2}$ over the interval $0 \le x \le 1$ corresponds to a **quarter circle** with radius 1, so it should make sense that the answer $\left(s = \frac{\pi}{2}\right)$ is one-fourth of the circumference.

❷ $s = \int_C ds = \int_C \sqrt{dx^2 + dy^2} = \int_C \sqrt{dx^2 \left[1 + \left(\frac{dy}{dx}\right)^2\right]} = \int_{x=0}^{\sqrt{3}/2} \sqrt{1 + \left(\frac{dy}{dx}\right)^2}\, dx$

$$s = \int_{x=0}^{\sqrt{3}/2} \sqrt{1 + \left(\frac{d}{dx}x^2\right)^2}\, dx = \int_{x=0}^{\sqrt{3}/2} \sqrt{1 + (2x)^2}\, dx = \int_{x=0}^{\sqrt{3}/2} \sqrt{1 + 4x^2}\, dx$$

Let $x = \frac{1}{2}\tan\theta$ such that $dx = \frac{1}{2}\sec^2\theta\, d\theta$. When $x = 0, \theta = 0$. When $x = \frac{\sqrt{3}}{2}, \theta = \frac{\pi}{3}$ because $\frac{1}{2}\tan\frac{\pi}{3} = \frac{1}{2}(\sqrt{3}) = \frac{\sqrt{3}}{2}$.

$$s = \int_{\theta=0}^{\pi/3} \sqrt{1 + 4\left(\frac{1}{4}\tan^2\theta\right)}\left(\frac{1}{2}\sec^2\theta\right) d\theta = \frac{1}{2}\int_{\theta=0}^{\pi/3} \sec^2\theta \sqrt{1+\tan^2\theta}\, d\theta = \frac{1}{2}\int_{\theta=0}^{\pi/3} \sec^3\theta\, d\theta$$

Integrate by parts with $u = \sec\theta$ such that $du = \sec\theta\tan\theta\, d\theta$ and $v = \tan\theta$ such that $dv = \sec^2\theta\, d\theta$. When $\theta = 0, u = 1$ and $v = 0$. When $\theta = \frac{\pi}{3}, u = 2$ and $v = \sqrt{3}$.

$$s = \frac{1}{2}\int_{\theta=0}^{\pi/3} \sec^3\theta\, d\theta = \frac{1}{2}\int_{v=0}^{\sqrt{3}} u\, dv = \frac{1}{2}[uv]_{u=1,v=0}^{u=2,v=\sqrt{3}} - \frac{1}{2}\int_{u=1}^{2} v\, du$$

$$s = \frac{1}{2}(2\sqrt{3} - 0) - \frac{1}{2}\int_{\theta=0}^{\pi/3} \tan\theta\sec\theta\tan\theta\, d\theta = \sqrt{3} - \frac{1}{2}\int_{\theta=0}^{\pi/3} \tan^2\theta\sec\theta\, d\theta$$

$$s = \sqrt{3} - \frac{1}{2}\int_{\theta=0}^{\pi/3} (\sec^2\theta - 1)\sec\theta\, d\theta = \sqrt{3} - \frac{1}{2}\int_{\theta=0}^{\pi/3} \sec^3\theta\, d\theta + \frac{1}{2}\int_{\theta=0}^{\pi/3} \sec\theta\, d\theta$$

Since $s = \frac{1}{2}\int_{\theta=0}^{\pi/3} \sec^3\theta\, d\theta$, the middle term on the right-hand side is simply s.

$s = \sqrt{3} - s + \frac{1}{2}[\ln|\sec\theta + \tan\theta|]_{\theta=0}^{\pi/3} = \sqrt{3} - s + \frac{1}{2}\ln\left|\sec\frac{\pi}{3} + \tan\frac{\pi}{3}\right| - \frac{1}{2}\ln|\sec 0 + \tan 0|$

Add s to both sides of the equation. The left side will be $s + s = 2s$.

$2s = \sqrt{3} + \frac{1}{2}\ln|2 + \sqrt{3}| - \frac{1}{2}\ln|1 + 0| = \sqrt{3} + \frac{1}{2}\ln(2 + \sqrt{3}) - \frac{1}{2}\ln(1) = \sqrt{3} + \frac{1}{2}\ln(2 + \sqrt{3})$

To solve for s, divide by 2 on both sides: $s = \boxed{\frac{\sqrt{3}}{2} + \frac{1}{4}\ln(2 + \sqrt{3})} \approx \boxed{1.195}$.

Notes: We used the trig identity $1 + \tan^2\theta = \sec^2\theta$ to replace $\sqrt{1 + \tan^2\theta}$ with $\sec\theta$ and again later to replace $\tan^2\theta$ with $\sec^2\theta - 1$. Recall that $\ln(1) = 0$. If you use a table of integrals, note that $\int \sec^3\theta\, d\theta = \frac{1}{2}\sec\theta\tan\theta + \frac{1}{2}\ln|\sec\theta + \tan\theta| + c$.

❸ $s = \int_C ds = \int_C \sqrt{dr^2 + r^2 d\theta^2} = \int_C \sqrt{\left[\left(\frac{dr}{d\theta}\right)^2 + r^2\right] d\theta^2} = \int_{\theta=0}^{\pi} \sqrt{\left(\frac{dr}{d\theta}\right)^2 + r^2}\, d\theta$

$s = \int_{\theta=0}^{\pi} \sqrt{\left(\frac{d}{d\theta}e^\theta\right)^2 + (e^\theta)^2}\, d\theta = \int_{\theta=0}^{\pi} \sqrt{(e^\theta)^2 + (e^\theta)^2}\, d\theta = \int_{\theta=0}^{\pi} \sqrt{2(e^\theta)^2}\, d\theta$

$s = \sqrt{2}\int_{\theta=0}^{\pi} \sqrt{(e^\theta)^2}\, d\theta = \sqrt{2}\int_{\theta=0}^{\pi} e^\theta\, d\theta = \sqrt{2}\left[e^\theta\right]_{\theta=0}^{\pi} = \sqrt{2}(e^\pi - e^0) =$

$\boxed{\sqrt{2}(e^\pi - 1)} \approx \boxed{31.31}$

Note: Recall that $\frac{d}{d\theta}e^\theta = e^\theta$, $\int e^\theta\, d\theta = e^\theta + c$, and $e^0 = 1$.

❹ $s = \int_C ds = \int_C \sqrt{dr^2 + r^2 d\theta^2} = \int_C \sqrt{\left[\left(\frac{dr}{d\theta}\right)^2 + r^2\right] d\theta^2} = \int_{\theta=0}^{1} \sqrt{\left(\frac{dr}{d\theta}\right)^2 + r^2}\, d\theta$

$s = \int_{\theta=0}^{1} \sqrt{\left(\frac{d}{d\theta}\theta\right)^2 + \theta^2}\, d\theta = \int_{\theta=0}^{1} \sqrt{(1)^2 + \theta^2}\, d\theta = \int_{\theta=0}^{1} \sqrt{1 + \theta^2}\, d\theta$

Let $\theta = \tan\alpha$ such that $d\theta = \sec^2\alpha\, d\alpha$. When $\theta = 0$, $\alpha = 0$. When $\theta = 1$, $\alpha = \frac{\pi}{4}$.

$s = \int_{\alpha=0}^{\pi/4} \sqrt{1 + \tan^2\alpha}\,(\sec^2\alpha)d\alpha = \int_{\alpha=0}^{\pi/4} \sec^3\alpha\, d\alpha = \left[\frac{1}{2}\sec\theta\tan\theta + \frac{1}{2}\ln|\sec\theta + \tan\theta|\right]_{\theta=0}^{\pi/4}$

$s = \frac{1}{2}\sec\frac{\pi}{4}\tan\frac{\pi}{4} - \frac{1}{2}\sec 0\tan 0 + \frac{1}{2}\ln\left|\sec\frac{\pi}{4} + \tan\frac{\pi}{4}\right| - \frac{1}{2}\ln|\sec 0 + \tan 0|$

$s = \frac{1}{2}\sqrt{2}(1) - \frac{1}{2}(1)(0) + \frac{1}{2}\ln|\sqrt{2} + 1| - \frac{1}{2}\ln|1 + 0| = \frac{\sqrt{2}}{2} - 0 + \frac{1}{2}\ln(1 + \sqrt{2}) - \frac{1}{2}\ln(1)$

$s = \frac{\sqrt{2}}{2} + \frac{1}{2}\ln(1 + \sqrt{2}) - \frac{1}{2}(0) = \boxed{\frac{\sqrt{2}}{2} + \frac{1}{2}\ln(1 + \sqrt{2})} \approx \boxed{1.148}$

Notes: We used the trig identity $1 + \tan^2\alpha = \sec^2\alpha$ to replace $\sqrt{1 + \tan^2\alpha}$ with $\sec\alpha$. Recall from the solution to Problem 2 that $\int \sec^3\theta\, d\theta = \frac{1}{2}\sec\theta\tan\theta + \frac{1}{2}\ln|\sec\theta + \tan\theta| + c$. Also recall that $\ln(1) = 0$.

Chapter 13, Part B

5 $\int_C \vec{\mathbf{F}} \cdot d\vec{s} = \int_C F_x\, dx + \int_C F_y\, dy = \int_C x^4y^2\, dx + \int_C x^2y^4\, dy$

$\int_C \vec{\mathbf{F}} \cdot d\vec{s} = \int_{x=0}^{2} x^4(x^2)^2\, dx + \int_{y=0}^{4} \left(\sqrt{y}\right)^2 y^4\, dy = \int_{x=0}^{2} x^4x^4\, dx + \int_{y=0}^{4} yy^4\, dy$

$\int_C \vec{\mathbf{F}} \cdot d\vec{s} = \int_{x=0}^{2} x^8\, dx + \int_{y=0}^{4} y^5\, dy = \left[\frac{x^9}{9}\right]_{x=0}^{2} + \left[\frac{y^6}{6}\right]_{y=0}^{4} = \left(\frac{2^9}{9} - \frac{0^9}{9}\right) + \left(\frac{4^6}{6} - \frac{0^4}{6}\right)$

$\int_C \vec{\mathbf{F}} \cdot d\vec{s} = \frac{512}{9} + \frac{4096}{6} = \frac{1024+12{,}288}{18} = \frac{13{,}312}{18} = \boxed{\frac{6656}{9}}$

Since $\frac{\partial F_x}{\partial y} = \frac{\partial}{\partial y} x^4y^2 = 2x^4y$ doesn't equal $\frac{\partial F_y}{\partial x} = \frac{\partial}{\partial x} x^2y^4 = 2xy^4$, $\vec{\mathbf{F}}$ is **nonconservative**.

6 $\vec{\mathbf{F}} = \vec{\nabla} x^3y = \hat{\mathbf{i}} \frac{\partial}{\partial x} x^3y + \hat{\mathbf{j}} \frac{\partial}{\partial y} x^3y = 3x^2y\hat{\mathbf{i}} + x^3\hat{\mathbf{j}}$

$\int_C \vec{\mathbf{F}} \cdot d\vec{s} = \int_C F_x\, dx + \int_C F_y\, dy = \int_C 3x^2y\, dx + \int_C x^3\, dy$

Since $y = 1 - x$,it follows that $x + y = 1$ and $x = 1 - y$. Note that x varies from -1 to 1, whereas y varies from 2 to 0.

$\int_C \vec{\mathbf{F}} \cdot d\vec{s} = \int_{x=-1}^{1} 3x^2(1 - x)\, dx + \int_{y=2}^{0} (1 - y)^3\, dy$

$\int_C \vec{\mathbf{F}} \cdot d\vec{s} = \int_{x=-1}^{1} (3x^2 - 3x^3)\, dx + \int_{y=2}^{0} (1 - 3y + 3y^2 - y^3)\, dy$

$\int_C \vec{\mathbf{F}} \cdot d\vec{s} = [x^3]_{x=-1}^{1} - \left[\frac{3x^4}{4}\right]_{x=-1}^{1} + [y]_{y=2}^{0} - \left[\frac{3y^2}{2}\right]_{y=2}^{0} + [y^3]_{y=2}^{0} - \left[\frac{y^4}{4}\right]_{y=2}^{0}$

$\int_C \vec{\mathbf{F}} \cdot d\vec{s} = 1^3 - (-1)^3 - \frac{3(1)^4}{4} + \frac{3(-1)^4}{4} + 0 - 2 - \frac{3(0)^2}{2} + \frac{3(2)^2}{2} + 0^3 - 2^3 - \frac{0^4}{4} + \frac{2^4}{4}$

$\int_C \vec{\mathbf{F}} \cdot d\vec{s} = 1 - (-1) - \frac{3}{4} + \frac{3}{4} - 2 + \frac{3(4)}{2} - 8 + \frac{16}{4} = 1 + 1 - \frac{3}{4} + \frac{3}{4} - 2 + 6 - 8 + 4 = \boxed{2}$

Since $\vec{\mathbf{F}}$ is the gradient of x^3y, $\frac{\partial F_x}{\partial y} = \frac{\partial}{\partial y} 3x^2y = 3x^2$ equals $\frac{\partial F_y}{\partial x} = \frac{\partial}{\partial x} x^3 = 3x^2$ and $\vec{\mathbf{F}}$ is **conservative**. Note: A simpler way to perform $\int_{y=2}^{0} (1 - y)^3\, dy$ is to make the substitution $u = 1 - y$ such that $du = -dy$.

Chapter 13, Part C

7 $\oint_C \vec{\mathbf{F}} \cdot d\vec{s} = \int_{C_1} F_x\, dx + \int_{C_1} F_y\, dy + \int_{C_2} F_x\, dx + \int_{C_2} F_y\, dy + \int_{C_3} F_x\, dx + \int_{C_3} F_y\, dy$

From $(1,1)$ to $(1,-1)$, $x = 1$. From $(1,-1)$ to $(-1,1)$, $y = -x$ since $m = \frac{1-(-1)}{-1-1} = \frac{2}{-2} = -1$ and the y-intercept is zero. From $(-1,1)$ to $(1,1)$, $y = 1$.

$\oint_C \vec{\mathbf{F}} \cdot d\vec{\mathbf{s}} = \int_{x=1}^{1} 1^4 y^2\, dx + \int_{y=1}^{-1} 1^5 y\, dy + \int_{x=1}^{-1} x^4(-x)^2\, dx + \int_{y=-1}^{1} (-y)^5 y\, dy +$
$\int_{x=-1}^{1} x^4 1^2\, dx + \int_{y=1}^{1} x^5 1\, dy$

$\oint_C \vec{\mathbf{F}} \cdot d\vec{\mathbf{s}} = 0 + \int_{y=1}^{-1} y\, dy + \int_{x=1}^{-1} x^4 x^2\, dx - \int_{y=-1}^{1} y^5 y\, dy + \int_{x=-1}^{1} x^4\, dx + 0$

$\oint_C \vec{\mathbf{F}} \cdot d\vec{\mathbf{s}} = \int_{y=1}^{-1} y\, dy + \int_{x=1}^{-1} x^6\, dx - \int_{y=-1}^{1} y^6\, dy + \int_{x=-1}^{1} x^4\, dx$

$\oint_C \vec{\mathbf{F}} \cdot d\vec{\mathbf{s}} = \left[\frac{y^2}{2}\right]_{y=1}^{-1} + \left[\frac{x^7}{7}\right]_{x=1}^{-1} - \left[\frac{y^7}{7}\right]_{y=-1}^{1} + \left[\frac{x^5}{5}\right]_{x=-1}^{1}$

$\oint_C \vec{\mathbf{F}} \cdot d\vec{\mathbf{s}} = \frac{(-1)^2}{2} - \frac{1^2}{2} + \frac{(-1)^7}{7} - \frac{1^7}{7} - \frac{1^7}{7} + \frac{(-1)^7}{7} + \frac{1^5}{5} - \frac{(-1)^5}{5}$

$\oint_C \vec{\mathbf{F}} \cdot d\vec{\mathbf{s}} = \frac{1}{2} - \frac{1}{2} + \left(-\frac{1}{7}\right) - \frac{1}{7} - \frac{1}{7} + \left(-\frac{1}{7}\right) + \frac{1}{5} - \left(-\frac{1}{5}\right)$

$\oint_C \vec{\mathbf{F}} \cdot d\vec{\mathbf{s}} = \frac{1}{2} - \frac{1}{2} - \frac{1}{7} - \frac{1}{7} - \frac{1}{7} - \frac{1}{7} + \frac{1}{5} + \frac{1}{5} = -\frac{4}{7} + \frac{2}{5} = -\frac{20}{35} + \frac{14}{35} = \frac{-20+14}{35} = \boxed{-\frac{6}{35}}$

Since $\frac{\partial F_x}{\partial y} = \frac{\partial}{\partial y} x^4 y^2 = 2x^4 y$ doesn't equal $\frac{\partial F_y}{\partial x} = \frac{\partial}{\partial x} x^5 y = 5x^4 y$, $\vec{\mathbf{F}}$ is **nonconservative**.

8 Notes: $d\vec{\mathbf{s}} = \hat{\mathbf{i}}\, dx + \hat{\mathbf{j}}\, dy$, $r = 2$ for the circle, $x = r\cos\theta = 2\cos\theta$, $y = r\sin\theta = 2\sin\theta$, $dx = -2\sin\theta\, d\theta$, $dy = 2\cos\theta\, d\theta$, $\hat{\mathbf{r}} = \hat{\mathbf{i}}\cos\theta + \hat{\mathbf{j}}\sin\theta$, and $\hat{\boldsymbol{\theta}} = -\hat{\mathbf{i}}\sin\theta + \hat{\mathbf{j}}\cos\theta$. Note that $\hat{\mathbf{r}}\cos\theta - \hat{\boldsymbol{\theta}}\sin\theta = \hat{\mathbf{i}}\cos^2\theta + \hat{\mathbf{j}}\sin\theta\cos\theta + \hat{\mathbf{i}}\sin^2\theta - \hat{\mathbf{j}}\sin\theta\cos\theta = \hat{\mathbf{i}}$ and $\hat{\mathbf{r}}\sin\theta + \hat{\boldsymbol{\theta}}\cos\theta = \hat{\mathbf{i}}\sin\theta\cos\theta + \hat{\mathbf{j}}\sin^2\theta - \hat{\mathbf{i}}\sin\theta\cos\theta + \hat{\mathbf{j}}\cos^2\theta = \hat{\mathbf{j}}$. Combine these expressions to see that $d\vec{\mathbf{s}} = \hat{\mathbf{i}}\, dx + \hat{\mathbf{j}}\, dy = (\hat{\mathbf{r}}\cos\theta - \hat{\boldsymbol{\theta}}\sin\theta)(-2\sin\theta\, d\theta) + (\hat{\mathbf{r}}\sin\theta + \hat{\boldsymbol{\theta}}\cos\theta)(2\cos\theta\, d\theta) = -2\hat{\mathbf{r}}\sin\theta\cos\theta\, d\theta + 2\hat{\boldsymbol{\theta}}\sin^2\theta\, d\theta + 2\hat{\mathbf{r}}\sin\theta\cos\theta\, d\theta + 2\hat{\boldsymbol{\theta}}\cos^2\theta\, d\theta = 2\hat{\boldsymbol{\theta}}d\theta$ because $\sin^2\theta + \cos^2\theta = 1$.

$\oint_C \vec{\mathbf{F}} \cdot d\vec{\mathbf{s}} = \oint_C r\hat{\boldsymbol{\theta}} \cdot 2\hat{\boldsymbol{\theta}}d\theta = 2\oint_C r\, d\theta$ since $\hat{\boldsymbol{\theta}} \cdot \hat{\boldsymbol{\theta}} = 1$ (since $\hat{\boldsymbol{\theta}}$ is a unit vector)

$\oint_C \vec{\mathbf{F}} \cdot d\vec{\mathbf{s}} = 2\oint_C 2\, d\theta = 4\oint_C d\theta$ (since $r = 2$ is a constant for the circle)

$\oint_C \vec{\mathbf{F}} \cdot d\vec{\mathbf{s}} = 4\int_{\theta=0}^{2\pi} d\theta = 4(2\pi) = \boxed{8\pi}$

$\vec{\mathbf{F}} = r\hat{\boldsymbol{\theta}} = -\hat{\mathbf{i}}\, r\sin\theta + \hat{\mathbf{j}}\, r\cos\theta = -y\hat{\mathbf{i}} + x\hat{\mathbf{j}}$ such that $F_x = -y$ and $F_y = x$.

Since $\frac{\partial F_x}{\partial y} = \frac{\partial}{\partial y}(-y) = -1$ doesn't equal $\frac{\partial F_y}{\partial x} = \frac{\partial}{\partial x} x = 1$, $\vec{\mathbf{F}}$ is **nonconservative**.

Note: This problem may seem simpler if you consider that $\vec{\mathbf{F}} = r\hat{\boldsymbol{\theta}} = 2\hat{\boldsymbol{\theta}}$ is tangential to the circle in a counterclockwise path, such that $\vec{\mathbf{F}}$ is parallel to the circle of integration. The scalar product is then $\oint_C \vec{\mathbf{F}} \cdot d\vec{\mathbf{s}} = \oint_C F\, ds = \oint_C r\, r d\theta = \oint_C 2(2)\, d\theta = 4\oint_C d\theta = 4\int_{\theta=0}^{2\pi} d\theta = 4(2\pi) = \boxed{8\pi}$.

Chapter 13, Part D

9 Since $\frac{\partial F_x}{\partial y} = \frac{\partial}{\partial y}(2xy - 3) = 2x$ equals $\frac{\partial F_y}{\partial x} = \frac{\partial}{\partial x}(x^2 - y^2) = 2x$, $\vec{\mathbf{F}}$ is **conservative**.

- Compare $\vec{\mathbf{F}} = \vec{\nabla} f = \hat{\mathbf{i}}\frac{\partial f}{\partial x} + \hat{\mathbf{j}}\frac{\partial f}{\partial y}$ with $\vec{\mathbf{F}} = (2xy - 3)\hat{\mathbf{i}} + (x^2 - y^2)\hat{\mathbf{j}}$ to see that $\frac{\partial f}{\partial x} = F_x = 2xy - 3$ and $\frac{\partial f}{\partial y} = F_y = x^2 - y^2$.
- Integrate $\frac{\partial f}{\partial x}$ over x to get $f(x, y) = x^2y - 3x + g(y)$.
- Now take a partial derivative of f with respect to y to get $\frac{\partial f}{\partial y} = x^2 + \frac{dg}{dy}$.
- Compare this with $\frac{\partial f}{\partial y} = F_y = x^2 - y^2$ to see that $\frac{dg}{dy} = -y^2$.
- Integrate $\frac{dg}{dy}$ over y to get $g(y) = -\frac{y^3}{3} + c$. Plug this expression for $g(y)$ into the previous expression for $f(x, y)$ to get $f(x, y) = \boxed{x^2y - 3x - \frac{y^3}{3} + c}$.

Check: $\vec{\nabla} f = \hat{\mathbf{i}}\frac{\partial f}{\partial x} + \hat{\mathbf{j}}\frac{\partial f}{\partial y} = \hat{\mathbf{i}}\frac{\partial}{\partial x}\left(x^2y - 3x - \frac{y^3}{3} + c\right) + \hat{\mathbf{j}}\frac{\partial f}{\partial y}\left(x^2y - 3x - \frac{y^3}{3} + c\right) =$ $\hat{\mathbf{i}}(2xy - 3 - 0 + 0) + \hat{\mathbf{j}}(x^2 - 0 - y^2 + 0) = (2xy - 3)\hat{\mathbf{i}} + (x^2 - y^2)\hat{\mathbf{j}} = \vec{\mathbf{F}}$.

10 Since $\frac{\partial F_x}{\partial y} = \frac{\partial}{\partial y}2x^5y^3 = 6x^5y^2$ equals $\frac{\partial F_y}{\partial x} = \frac{\partial}{\partial x}(x^6y^2 - y^8) = 6x^5y^2$, $\vec{\mathbf{F}}$ is **conservative**

- Compare $\vec{\mathbf{F}} = \vec{\nabla} f = \hat{\mathbf{i}}\frac{\partial f}{\partial x} + \hat{\mathbf{j}}\frac{\partial f}{\partial y}$ with $\vec{\mathbf{F}} = 2x^5y^3\hat{\mathbf{i}} + (x^6y^2 - y^8)\hat{\mathbf{j}}$ to see that $\frac{\partial f}{\partial x} = F_x = 2x^5y^3$ and $\frac{\partial f}{\partial y} = F_y = x^6y^2 - y^8$.
- Integrate $\frac{\partial f}{\partial x}$ over x to get $f(x, y) = \frac{x^6y^3}{3} + g(y)$.
- Now take a partial derivative of f with respect to y to get $\frac{\partial f}{\partial y} = x^6y^2 + \frac{dg}{dy}$.
- Compare this with $\frac{\partial f}{\partial y} = F_y = x^6y^2 - y^8$ to see that $\frac{dg}{dy} = -y^8$.
- Integrate $\frac{dg}{dy}$ over y to get $g(y) = -\frac{y^9}{9} + c$. Plug this expression for $g(y)$ into the previous expression for $f(x, y)$ to get $f(x, y) = \boxed{\frac{x^6y^3}{3} - \frac{y^9}{9} + c}$.

Check: $\vec{\nabla} f = \hat{\mathbf{i}}\frac{\partial f}{\partial x} + \hat{\mathbf{j}}\frac{\partial f}{\partial y} = \hat{\mathbf{i}}\frac{\partial}{\partial x}\left(\frac{x^6y^3}{3} - \frac{y^9}{9} + c\right) + \hat{\mathbf{j}}\frac{\partial}{\partial y}\left(\frac{x^6y^3}{3} - \frac{y^9}{9} + c\right)$
$= \hat{\mathbf{i}}(2x^5y^3 - 0 + 0) + \hat{\mathbf{j}}(x^6y^2 - y^8 + 0) = 2x^5y^3\hat{\mathbf{i}} + (x^6y^2 - y^8)\hat{\mathbf{j}} = \vec{\mathbf{F}}$.

⓫ Since $\frac{\partial F_x}{\partial y} = \frac{\partial}{\partial y} yz = z$ equals $\frac{\partial F_y}{\partial x} = \frac{\partial}{\partial x} xz = z$, $\frac{\partial F_x}{\partial z} = \frac{\partial}{\partial z} yz = y$ equals $\frac{\partial F_z}{\partial x} = \frac{\partial}{\partial x} xy = y$, and $\frac{\partial F_z}{\partial y} = \frac{\partial}{\partial y} xy = x$ equals $\frac{\partial F_y}{\partial z} = \frac{\partial}{\partial z} xz = x$, $\vec{\mathbf{F}}$ is <u>**conservative**</u>.

- Compare $\vec{\mathbf{F}} = \vec{\nabla} f = \hat{\mathbf{i}}\frac{\partial f}{\partial x} + \hat{\mathbf{j}}\frac{\partial f}{\partial y} + \hat{\mathbf{k}}\frac{\partial f}{\partial z}$ with $\vec{\mathbf{F}} = yz\hat{\mathbf{i}} + xz\hat{\mathbf{j}} + xy\hat{\mathbf{k}}$ to see that $\frac{\partial f}{\partial x} = F_x = yz$, $\frac{\partial f}{\partial y} = F_y = xz$, and $\frac{\partial f}{\partial z} = F_z = xy$.
- Integrate $\frac{\partial f}{\partial x}$ over x to get $f(x, y) = xyz + g(y, z)$.
- Now take a partial derivative of f with respect to y to get $\frac{\partial f}{\partial y} = xz + \frac{dg}{dy}$.
- Compare this with $\frac{\partial f}{\partial y} = F_y = xz$ to see that $\frac{dg}{dy} = 0$. It follows that $g(y, z) = h(z)$ (since g is constant with respect to y) and $f(x, y) = xyz + h(z)$.
- Now take a partial derivative of f with respect to z to get $\frac{\partial f}{\partial z} = xy + \frac{dh}{dz}$. It follows that $h(z) = c$ and $f(x, y) = \boxed{xyz + c}$.

Check: $\vec{\nabla} f = \hat{\mathbf{i}}\frac{\partial f}{\partial x} + \hat{\mathbf{j}}\frac{\partial f}{\partial y} + \hat{\mathbf{k}}\frac{\partial f}{\partial z} = \hat{\mathbf{i}}\frac{\partial}{\partial x} xyz + \hat{\mathbf{j}}\frac{\partial}{\partial y} xyz + \hat{\mathbf{k}}\frac{\partial}{\partial z} xyz = yz\hat{\mathbf{i}} + xz\hat{\mathbf{j}} + xy\hat{\mathbf{k}} = \vec{\mathbf{F}}$.

⓬ $\vec{\mathbf{F}} = r\hat{\mathbf{r}} = r(\hat{\mathbf{i}}\cos\theta + \hat{\mathbf{j}}\sin\theta) = x\hat{\mathbf{i}} + y\hat{\mathbf{j}}$ since $x = r\cos\theta$ and $y = r\sin\theta$.

Since $\frac{\partial F_x}{\partial y} = \frac{\partial}{\partial y} x = 0$ equals $\frac{\partial F_y}{\partial x} = \frac{\partial}{\partial x} y = 0$, $\vec{\mathbf{F}}$ is <u>**conservative**</u>.

- Compare $\vec{\mathbf{F}} = \vec{\nabla} f = \hat{\mathbf{i}}\frac{\partial f}{\partial x} + \hat{\mathbf{j}}\frac{\partial f}{\partial y}$ with $\vec{\mathbf{F}} = x\hat{\mathbf{i}} + y\hat{\mathbf{j}}$ to see that $\frac{\partial f}{\partial x} = F_x = x$ and $\frac{\partial f}{\partial y} = F_y = y$.
- Integrate $\frac{\partial f}{\partial x}$ over x to get $f(x, y) = \frac{x^2}{2} + g(y)$.
- Now take a partial derivative of f with respect to y to get $\frac{\partial f}{\partial y} = 0 + \frac{dg}{dy}$.
- Compare this with $\frac{\partial f}{\partial y} = F_y = y$ to see that $\frac{dg}{dy} = y$.
- Integrate $\frac{dg}{dy}$ over y to get $g(y) = \frac{y^2}{2} + c$. Plug this expression for $g(y)$ into the previous expression for $f(x, y)$ to get $f(x, y) = \boxed{\frac{x^2}{2} + \frac{y^2}{2} + c}$.

Check: $\vec{\nabla} f = \hat{\mathbf{i}}\frac{\partial f}{\partial x} + \hat{\mathbf{j}}\frac{\partial f}{\partial y} = \hat{\mathbf{i}}\frac{\partial}{\partial x}\left(\frac{x^2}{2} + \frac{y^2}{2} + c\right) + \hat{\mathbf{j}}\frac{\partial}{\partial y}\left(\frac{x^2}{2} + \frac{y^2}{2} + c\right)$
$= \hat{\mathbf{i}}(x + 0 + 0) + \hat{\mathbf{j}}(y + 0 + 0) = x\hat{\mathbf{i}} + y\hat{\mathbf{j}} = r(\hat{\mathbf{i}}\cos\theta + \hat{\mathbf{j}}\sin\theta) = r\hat{\mathbf{r}} = \vec{\mathbf{F}}$.

Chapter 14, Part A

1 $A = \int_{x=0}^{1}\int_{y=1-x}^{\sqrt{1-x^2}} dy\,dx = \int_{x=0}^{1}[y]_{y=1-x}^{\sqrt{1-x^2}} dx = \int_{x=0}^{1}\sqrt{1-x^2}\,dx - \int_{x=0}^{1}(1-x)\,dx$

For the first integral, let $x = \sin\theta$ such that $dx = \cos\theta\,d\theta$. When $x = 0, \theta = 0$. When $x = 1, \theta = \frac{\pi}{2}$.

$$A = \int_{\theta=0}^{\pi/2}\sqrt{1-\sin^2\theta}\cos\theta\,d\theta - \left[x - \frac{x^2}{2}\right]_{x=0}^{1} = \int_{\theta=0}^{\pi/2}\sqrt{\cos^2\theta}\cos\theta\,d\theta - \left(1 - 0 - \frac{1^2}{2} + \frac{0^2}{2}\right)$$

$$A = \int_{\theta=0}^{\pi/2}\cos^2\theta\,d\theta - \left(1 - \frac{1}{2}\right) = \int_{\theta=0}^{\pi/2}\frac{1+\cos(2\theta)}{2}d\theta - \frac{1}{2} = \int_{\theta=0}^{\pi/2}\frac{1}{2}d\theta + \int_{\theta=0}^{\pi/2}\frac{\cos(2\theta)}{2}d\theta - \frac{1}{2}$$

We used the trig identities $\sin^2\theta + \cos^2\theta = 1$ and $\cos^2\theta = \frac{1+\cos(2\theta)}{2}$.

$$A = \left[\frac{\theta}{2}\right]_{\theta=0}^{\pi/2} + \left[\frac{\sin(2\theta)}{4}\right]_{\theta=0}^{\pi/2} - \frac{1}{2} = \frac{1}{2}\frac{\pi}{2} - \frac{0}{2} + \frac{\sin(\pi)}{4} - \frac{\sin(0)}{4} - \frac{1}{2} = \frac{\pi}{4} + \frac{0}{4} - \frac{1}{2} = \boxed{\frac{\pi}{4} - \frac{1}{2}} = \boxed{\frac{\pi-2}{4}}$$

Note: Since the line makes a 45° right triangle with the coordinate axes, the answer can be checked by subtracting the area of the triangle from the area of the quarter circle: $\frac{\pi(1)^2}{4} - \frac{1}{2}(1)(1) = \frac{\pi}{4} - \frac{1}{2} = \frac{\pi}{4} - \frac{2}{4} = \frac{\pi-2}{4}$.

2 $A = \int_{r=0}^{1+\sin\theta}\int_{\theta=0}^{2\pi} r\,dr\,d\theta = \int_{\theta=0}^{2\pi}\int_{r=0}^{1+\sin\theta} r\,dr\,d\theta = \int_{\theta=0}^{2\pi}\left[\frac{r^2}{2}\right]_{r=0}^{1+\sin\theta} d\theta$

$$A = \frac{1}{2}\int_{\theta=0}^{2\pi}(1+\sin\theta)^2\,d\theta = \frac{1}{2}\int_{\theta=0}^{2\pi}(1 + 2\sin\theta + \sin^2\theta)\,d\theta$$

We used the trig identity $\sin^2\theta = \frac{1-\cos(2\theta)}{2}$.

$$A = \frac{1}{2}\int_{\theta=0}^{2\pi}d\theta + \frac{1}{2}\int_{\theta=0}^{2\pi}2\sin\theta\,d\theta + \frac{1}{2}\int_{\theta=0}^{2\pi}\sin^2\theta\,d\theta = \frac{1}{2}[\theta]_{\theta=0}^{2\pi} + \frac{1}{2}[-2\cos\theta]_{\theta=0}^{2\pi} + \frac{1}{2}\int_{\theta=0}^{2\pi}\frac{1-\cos(2\theta)}{2}$$

$$A = \frac{1}{2}(2\pi - 0) - \cos(2\pi) + \cos 0 + \frac{1}{2}\int_{\theta=0}^{2\pi}\frac{1}{2}d\theta - \frac{1}{2}\int_{\theta=0}^{2\pi}\frac{\cos(2\theta)}{2}d\theta$$

$$A = \pi - 1 + 1 + \frac{1}{2}\left[\frac{\theta}{2}\right]_{\theta=0}^{2\pi} - \frac{1}{2}\left[\frac{\sin(2\theta)}{4}\right]_{\theta=0}^{2\pi} = \pi + 0 + \frac{1}{2}\left(\frac{2\pi}{2} - \frac{0}{2}\right) - \frac{1}{2}\left(\frac{\sin 4\pi}{4} - \frac{\sin 0}{4}\right)$$

$$A = \pi + \frac{1}{2}(\pi) - \frac{1}{2}(0 - 0) = \pi + \frac{\pi}{2} = \frac{2\pi}{2} + \frac{\pi}{2} = \boxed{\frac{3\pi}{2}}$$

3 $A = \iint_S xy\sqrt{1 + \left(\frac{\partial z}{\partial x}\right)^2 + \left(\frac{\partial z}{\partial y}\right)^2}\,dxdy = \iint_S\sqrt{1 + \left[\frac{\partial}{\partial x}(x^2 - y^2)\right]^2 + \left[\frac{\partial}{\partial y}(x^2 - y^2)\right]^2}\,dxdy$

$$A = \iint_S\sqrt{1 + (2x)^2 + (-2y)^2}\,dxdy = \iint_S\sqrt{1 + 4x^2 + 4y^2}\,dxdy$$

It is convenient to change variables from Cartesian coordinates to cylindrical coordinates. Note that $dA = dxdy = r_c dr_c d\theta$ and $x^2 + y^2 = r_c^2$. Note the distinction between the surface of integration $z = x^2 - y^2$ (used above) and the disc $x^2 + y^2 \leq 4$ that defines the limits of integration. We want the surface area of $z = x^2 - y^2$ that lies above the disc. The disc $x^2 + y^2 \leq 4$ is mapped by $0 \leq r_c \leq 2$ and $0 \leq \theta \leq 2\pi$ since $x^2 + y^2 \leq 4$ is a disc with a radius of 2 (since $2^2 = 4$). Don't forget the important r_c in $dA = dxdy = r_c dr_c d\theta$.

$A = \int_{r_c=0}^{2} \int_{\theta=0}^{2\pi} \sqrt{1 + 4r_c^2}\, r_c\, dr_c d\theta = 2\pi \int_{r_c=0}^{2} r_c \sqrt{1 + 4r_c^2}\, dr_c$

Let $u = 1 + 4r_c^2$ such that $du = 8r_c dr_c$, for which $r_c dr_c = \frac{du}{8}$. When $r_c = 0, u = 1$.

When $r_c = 2, u = 1 + 4(2)^2 = 1 + 4(4) = 1 + 16 = 17$.

$A = 2\pi \int_{u=1}^{17} \sqrt{u} \frac{du}{8} = \frac{\pi}{4} \int_{u=1}^{17} u^{1/2}\, du = \frac{\pi}{4} \left[\frac{2u^{3/2}}{3}\right]_{u=1}^{17} = \boxed{\frac{\pi}{6}\left(17^{3/2} - 1\right)} \approx \boxed{36.18}$

❹ Notes: The πa^2 term accounts for the area of the circular base. The upper limit for φ is $\frac{\pi}{2}$ so that the integral gives the top surface of the hemisphere (where $z > 0$).

$A = \pi a^2 + \int_{\theta=0}^{2\pi} \int_{\varphi=0}^{\pi/2} a^2 \sin\varphi\, d\theta\, d\varphi = \pi a^2 + a^2[\theta]_{\theta=0}^{2\pi}[-\cos\varphi]_{\varphi=0}^{\pi/2}$

$A = \pi a^2 + a^2(2\pi - 0)\left(-\cos\frac{\pi}{2} + \cos 0\right) = \pi a^2 + 2\pi a^2(-0 + 1)$

$A = \pi a^2 + 2\pi a^2(1) = \pi a^2 + 2\pi a^2 = \boxed{3\pi a^2}$

Notes: The surface area of a complete sphere is $4\pi a^2$. The area of the hemisphere equals one-half of the area of a complete sphere ($2\pi a^2$) plus the area of its circular base (πa^2).

Chapter 14, Part B

❺ Use cylindrical coordinates. Note that $z = x^2 + y^2 = r_c^2$ and $dV = r_c dr_c d\theta dz$. The circular paraboloid $z = r_c^2$ intersects the plane $z = 9$ when $r_c = 3$.

$V = \int_{r_c=0}^{3} \int_{\theta=0}^{2\pi} \int_{z=0}^{r_c^2} r_c\, dr_c\, d\theta\, dz = \int_{r_c=0}^{3} \int_{\theta=0}^{2\pi} \int_{z=0}^{r_c^2} r_c\, dz\, d\theta\, dr_c = \int_{r_c=0}^{3} r_c [\theta]_{\theta=0}^{2\pi} [z]_{z=0}^{r_c^2}\, dr_c$

$V = \int_{r_c=0}^{3} 2\pi r_c r_c^2\, dr_c = \int_{r_c=0}^{3} 2\pi r_c^3\, dr_c = 2\pi \left[\frac{r_c^4}{4}\right]_{r_c=0}^{3} = 2\pi\left(\frac{3^4}{4} - \frac{0^4}{4}\right) = 2\pi\left(\frac{81}{4}\right) = \boxed{\frac{81\pi}{2}}$

Note: This is one-half of the volume of a cylinder of the same height.

❻ $V = \int_{x=0}^{\pi/2} \int_{y=0}^{\pi/2} \int_{z=0}^{\sin x \cos y} dx\, dy\, dz = \int_{x=0}^{\pi/2} \int_{y=0}^{\pi/2} [z]_{z=0}^{\sin x \cos y}\, dx\, dy$

$V = \int_{x=0}^{\pi/2} \int_{y=0}^{\pi/2} \sin x \cos y\, dx\, dy = [-\cos x]_{x=0}^{\pi/2} [\sin y]_{y=0}^{\pi/2}$

$V = \left(-\cos\frac{\pi}{2} + \cos 0\right)\left(\sin\frac{\pi}{2} - \sin 0\right) = (-0 + 1)(1 - 0) = (1)(1) = \boxed{1}$

❼ The line $y = 1 - x$ connects (1,0,0) and (0,1,0) in the xy plane, while the plane $z = 1 - x - y$ connects (1,0,0), (0,1,0), and (0,0,1). Integrate x from 0 to 1, y from 0 to $1 - x$, and z from 0 to $1 - x - y$. Note that although this is a tetrahedron, it is **not** a regular tetrahedron (since the faces meet at right angles at the origin).

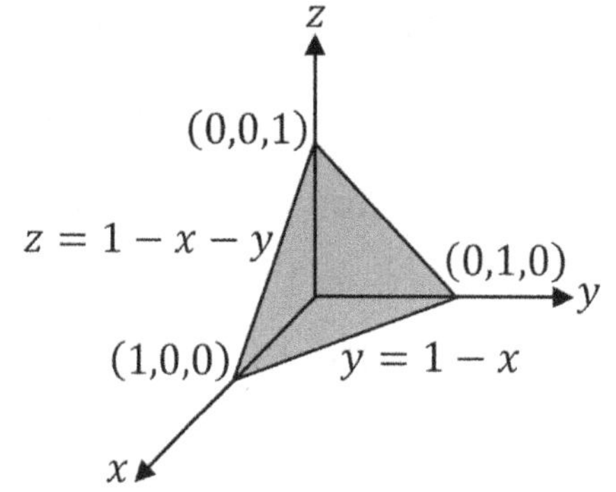

$$V = \int_{x=0}^{1}\int_{y=0}^{1-x}\int_{z=0}^{1-x-y} dx\,dy\,dz = \int_{x=0}^{1}\int_{y=0}^{1-x}[z]_{z=0}^{1-x-y}\,dx\,dy$$

$$V = \int_{x=0}^{1}\int_{y=0}^{1-x}(1 - x - y)\,dy\,dx = \int_{x=0}^{1}\int_{y=0}^{1-x}dy\,dx - \int_{x=0}^{1}\int_{y=0}^{1-x}x\,dy\,dx - \int_{x=0}^{1}\int_{y=0}^{1-x}y\,dy\,d$$

$$V = \int_{x=0}^{1}[y]_{y=0}^{1-x}dx - \int_{x=0}^{1}x[y]_{y=0}^{1-x}\,dx - \int_{x=0}^{1}\left[\frac{y^2}{2}\right]_{y=0}^{1-x}dx$$

$$V = \int_{x=0}^{1}(1 - x)dx - \int_{x=0}^{1}x(1 - x)\,dx - \frac{1}{2}\int_{x=0}^{1}(1 - x)^2\,dx$$

$$V = \int_{x=0}^{1}(1 - x)dx - \int_{x=0}^{1}(x - x^2)\,dx - \frac{1}{2}\int_{x=0}^{1}(1 - 2x + x^2)\,dx$$

$$V = \left[x - \frac{x^2}{2}\right]_{x=0}^{1} - \left[\frac{x^2}{2} - \frac{x^3}{3}\right]_{x=0}^{1} - \frac{1}{2}\left[x - x^2 + \frac{x^3}{3}\right]_{x=0}^{1} = 1 - \frac{1}{2} - \left(\frac{1}{2} - \frac{1}{3}\right) - \frac{1}{2}\left(1 - 1 + \frac{1}{3}\right)$$

$$V = \frac{1}{2} - \left(\frac{1}{6}\right) - \frac{1}{2}\left(\frac{1}{3}\right) = \frac{1}{2} - \frac{1}{6} - \frac{1}{6} = \frac{1}{2} - \frac{2}{6} = \frac{3}{6} - \frac{2}{6} = \boxed{\frac{1}{6}}$$

Note: The volume of a pyramid equals one-third of the area of the base times the height. The area of the base is the area of a triangle with a base of 1 and a height of 1; the area of the base is $B = \frac{1}{2}(1)(1) = \frac{1}{2}$. Since the height of the pyramid is 1, the volume of the pyramid is $V = \frac{1}{3}Bh = \frac{1}{3}\left(\frac{1}{2}\right)(1) = \frac{1}{6}$.

❽ This integral is simplest in cylindrical coordinates. (It is actually more challenging in spherical coordinates. Note that $\varphi = c$ in spherical coordinates makes a "cone" with a rounded "base" like an ice-cream cone with one scoop of ice-cream inside, whereas we need a cone with a flat base. The challenge with spherical coordinates is setting integration limits for a flat base.) In cylindrical coordinates, the equation of a right-circular cone with its base lying in the $z = h$ plane and its apex at $(0,0,0)$ is $z = \frac{h}{a} r_c$. Observe that $z = 0$ when $r_c = 0$, which puts with the apex at $(0,0,0)$, and that $z = h$ when $r_c = a$, which puts the circular base in the $z = h$ plane. As r_c varies from 0 to a, z varies from $\frac{hr_c}{a}$ to h. See the diagram that follows.

$$V = \int_{r_c=0}^{a} \int_{\theta=0}^{2\pi} \int_{z=hr_c/a}^{h} r_c\, dr_c\, d\theta\, dz = \int_{r_c=0}^{a} [\theta]_{\theta=0}^{2\pi} [z]_{z=hr_c/a}^{h} r_c\, dr_c$$

$$V = \int_{r_c=0}^{a} (2\pi)\left(h - \frac{hr_c}{a}\right) r_c\, dr_c = 2\pi \int_{r_c=0}^{a} \left(hr_c - \frac{hr_c^2}{a}\right) dr_c = 2\pi \left[\frac{hr_c^2}{2} - \frac{hr_c^3}{3a}\right]_{r_c=0}^{a}$$

$$V = 2\pi\left(\frac{ha^2}{2} - \frac{ha^3}{3a}\right) = 2\pi\left(\frac{ha^2}{2} - \frac{ha^2}{3}\right) = 2\pi ha^2\left(\frac{1}{2} - \frac{1}{3}\right) = 2\pi ha^2\left(\frac{3}{6} - \frac{2}{6}\right) = \frac{2\pi ha^2}{6} = \boxed{\frac{\pi ha^2}{3}}$$

Note: In the diagram below, for a given value of r_c, z varies from $\frac{hr_c}{a}$ to h (the "base" of the cone, which is at the top). The surface of the cone has slope $\frac{h}{a}$, so that $z = \frac{hr_c}{a}$ describes the cone's surface. The answer, $V = \frac{1}{3}\pi a^2 h$, is the well-known formula for the volume of a cone. A common mistake is to use 0 for the lower limit of z for the cone shown below. (For a cone with the base in the xy plane, see Chapter 15, Problem 8.)

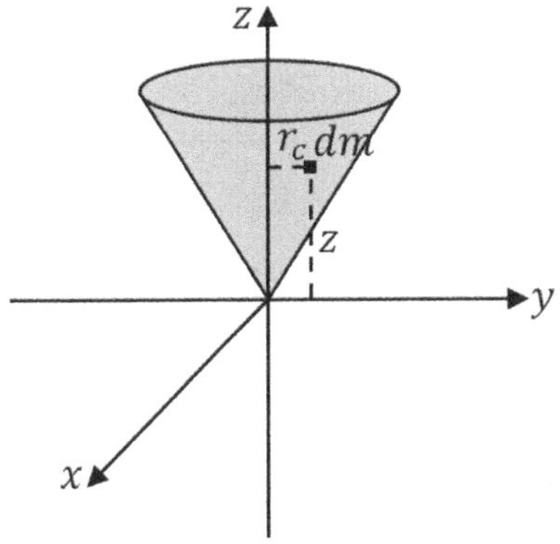

Chapter 14, Part C

❾ The line $y = 3 - x$ connects $(1,2)$ to $(2,1)$ since the slope is $m = \frac{1-2}{2-1} = -\frac{1}{1} = -1$ and the y-intercept is 3 (to see this, set $y = 2$ and $x = 1$ in $y = -x + b$ to get $2 = -1 + b$, and then add 1 to both sides to get $3 = b$).

$$I = \int_{x=1}^{2} \int_{y=1}^{3-x} xy\, dx\, dy = \int_{x=1}^{2} x \int_{y=1}^{3-x} y\, dy\, dx = \int_{x=1}^{2} x \left[\frac{y^2}{2}\right]_{y=1}^{3-x} dx$$

$$I = \frac{1}{2}\int_{x=1}^{2} x[(3-x)^2 - 1^2]\,dx = \frac{1}{2}\int_{x=1}^{2} x(9 - 6x + x^2 - 1)\,dx = \frac{1}{2}\int_{x=1}^{2} x(8 - 6x + x^2)\,dx$$

$$I = \frac{8}{2}\int_{x=1}^{2} x\,dx - \frac{6}{2}\int_{x=1}^{2} x^2\,dx + \frac{1}{2}\int_{x=1}^{2} x^3\,dx = 4\left[\frac{x^2}{2}\right]_{x=1}^{2} - 3\left[\frac{x^3}{3}\right]_{x=1}^{2} + \frac{1}{2}\left[\frac{x^4}{4}\right]_{x=1}^{2}$$

$$I = 2(2^2 - 1^2) - (2^3 - 1^3) + \frac{1}{8}(2^4 - 1^4) = 2(4-1) - (8-1) + \frac{1}{8}(16-1)$$

$$I = 2(3) - 7 + \frac{1}{8}(15) = 6 - 7 + \frac{15}{8} = -1 + \frac{15}{8} = -\frac{8}{8} + \frac{15}{8} = \boxed{\frac{7}{8}}$$

10 $I = \int_{r=0}^{4}\int_{\theta=0}^{2\pi}\int_{\varphi=0}^{\pi/2} z^2 r^2 \sin\varphi\,dr\,d\theta\,d\varphi$ Note: $z = r\cos\varphi$, where φ is the **polar** angle.

$$I = \int_{r=0}^{4}\int_{\theta=0}^{2\pi}\int_{\varphi=0}^{\pi/2} r^2\cos^2\varphi\, r^2 \sin\varphi\,dr\,d\theta\,d\varphi = \int_{r=0}^{a}\int_{\theta=0}^{2\pi}\int_{\varphi=0}^{\pi/2} r^4\cos^2\varphi \sin\varphi\,dr\,d\theta\,d\varphi$$

Notes: $r^2r^2 = r^4$ (where the first r^2 came from $z^2 = r^2\cos^2\varphi$). Let $u = \cos\varphi$ such that $du = -\sin\varphi\,d\varphi$. When $\varphi = 0$, $u = 1$. When $\varphi = \frac{\pi}{2}$, $u = 0$.

$$I = \left[\frac{r^5}{5}\right]_{r=0}^{4} [\theta]_{\theta=0}^{2\pi} \int_{u=1}^{0}(-u^2)\,du = -\frac{4^5}{5}(2\pi)\left[\frac{u^3}{3}\right]_{u=1}^{0} = -\frac{1024}{5}(2\pi)\left(\frac{0^3}{3} - \frac{1^3}{3}\right)$$

$$I = -\frac{2048\pi}{5}\left(-\frac{1}{3}\right) = \boxed{\frac{2048\pi}{15}}$$

Note: This is similar to the example, except that φ only varies up to $\frac{\pi}{2}$ and there is an extra factor of z^2 in the integrand.

11 When integrating over (x, y) coordinates, for a rectangle every limit is a constant.

$$I = \int_{x=0}^{2}\int_{y=0}^{4} xy\sqrt{1 + \left[\frac{\partial}{\partial x}(x^2 + y)\right]^2 + \left[\frac{\partial}{\partial y}(x^2 + y)\right]^2}\,dx\,dy$$

$$I = \int_{x=0}^{2}\int_{y=0}^{4} xy\sqrt{1 + (2x)^2 + 1^2}\,dx\,dy = \int_{x=0}^{2}\int_{y=0}^{4} xy\sqrt{2 + 4x^2}\,dx\,dy$$

Let $u = 2 + 4x^2$ such that $du = 8x\,dx$ and $\frac{du}{8} = x\,dx$. When $x = 0$, $u = 2$. When $x = 2$, $u = 2 + 4(2)^2 = 2 + 4(4) = 2 + 16 = 18$.

$$I = \int_{x=0}^{2} x\sqrt{2 + 4x^2}\,dx\left[\frac{y^2}{2}\right]_{y=0}^{4} = \int_{u=2}^{18}\sqrt{u}\,\frac{du}{8}\left(\frac{4^2}{2}\right) = \int_{u=2}^{18} u^{1/2}\frac{du}{8}(8) = \int_{u=2}^{18} u^{1/2}\,du$$

$$I = \left[\frac{2u^{3/2}}{3}\right]_{u=2}^{18} = \frac{2}{3}(18)^{3/2} - \frac{2}{3}(2)^{2/3} = \boxed{\frac{2}{3}\left(18^{3/2} - 2^{3/2}\right)} = \boxed{\frac{104}{3}\sqrt{2}} \approx \boxed{49.026}$$

Note: $18^{3/2} - 2^{3/2} = 18\sqrt{18} - 2\sqrt{2} = 18\sqrt{(9)(2)} - 2\sqrt{2} = 18(3)\sqrt{2} - 2\sqrt{2} = 54\sqrt{2} - 2\sqrt{2} = 52\sqrt{2}$ such that $\frac{2}{3}\left(18^{3/2} - 2^{3/2}\right) = \frac{2}{3}52\sqrt{2} = \frac{104}{3}\sqrt{2}$.

Chapter 14, Part D

⓬ For the surface $z(x,y) = 6 - 3x - 2y$, the flux integral becomes:

$\Phi = \iint_S \vec{\mathbf{F}} \cdot d\vec{\mathbf{A}} = \iint_S \left(-F_x \frac{\partial z}{\partial x} - F_y \frac{\partial z}{\partial y} + F_z\right) dxdy$

Compare $\vec{\mathbf{F}} = x\hat{\mathbf{i}} + y\hat{\mathbf{j}} + z\hat{\mathbf{k}}$ to $\vec{\mathbf{F}} = F_x\hat{\mathbf{i}} + F_y\hat{\mathbf{j}} + F_z\hat{\mathbf{k}}$ to see that $F_x = x$, $F_y = y$, and $F_z = z$. The plane $z = 6 - 3x - 2y$ intersects the axes at (2,0,0), (0,3,0), and (0,0,6) (to find these points, set two coordinates to zero and solve for the third in $z = 6 - 3x - 2y$.) Therefore, the part of the xy plane that lies below $z = 6 - 3x - 2y$ is the triangle with vertices at (0,0), (2,0), and (0,3). The line $y = 3 - \frac{3}{2}x$ connects (2,0), and (0,3) since the slope is $m = \frac{3-0}{0-2} = \frac{3}{-2} = -\frac{3}{2}$ and the y-intercept is 3. As x varies from 0 to 2, y varies from 0 to $3 - \frac{3}{2}x$.

$\Phi = \int_{x=0}^{2} \int_{y=0}^{3-3x/2} \left[-x\frac{\partial}{\partial x}(6 - 3x - 2y) - y\frac{\partial}{\partial y}(6 - 3x - 2y) + z\right] dx\,dy$

Replace z with $6 - 3x - 2y$ (since $z = 6 - 3x - 2y$).

$\Phi = \int_{x=0}^{2} \int_{y=0}^{3-3x/2} \left[-x(-3) - y\frac{\partial}{\partial y}(-2) + 6 - 3x - 2y\right] dx\,dy$

$\Phi = \int_{x=0}^{2} \int_{y=0}^{3-3x/2} (3x + 2y + 6 - 3x - 2y)\,dx\,dy = \int_{x=0}^{2} \int_{y=0}^{3-3x/2} 6\,dx\,dy$

$\Phi = 6\int_{x=0}^{2} [y]_{y=0}^{3-3x/2}\,dx = 6\int_{x=0}^{2}\left(3 - \frac{3}{2}x\right) dx = 6\left[3x - \frac{3x^2}{4}\right]_{x=0}^{2}$

$\Phi = 6\left[3(2) - \frac{3(2)^2}{4}\right] = 6\left[6 - \frac{3(4)}{4}\right] = 6\left(6 - \frac{12}{4}\right) = 6(6-3) = 6(3) = \boxed{18}$

⓭ $\vec{\mathbf{r}}_\varphi \times \vec{\mathbf{r}}_\theta = a^2\hat{\mathbf{i}}\cos\theta\sin^2\varphi + a^2\hat{\mathbf{j}}\sin\theta\sin^2\varphi + a^2\hat{\mathbf{k}}\sin\varphi\cos\varphi$ (as shown in the text for the chapter for the case of a sphere of radius a)

$\vec{\mathbf{F}} \cdot (\vec{\mathbf{r}}_\varphi \times \vec{\mathbf{r}}_\theta) = (z^3\hat{\mathbf{k}}) \cdot (3^2\hat{\mathbf{i}}\cos\theta\sin^2\varphi + 3^2\hat{\mathbf{j}}\sin\theta\sin^2\varphi + 3^2\hat{\mathbf{k}}\sin\varphi\cos\varphi)$

$\vec{\mathbf{F}} \cdot (\vec{\mathbf{r}}_\varphi \times \vec{\mathbf{r}}_\theta) = 9z^3\sin\varphi\cos\varphi = 9(3\cos\varphi)^3\sin\varphi\cos\varphi = 243\sin\varphi\cos^4\varphi$

$\Phi = \iint_S \vec{\mathbf{F}} \cdot (\vec{\mathbf{r}}_\varphi \times \vec{\mathbf{r}}_\theta) d\theta d\varphi = 243\int_{\theta=0}^{2\pi}\int_{\varphi=0}^{\pi} \sin\varphi\cos^4\varphi\,d\theta\,d\varphi = 243(2\pi)\int_{\varphi=0}^{\pi}\sin\varphi\cos^4\varphi\,d\varphi$

Let $u = \cos\varphi$, such that $du = -\sin\varphi\,d\varphi$. When $\varphi = 0$, $u = 1$. When $\varphi = \pi$, $u = -1$.

$\Phi = 486\pi\int_{u=1}^{-1} u^4(-du) = -486\pi\left[\frac{u^5}{5}\right]_{u=1}^{-1} = -486\pi\left[\frac{(-1)^5}{5} - \frac{1^5}{5}\right] = -486\pi\left(-\frac{1}{5} - \frac{1}{5}\right)$

$\Phi = -486\pi\left(-\frac{2}{5}\right) = \boxed{\frac{972\pi}{5}} \approx \boxed{610.73}$ Note: In this book, φ is the **polar** angle.

Alternative solution: $d\vec{\mathbf{A}} = \hat{\mathbf{n}}\,dA = \hat{\mathbf{r}}\,dA$, since $\hat{\mathbf{r}}$ is an outward unit vector for a sphere, such that $\vec{\mathbf{F}} \cdot d\vec{\mathbf{A}} = \vec{\mathbf{F}} \cdot \hat{\mathbf{r}}\,dA = z^3\hat{\mathbf{k}} \cdot \hat{\mathbf{r}}\,dA$. Since $\hat{\mathbf{r}} = \hat{\mathbf{i}}\cos\theta\sin\varphi + \hat{\mathbf{j}}\sin\theta\sin\varphi + \hat{\mathbf{k}}\cos\varphi$, $\hat{\mathbf{k}} \cdot \hat{\mathbf{r}} = \cos\varphi$, such that $\vec{\mathbf{F}} \cdot d\vec{\mathbf{A}} = z^3\cos\varphi\,dA = (3\cos\varphi)^3\cos\varphi\,dA = 27\cos^4\varphi\,dA$. For a sphere with radius 3, $dA = 3^2\sin\varphi\,d\theta d\varphi = 9\sin\varphi\,d\theta d\varphi$.

$$\Phi = \iint_S \vec{\mathbf{F}} \cdot d\vec{\mathbf{A}} = \int_{\theta=0}^{2\pi}\int_{\varphi=0}^{\pi} 27\cos^4\varphi\,(9\sin\varphi\,d\theta d\varphi) = 243\int_{\theta=0}^{2\pi}\int_{\varphi=0}^{\pi}\sin\varphi\cos^4\varphi\,d\theta\,d\varphi$$

⑭ For the surface $z(x,y) = x^2 + y^2$, the flux integral has an overall minus sign out front because the outward direction is oriented downward for this surface.

$$\Phi = -\iint_S \vec{\mathbf{F}} \cdot d\vec{\mathbf{A}} = \iint_S \left(-F_x\frac{\partial z}{\partial x} - F_y\frac{\partial z}{\partial y} + F_z\right) dxdy$$

Compare $\vec{\mathbf{F}} = y\hat{\mathbf{i}} - z\hat{\mathbf{k}}$ to $\vec{\mathbf{F}} = F_x\hat{\mathbf{i}} + F_y\hat{\mathbf{j}} + F_z\hat{\mathbf{k}}$ to see that $F_x = y$, $F_y = 0$, and $F_z = -z$.

$$\Phi = -\iint_S \left[-y\frac{\partial}{\partial x}(x^2 + y^2) - 0\frac{\partial}{\partial y}(x^2 + y^2) + (-z)\right] dxdy$$

Replace $-z$ with $-x^2 - y^2$ (since $z = x^2 + y^2$).

$$\Phi = -\iint_S \left[-y(2x) - 0\frac{\partial}{\partial y}(2y) - x^2 - y^2\right] dxdy = -\iint_S (-2xy - x^2 - y^2)\,dxdy$$

$$\Phi = \iint_S 2xy\,dxdy + \iint_S x^2\,dxdy + \iint_S y^2\,dxdy$$

Change variables to cylindrical coordinates: $dA = dxdy = r_c dr_c d\theta$. Note that $x^2 + y^2 = r_c^2$ such that $z = 9$ when $r_c = 3$. Recall that $x = r_c\cos\theta$ and $y = r_c\sin\theta$.

$$\Phi = \int_{r_c=0}^{3}\int_{\theta=0}^{2\pi} 2xy\,r_c dr_c\,d\theta + \int_{r_c=0}^{3}\int_{\theta=0}^{2\pi} x^2\,r_c dr_c\,d\theta + \int_{r_c=0}^{3}\int_{\theta=0}^{2\pi} y^2\,r_c dr_c\,d\theta$$

$$\Phi = \int_{r_c=0}^{3}\int_{\theta=0}^{2\pi} r_c^3 2\cos\theta\sin\theta\,dr_c\,d\theta + \int_{r_c=0}^{3}\int_{\theta=0}^{2\pi} r_c^3\cos^2\theta\,dr_c\,d\theta + \int_{r_c=0}^{3}\int_{\theta=0}^{2\pi} r_c^3\sin^2\theta\,dr_c$$

Recall the trig identities $\sin 2\theta = 2\cos\theta\sin\theta$, $\cos^2\theta = \frac{1+\cos 2\theta}{2}$, and $\sin^2\theta = \frac{1-\cos 2\theta}{2}$.

$$\Phi = \int_{\theta=0}^{2\pi}\left[\frac{r_c^4}{4}\right]_{r_c=0}^{3}\sin 2\theta\,d\theta + \int_{\theta=0}^{2\pi}\left[\frac{r_c^4}{4}\right]_{r_c=0}^{3}\frac{1+\cos 2\theta}{2}\,d\theta + \int_{\theta=0}^{2\pi}\left[\frac{r_c^4}{4}\right]_{r_c=0}^{3}\frac{1-\cos 2\theta}{2}\,d\theta$$

$$\Phi = \left(\frac{3^4}{4}\right)\left[-\frac{\cos 2\theta}{2}\right]_{\theta=0}^{2\pi} + \left(\frac{3^4}{4}\right)\left[\frac{\theta}{2} + \frac{\sin 2\theta}{4}\right]_{\theta=0}^{2\pi} + \left(\frac{3^4}{4}\right)\left[\frac{\theta}{2} - \frac{\sin 2\theta}{4}\right]_{\theta=0}^{2\pi}$$

$$\Phi = \left(\frac{81}{4}\right)\left(-\frac{\cos 4\pi}{2} + \frac{\cos 0}{2}\right) + \left(\frac{81}{4}\right)\left(\frac{2\pi}{2} + \frac{\sin 4\pi}{4} - \frac{0}{2} - \frac{\sin 0}{4}\right) + \left(\frac{81}{4}\right)\left(\frac{2\pi}{2} - \frac{\sin 4\pi}{4} - \frac{0}{2} + \frac{\sin 0}{4}\right)$$

$$\Phi = \frac{81}{4}\left(-\frac{1}{2} + \frac{1}{2}\right) + \frac{81}{4}(\pi) + \frac{81}{4}(\pi) = \frac{81}{4}(0) + \frac{81\pi}{4} + \frac{81\pi}{4} = \frac{162\pi}{4} = \frac{81\pi}{2}$$

For the disc $z = 9$, $r_c \leq 3$, the upward orientation is outward, such that $d\vec{\mathbf{A}} = \hat{\mathbf{k}}\,dA$.

$$\Phi = \iint_S \vec{\mathbf{F}} \cdot d\vec{\mathbf{A}} = \iint_S (y\hat{\mathbf{i}} - z\hat{\mathbf{k}}) \cdot \hat{\mathbf{k}}\,dA = \iint_S (-z)\,dA = -9\iint_S dA = -9A = -9(\pi 3^2) = -81\pi$$

Add these to get the net flux: $\Phi_{\text{net}} = \frac{81\pi}{2} - 81\pi = \frac{81\pi}{2} - \frac{162\pi}{2} = \boxed{-\frac{81\pi}{2}}$.

Chapter 15, Part A

1 $y_{cm} = \frac{1}{m}\int y\,dm = \frac{1}{m}\int y\,\lambda ds = \frac{1}{m}\int_{y=0}^{L} y\,\lambda dy = \frac{1}{m}\int_{y=0}^{L} y\left(k\sqrt{y}\right)dy = \frac{k}{m}\int_{y=0}^{L} y\left(y^{1/2}\right)dy$

$$y_{cm} = \frac{k}{m}\int_{y=0}^{L} y^{3/2}\,dy = \frac{k}{m}\left[\frac{2y^{5/2}}{5}\right]_{y=0}^{L} = \frac{k}{m}\left(\frac{2L^{5/2}}{5} - 0\right) = \frac{2kL^{5/2}}{5m}$$

$$m = \int dm = \int \lambda\,ds = \int_{y=0}^{L} \lambda\,dy = \int_{x=0}^{L} k\sqrt{y}\,dy = k\int_{y=0}^{L} y^{1/2}\,dy = k\left[\frac{2y^{3/2}}{3}\right]_{y=0}^{L} = \frac{2kL^{3/2}}{3}$$

$$y_{cm} = \frac{2kL^{5/2}}{5m} = \frac{2kL^{5/2}}{5}\frac{1}{m} = \frac{2kL^{5/2}}{5}\frac{3}{2kL^{3/2}} = \boxed{\frac{3L}{5}}$$

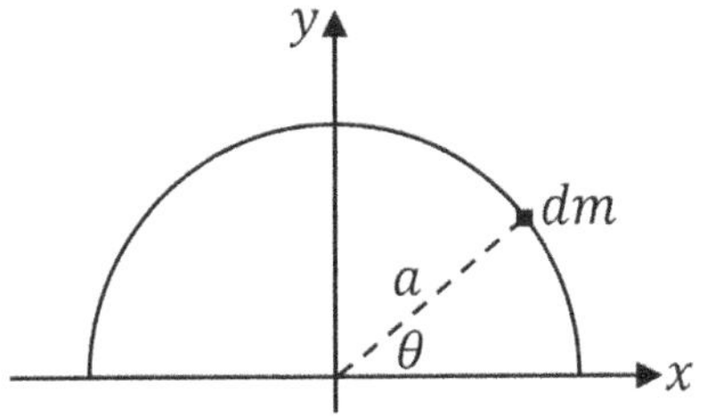

2 $y_{cm} = \frac{1}{m}\int y\,dm = \frac{1}{m}\int y\,\lambda ds = \frac{1}{m}\int_{\theta=0}^{\pi} y\left(\frac{m}{\pi a}\right)a d\theta = \frac{1}{\pi}\int_{\theta=0}^{\pi}(a\sin\theta)\,d\theta = \frac{a}{\pi}\int_{\theta=0}^{\pi}\sin\theta\,d\theta$

$$y_{cm} = \frac{a}{\pi}[-\cos\theta]_{\theta=0}^{\pi} = \frac{a}{\pi}(-\cos\pi + \cos 0) = \frac{a}{\pi}(1+1) = \boxed{\frac{2a}{\pi}} \approx \boxed{0.6366a} \quad , \quad x_{cm} = \boxed{0}$$

Notes: The mass per unit length of the semicircle is the mass divided by one-half of the circumference: $\lambda = \frac{m}{\pi a}$. Unlike the example with the solid disc, the semicircular arc actually has more of its mass above one-half of the radius.

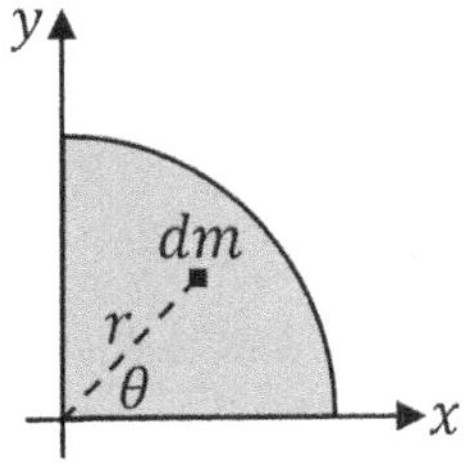

3 $x_{cm} = \frac{1}{m}\int x\,dm = \frac{1}{m}\int x\,\sigma dA = \frac{1}{m}\int_{r=0}^{a}\int_{\theta=0}^{\pi/2}(r\cos\theta)\left(\frac{m}{A}\right)rdrd\theta$

$$x_{cm} = \frac{1}{A}\int_{r=0}^{a}\int_{\theta=0}^{\pi/2} r^2\cos\theta\,dr\,d\theta = \frac{1}{\pi a^2/4}\left[\frac{r^3}{3}\right]_{r=0}^{a}[\sin\theta]_{\theta=0}^{\pi/2} = \frac{4}{\pi a^2}\frac{a^3}{3}\left(\sin\frac{\pi}{2} - \sin 0\right)$$

$$x_{cm} = \frac{4a}{3\pi}(1-0) = \boxed{\frac{4a}{3\pi}} \quad , \quad y_{cm} = x_{cm} = \boxed{\frac{4a}{3\pi}}$$

Notes: By symmetry, $y_{cm} = x_{cm}$. The mass per unit area of the semicircle is the mass divided by one-fourth of the area of a full circle: $\sigma = \frac{m}{A} = \frac{m}{\pi a^2/4} = \frac{4m}{\pi a^2}$.

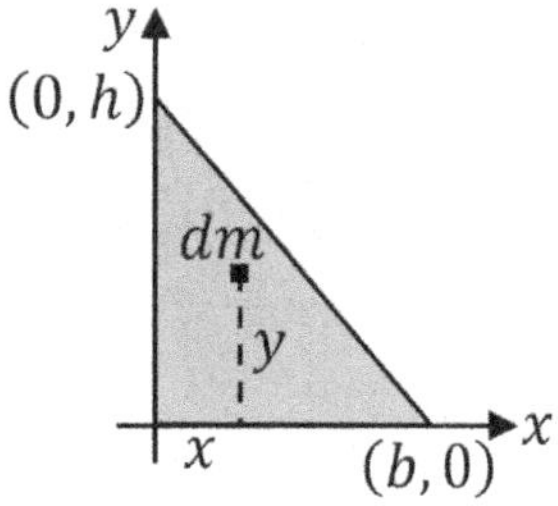

❹ The equation for the hypotenuse is $y = h - \frac{hx}{b}$ because the slope is $\frac{0-h}{b-0} = -\frac{h}{b}$ and the y-intercept is h. The area of the triangle is $A = \frac{1}{2}bh$.

$$x_{cm} = \frac{1}{m}\int x\,dm = \frac{1}{m}\int x\,\sigma dA = \frac{1}{m}\int_{x=0}^{b}\int_{y=0}^{h-hx/b} x\left(\frac{m}{A}\right)dxdy = \frac{1}{A}\int_{x=0}^{b} x[y]_{y=0}^{h-\frac{hx}{b}}\,dx$$

$$x_{cm} = \frac{1}{bh/2}\int_{x=0}^{b} x\left(h - \frac{hx}{b}\right)dx = \frac{2}{bh}\int_{x=0}^{b}\left(hx - \frac{hx^2}{b}\right)dx = \frac{2}{bh}\left[\frac{hx^2}{2} - \frac{hx^3}{3b}\right]_{x=0}^{b}$$

$$x_{cm} = \frac{2}{bh}\left(\frac{hb^2}{2} - \frac{hb^3}{3b}\right) = \frac{2}{bh}\left(\frac{hb^2}{2} - \frac{hb^2}{3}\right) = \frac{2hb^2}{2bh} - \frac{2hb^2}{3bh} = b - \frac{2b}{3} = \boxed{\frac{b}{3}}$$

$$y_{cm} = \frac{1}{m}\int y\,\sigma dA = \frac{1}{m}\int_{x=0}^{b}\int_{y=0}^{h-hx/b} y\left(\frac{m}{A}\right)dxdy = \frac{1}{A}\int_{x=0}^{b}\left[\frac{y^2}{2}\right]_{y=0}^{h-\frac{hx}{b}}dx$$

$$y_{cm} = \frac{1}{bh/2}\int_{x=0}^{b}\left[\frac{1}{2}\left(h - \frac{hx}{b}\right)^2\right]dx = \frac{2}{bh}\int_{x=0}^{b}\left(\frac{h^2}{2} - \frac{h^2x}{b} + \frac{h^2x^2}{2b^2}\right)dx = \frac{2}{bh}\left[\frac{h^2x}{2} - \frac{h^2x^2}{2b} + \frac{h^2x^3}{6b^2}\right]_{x=0}^{b}$$

$$y_{cm} = \frac{2}{bh}\left(\frac{h^2b}{2} - \frac{h^2b^2}{2b} + \frac{h^2b^3}{6b^2}\right) = \frac{2}{bh}\left(\frac{h^2b}{2} - \frac{h^2b}{2} + \frac{h^2b}{6}\right) = \frac{2}{bh}\left(\frac{h^2b}{6}\right) = \boxed{\frac{h}{3}}$$

Note: These answers agree with the well-known proof in geometry that the centroid of any triangle lies one-third of the distance along a median from the midpoint. By drawing medians and making similar triangles, you can show that this means that the centroid of the given right triangle lies at $\left(\frac{b}{3}, \frac{h}{3}\right)$.

Chapter 15, Part B

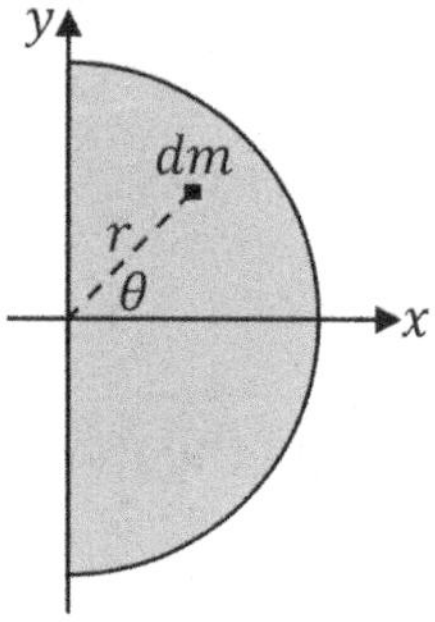

❺ $x_{cm} = \frac{1}{m}\int x\, dm = \frac{1}{m}\int x\, \sigma dA = \frac{1}{m}\int_{r=0}^{a}\int_{\theta=-\pi/2}^{\pi/2}(r\cos\theta)(kr)\, r dr d\theta$

$$x_{cm} = \frac{k}{m}\int_{r=0}^{a}\int_{\theta=-\pi/2}^{\pi/2} r^3\cos\theta\, dr\, d\theta = \frac{k}{m}\left[\frac{r^4}{4}\right]_{r=0}^{a}[\sin\theta]_{\theta=-\pi/2}^{\pi/2}$$

$$x_{cm} = \frac{k}{m}\frac{a^4}{4}\left[\sin\frac{\pi}{2} - \sin\left(-\frac{\pi}{2}\right)\right] = \frac{ka^4}{4m}[1-(-1)] = \frac{ka^4}{2m}$$

$$m = \int dm = \int \sigma\, dA = \int_{r=0}^{a}\int_{\theta=-\pi/2}^{\pi/2}(kr)\, r dr d\theta = k\int_{r=0}^{a}\int_{\theta=-\pi/2}^{\pi/2} r^2\, dr\, d\theta$$

$$m = k\left[\frac{r^3}{3}\right]_{r=0}^{a}[\theta]_{\theta=-\pi/2}^{\pi/2} = k\left(\frac{a^3}{3}\right)\left[\frac{\pi}{2} - \left(-\frac{\pi}{2}\right)\right] = \frac{ka^3}{3}\left(\frac{\pi}{2}+\frac{\pi}{2}\right) = \frac{ka^3}{3}(\pi) = \frac{\pi k a^3}{3}$$

$$x_{cm} = \frac{ka^4}{2m} = \frac{ka^4}{2}\frac{1}{m} = \frac{ka^4}{2}\frac{3}{\pi k a^3} = \boxed{\frac{3a}{2\pi}} \quad , \quad y_{cm} = \boxed{0}$$

❻ The plane $z = 9$ intersects the circular paraboloid $z = r_c^2$ at $r_c = 3$. Integrate z from r_c^2 (the bottom of the paraboloid) to 9 (the horizontal plane) and r_c from 0 to 3.

$$z_{cm} = \frac{1}{m}\int z\, dm = \frac{1}{m}\int z\, \rho dV = \frac{1}{m}\int_{r_c=0}^{3}\int_{\theta=0}^{2\pi}\int_{z=r_c^2}^{9} z\left(\frac{m}{V}\right)(r_c dr_c d\theta dz)$$

$$z_{cm} = \frac{1}{V}\int_{r_c=0}^{3}\int_{\theta=0}^{2\pi}\left[\frac{z^2}{2}\right]_{z=r_c^2}^{9} r_c dr_c\, d\theta = \frac{1}{V}\int_{r_c=0}^{3}\int_{\theta=0}^{2\pi}\left[\frac{9^2}{2} - \frac{(r_c^2)^2}{2}\right] r_c dr_c\, d\theta$$

$$z_{cm} = \frac{1}{V}\int_{r_c=0}^{3}\int_{\theta=0}^{2\pi}\left(\frac{81}{2} - \frac{r_c^4}{2}\right) r_c\, dr_c\, d\theta = \frac{1}{V}\int_{r_c=0}^{3}\int_{\theta=0}^{2\pi}\left(\frac{81 r_c}{2} - \frac{r_c^5}{2}\right) dr_c\, d\theta$$

$$z_{cm} = \frac{1}{V}\left[\frac{81 r_c^2}{4} - \frac{r_c^6}{12}\right]_{r_c=0}^{3}[\theta]_{\theta=0}^{2\pi} = \frac{1}{V}\left[\frac{81(3)^2}{4} - \frac{3^6}{12}\right](2\pi) = \frac{2\pi}{V}\left(\frac{729}{4} - \frac{729}{12}\right) = \frac{2\pi(729)}{V}\left(\frac{1}{4} - \frac{1}{12}\right)$$

$$z_{cm} = \frac{2\pi(729)}{V}\left(\frac{3}{12} - \frac{1}{12}\right) = \frac{2\pi(729)}{V}\left(\frac{2}{12}\right) = \frac{2\pi(729)}{V}\left(\frac{1}{6}\right) = \frac{729\pi}{3V} = \frac{243\pi}{V}$$

$$V = \int dV = \int_{r_c=0}^{3}\int_{\theta=0}^{2\pi}\int_{z=r_c^2}^{9} r_c\, dr_c\, d\theta\, dz = \int_{r_c=0}^{3}\int_{\theta=0}^{2\pi}[z]_{z=r_c^2}^{9} r_c dr_c\, d\theta$$

$$V = \int_{r_c=0}^{3}\int_{\theta=0}^{2\pi}(9 - r_c^2)\, r_c dr_c\, d\theta = \int_{r_c=0}^{3}\int_{\theta=0}^{2\pi}(9r_c - r_c^3)\, dr_c\, d\theta = \left[\frac{9r_c^2}{2} - \frac{r_c^4}{4}\right]_{r_c=0}^{3}[\theta]_{\theta=0}^{2\pi}$$

$$V = \left[\frac{9(3)^2}{2} - \frac{3^4}{4}\right](2\pi) = \left(\frac{81}{2} - \frac{81}{4}\right)(2\pi) = \left(\frac{162}{4} - \frac{81}{4}\right)(2\pi) = \left(\frac{81}{4}\right)(2\pi) = \frac{81\pi}{2}$$

$$z_{cm} = \frac{243\pi}{V} = 243\pi\frac{1}{V} = 243\pi\frac{2}{81\pi} = (3)(2) = \boxed{6} \quad , \quad x_{cm} = y_{cm} = \boxed{0}$$

Note: It should make sense that $z_{cm} = 6$ is greater than one-half of 9, since more mass lies above the halfway point ($z = 4.5$) than below it.

❼ $z_{cm} = \frac{1}{m}\int z\,dm = \frac{1}{m}\int (r\cos\varphi)\,\rho dV = \int_{r=0}^{a}\int_{\theta=0}^{2\pi}\int_{\varphi=0}^{\pi/2} r\cos\varphi\left(\frac{m}{V}\right) r^2 \sin\varphi\, dr d\theta d\varphi$

$$z_{cm} = \frac{1}{V}\int_{r=0}^{a}\int_{\theta=0}^{2\pi}\int_{\varphi=0}^{\pi/2} r^3 \sin\varphi\cos\varphi\, dr\, d\theta\, d\varphi = \frac{1}{2\pi a^3/3}\left[\frac{r^4}{4}\right]_{r=0}^{a} [\theta]_{\theta=0}^{2\pi}\int_{\varphi=0}^{\pi/2}\frac{\sin(2\varphi)}{2}\,d\varphi$$

Recall the trig identity $\sin(2\varphi) = 2\sin\varphi\cos\varphi$, such that $\frac{\sin(2\varphi)}{2} = \sin\varphi\cos\varphi$.

$$z_{cm} = \frac{3}{2\pi a^3}\left(\frac{a^4}{4}\right)(2\pi)\left[-\frac{\cos(2\varphi)}{4}\right]_{\varphi=0}^{\pi/2} = \frac{3a}{4}\left(-\frac{\cos\pi}{4} + \frac{\cos 0}{4}\right) = \frac{3a}{4}\left[-\left(-\frac{1}{4}\right) + \frac{1}{4}\right]$$

$$z_{cm} = \frac{3a}{4}\left(\frac{1}{4} + \frac{1}{4}\right) = \frac{3a}{4}\left(\frac{1}{2}\right) = \boxed{\frac{3a}{8}} \quad , \quad x_{cm} = y_{cm} = \boxed{0}$$

Notes: It should make sense that $z_{cm} = \frac{3a}{8} = 0.375a$ is less than $\frac{a}{2}$, since more mass lies below the halfway point than above it. The volume of the solid hemisphere is the mass divided by the volume of **one-half** of a sphere: $\rho = \frac{m}{V} = \frac{m}{2\pi a^3/3} = \frac{3m}{2\pi a^3}$.

❽ This integral is simplest in cylindrical coordinates. (It is actually more challenging in spherical coordinates. Note that $\varphi = c$ in spherical coordinates makes a "cone" with a rounded "base" like an ice-cream cone with one scoop of ice-cream inside, whereas we need a cone with a flat base. The challenge with spherical coordinates is setting integration limits for a flat base.) In cylindrical coordinates, the equation of a right-circular cone with its base lying in the xy plane and its apex at $(0,0,h)$ is $z = h - \frac{h}{a}r_c$. Observe that $z = h$ when $r_c = 0$, which puts with the apex at $(0,0,h)$, and that $z = 0$ when $r_c = a$, which puts the circular base in the xy plane. **Note**: This cone is different from the cone of Chapter 14, Problem 8, since the apex of this cone lies at $(0,0,h)$, **not** the origin. The limits for z are different for this problem.

$$z_{cm} = \frac{1}{m}\int z\,dm = \frac{1}{m}\int z\,\rho dV = \frac{1}{m}\int_{r_c=0}^{a}\int_{\theta=0}^{2\pi}\int_{z=0}^{h-hr_c/a} z\left(\frac{m}{V}\right)(r_c dr_c d\theta dz)$$

$$z_{cm} = \frac{1}{V}\int_{r_c=0}^{a}\int_{\theta=0}^{2\pi}\left[\frac{z^2}{2}\right]_{z=0}^{h-\frac{hr_c}{a}} r_c dr_c\, d\theta = \frac{1}{\pi a^2 h/3}\int_{r_c=0}^{a}\int_{\theta=0}^{2\pi}\left[\frac{1}{2}\left(h - \frac{hr_c}{a}\right)^2\right] r_c dr_c\, d\theta$$

$$z_{cm} = \frac{3}{\pi a^2 h}\int_{r_c=0}^{a}\int_{\theta=0}^{2\pi}\frac{1}{2}\left(h^2 - \frac{2h^2 r_c}{a} + \frac{h^2 r_c^2}{a^2}\right) r_c\, dr_c\, d\theta$$

$$z_{cm} = \frac{3}{2\pi a^2 h}\int_{r_c=0}^{a}\int_{\theta=0}^{2\pi}\left(h^2 r_c - \frac{2h^2 r_c^2}{a} + \frac{h^2 r_c^3}{a^2}\right) dr_c\, d\theta$$

$$z_{cm} = \frac{3}{2\pi a^2 h}\left[\left(\frac{h^2 r_c^2}{2} - \frac{2h^2 r_c^3}{3a} + \frac{h^2 r_c^4}{4a^2}\right)\right]_{r_c=0}^{a} [\theta]_{\theta=0}^{2\pi} = \frac{3}{2\pi a^2 h}\left(\frac{h^2 a^2}{2} - \frac{2h^2 a^3}{3a} + \frac{h^2 a^4}{4a^2}\right)(2\pi)$$

$$z_{cm} = \frac{3(2\pi)}{2\pi a^2 h}\left(\frac{h^2a^2}{2} - \frac{2h^2a^2}{3} + \frac{h^2a^2}{4}\right) = \frac{3}{a^2h}\, h^2a^2\left(\frac{1}{2} - \frac{2}{3} + \frac{1}{4}\right) = 3h\left(\frac{6}{12} - \frac{8}{12} + \frac{3}{12}\right)$$

$$z_{cm} = 3h\left(\frac{6-8+3}{12}\right) = 3h\left(\frac{1}{12}\right) = \boxed{\frac{h}{4}} \quad , \quad x_{cm} = y_{cm} = \boxed{0}$$

Notes: It should make sense that $z_{cm} = \frac{h}{4}$ is less than one-half of h, since more mass lies below the halfway point than above it. That is, the center of mass lies closer to the base than to the apex. The volume of a right-circular cone is $V = \frac{Bh}{3} = \frac{\pi a^2 h}{3}$.

Chapter 15, Part C

❾ The x-axis is the axis of rotation. The distance from each dm to the x-axis is y. Therefore, $r_\perp = y$ in this problem.

$$I = \int r_\perp^2\, dm = \int y^2\, \lambda ds = \int_{y=0}^{L} y^2\left(\frac{m}{L}\right) dy = \frac{m}{L}\int_{y=0}^{L} y^2\, dy = \frac{m}{L}\left[\frac{y^3}{3}\right]_{y=0}^{L} = \frac{m}{L}\left(\frac{L^3}{3}\right) = \boxed{\frac{mL^2}{3}}$$

Note: The moment of inertia $\left(\frac{mL^2}{3}\right)$ is larger in this problem than it was in the similar example $\left(\text{where } \frac{mL^2}{12}\right)$ because more mass is farther from the axis on average (since the axis is at the end of the rod in this problem, but was instead at the center of the rod in the similar example). The two formulas for the moment of inertia of the rod can be related via the parallel-axis theorem.

❿ The distance from each dm to the line $x = \frac{L}{4}$ is $x - \frac{L}{4}$. Therefore, $r_\perp = x - \frac{L}{4}$.

$$I = \int r_\perp^2\, dm = \int \left(x - \frac{L}{4}\right)^2 \lambda ds = \int_{x=0}^{L}\left(x^2 - \frac{2xL}{4} + \frac{L^2}{16}\right)(kx)\, dx = k\int_{x=0}^{L}\left(x^3 - \frac{x^2L}{2} + \frac{xL^2}{16}\right) dx$$

$$I = k\left[\frac{x^4}{4} - \frac{x^3L}{6} + \frac{x^2L^2}{32}\right]_{x=0}^{L} = k\left(\frac{L^4}{4} - \frac{L^3L}{6} + \frac{L^2L^2}{32}\right) = k\left(\frac{L^4}{4} - \frac{L^4}{6} + \frac{L^4}{32}\right) = \frac{k}{2}\left(\frac{L^4}{2} - \frac{L^4}{3} + \frac{L^4}{16}\right)$$

$$I = \frac{kL^4}{2}\left(\frac{1}{2} - \frac{1}{3} + \frac{1}{16}\right) = \frac{kL^4}{2}\left(\frac{24}{48} - \frac{16}{48} + \frac{3}{48}\right) = \frac{kL^4}{2}\left(\frac{11}{48}\right)$$

$$m = \int dm = \int \lambda\, ds = \int_{x=0}^{L} \lambda\, dx = \int_{x=0}^{L} kx\, dx = k\left[\frac{x^2}{2}\right]_{x=0}^{L} = \frac{kL^2}{2}$$

$$I = \frac{kL^4}{2}\left(\frac{11}{48}\right) = \left(\frac{kL^2}{2}\right)L^2\left(\frac{11}{48}\right) = mL^2\left(\frac{11}{48}\right) = \boxed{\frac{11mL^2}{48}}$$

⓫ This problem is similar to the example with a uniform solid disc, but with a few important exceptions:

- $dm = \lambda ds$ (instead of σdA) for a very thin ring (assuming that it is infinitesimally thin; if a problem involves a ring with finite thickness, the problem will give you both inner and outer radii).
- $ds = a d\theta$ and $x = a\cos\theta$ (since every dm lies on the circumference).
- $r_\perp = x$ because the axis of integration is the y-axis. The distance from each dm to the y-axis is equal to x, where $x = a\cos\theta$.

$$I = \int r_\perp^2\, dm = \int x^2\, \lambda ds = \int_{\theta=0}^{2\pi} (a\cos\theta)^2 \left(\frac{m}{2\pi a}\right)(a d\theta) = \frac{m}{2\pi a}\int_{\theta=0}^{2\pi} (a^2\cos^2\theta)\, a\, d\theta$$

Recall the trig identity $\cos^2\theta = \frac{1+\cos 2\theta}{2}$.

$$I = \frac{ma^2}{2\pi}\int_{\theta=0}^{2\pi} \cos^2\theta\, d\theta = \frac{ma^2}{2\pi}\int_{\theta=0}^{2\pi} \frac{1+\cos 2\theta}{2}\, d\theta = \frac{ma^2}{2\pi}\left[\frac{\theta}{2} + \frac{\sin 2\theta}{4}\right]_{\theta=0}^{2\pi}$$

$$I = \frac{ma^2}{2\pi}\left(\frac{2\pi}{2} - 0 + \frac{\sin 4\pi}{4} - \frac{\sin 0}{4}\right) = \frac{ma^2}{2\pi}(\pi + 0 - 0) = \boxed{\frac{ma^2}{2}}$$

Notes: The moment of inertia of a very thin ring is $\frac{ma^2}{2}$ in flipping mode (which is the case here, where the axis of rotation is a diameter), whereas the moment of inertia of a very thin ring is ma^2 in rolling mode (which would be about the z-axis instead). If you look up the moment of inertia in a table, make sure that you don't check your answer with the common expression for a "rolling" ring since this one is "flipping."

⓬ For rotation about the z-axis, $r_\perp = r$ because r in 2D polar coordinates is the distance from the origin. (Since the disc lies in the xy plane, r is also the distance from the z-axis.)

$$I = \int r_\perp^2\, dm = \int r^2\, \sigma dA = \int_{r=0}^{a}\int_{\theta=0}^{2\pi} r^2 (kr)\, r dr d\theta = k\int_{r=0}^{a}\int_{\theta=0}^{2\pi} r^4\, dr\, d\theta$$

$$I = k\left[\frac{r^5}{5}\right]_{r=0}^{a} [\theta]_{\theta=0}^{2\pi} = k\left(\frac{a^5}{5}\right)(2\pi) = \frac{2\pi k a^5}{5}$$

$$m = \int dm = \int \sigma\, dA = \int_{r=0}^{a}\int_{\theta=0}^{2\pi} (kr)\, r dr d\theta = k\int_{r=0}^{a}\int_{\theta=0}^{2\pi} r^2\, dr\, d\theta$$

$$m = k\left[\frac{r^3}{3}\right]_{r=0}^{a} [\theta]_{\theta=0}^{2\pi} = k\left(\frac{a^3}{3}\right)(2\pi) = \frac{2\pi k a^3}{3}$$

$$I = \frac{2\pi k a^5}{5} = \frac{2\pi k a^3 a^2}{5}\frac{3}{3} = \frac{2\pi k a^3}{3}\frac{3a^2}{5} = m\frac{3a^2}{5} = \boxed{\frac{3ma^2}{5}}$$

Chapter 15, Part D

⑬ This problem is similar to the example with a uniform solid sphere, but with a few important exceptions:

- $dm = \sigma dA$ (instead of ρdV) for a very thin hollow sphere (assuming that it is infinitesimally thin; if the thickness were finite, the problem would give both the inner and outer radii instead of just one radius).
- $dA = a^2 \sin\varphi \, d\theta d\varphi$. Every dm lies on the surface of the sphere.
- $r_\perp = a \sin\varphi$ because the axis of integration is the y-axis. The distance from each dm to the y-axis is equal to $a \sin\varphi$. See the diagram in the example, but note that dm lies on the surface, a distance a from the origin.
- The mass per unit area is $\sigma = \frac{m}{A} = \frac{m}{4\pi a^2}$ because the surface area of a sphere equals $4\pi a^2$.

$$I = \int r_\perp^2 \, dm = \int (a \sin\varphi)^2 \sigma dA = \int_{\theta=0}^{2\pi} \int_{\varphi=0}^{\pi} a^2 \sin^2\varphi \left(\frac{m}{4\pi a^2}\right) a^2 \sin\varphi \, d\theta \, d\varphi$$

$$I = \frac{ma^4}{4\pi a^2} \int_{\theta=0}^{2\pi} \int_{\varphi=0}^{\pi} \sin^3\varphi \, d\theta \, d\varphi = \frac{ma^2}{4\pi} [\theta]_{\theta=0}^{2\pi} \int_{\varphi=0}^{\pi} \sin^3\varphi \, d\varphi$$

Recall the trig identity $\sin^2\varphi = 1 - \cos^2\varphi$.

$$I = \frac{ma^2}{4\pi}(2\pi) \int_{\varphi=0}^{\pi} \sin\varphi \, (1 - \cos^2\varphi) \, d\varphi = \frac{ma^2}{2} \int_{\varphi=0}^{\pi} \sin\varphi \, d\varphi - \frac{ma^2}{2} \int_{\varphi=0}^{\pi} \sin\varphi \cos^2\varphi \, d\varphi$$

Let $u = \cos\varphi$ such that $du = -\sin\varphi \, d\varphi$. When $\varphi = 0, u = 1$. When $\varphi = \pi, u = -1$.

$$I = \frac{ma^2}{2} [-\cos\varphi]_{\varphi=0}^{\pi} - \frac{ma^2}{2} \int_{u=1}^{-1} u^2 \, (-du) = \frac{ma^2}{2}(-\cos\pi + \cos 0) + \frac{ma^2}{2} \left[\frac{u^3}{3}\right]_{u=1}^{-1}$$

Note: The two minus signs made a plus sign for the second term.

$$I = \frac{ma^2}{2}(1+1) + \frac{ma^2}{2}\left[\frac{(-1)^3}{3} - \frac{1^3}{3}\right] = \frac{ma^2}{2}(2) + \frac{ma^2}{2}\left(-\frac{1}{3} - \frac{1}{3}\right)$$

$$I = ma^2 + \frac{ma^2}{2}\left(-\frac{2}{3}\right) = ma^2 - \frac{ma^2}{3} = \frac{3ma^2}{3} - \frac{ma^2}{3} = \boxed{\frac{2ma^2}{3}}$$

Note: It should make sense that the moment of inertia of a hollow sphere $\left(\frac{2ma^2}{3}\right)$ is larger than the moment of inertia of a solid sphere $\left(\frac{2ma^2}{5}\right)$, as $\frac{2}{3} > \frac{2}{5}$, because a greater percentage of the mass is farther away from the axis of rotation on average for the hollow sphere. In the case of the hollow sphere, all of the mass lies on the surface of the sphere.

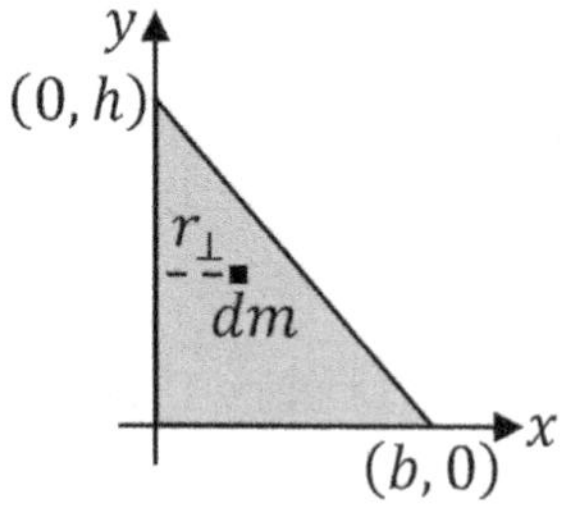

⓮ The y-axis is the axis of rotation. The distance from each dm to the y-axis is x. Therefore, $r_\perp = x$ in this problem.

$$I = \int r_\perp^2\, dm = \int x^2\, \sigma dA = \int_{x=0}^{b} \int_{y=0}^{h-hx/b} x^2 \left(\frac{m}{A}\right) dxdy = \frac{m}{A} \int_{x=0}^{b} x^2 [y]_{y=0}^{h-\frac{hx}{b}}\, dx$$

$$I = \frac{m}{bh/2} \int_{x=0}^{b} x^2 \left(h - \frac{hx}{b}\right) dx = \frac{2m}{bh} \int_{x=0}^{b} \left(hx^2 - \frac{hx^3}{b}\right) dx = \frac{2m}{bh} \left[\frac{hx^3}{3} - \frac{hx^4}{4b}\right]_{x=0}^{b}$$

$$I = \frac{2m}{bh}\left(\frac{hb^3}{3} - \frac{hb^4}{4b}\right) = \frac{2m}{bh}\left(\frac{hb^3}{3} - \frac{hb^3}{4}\right) = \frac{2m}{bh}(hb^3)\left(\frac{1}{3} - \frac{1}{4}\right) = 2mb^2\left(\frac{4}{12} - \frac{3}{12}\right) = \boxed{\frac{mb^2}{6}}$$

⓯ $I = \int r_\perp^2\, dm = \int (r \sin\varphi)^2 \rho dV = \int_{r=0}^{a} \int_{\theta=0}^{2\pi} \int_{\varphi=0}^{\pi} r^2 \sin^2\varphi\, (kr)\, r^2 \sin\varphi\, dr d\theta d\varphi$

$$I = k \int_{r=0}^{a} \int_{\theta=0}^{2\pi} \int_{\varphi=0}^{\pi} r^5 \sin^3\varphi\, dr\, d\theta\, d\varphi = k \left[\frac{r^6}{6}\right]_{r=0}^{a} [\theta]_{\theta=0}^{2\pi} \int_{\varphi=0}^{\pi} \sin^3\varphi\, d\varphi$$

Recall the trig identity $\sin^2\varphi = 1 - \cos^2\varphi$.

$$I = k\left(\frac{a^6}{6}\right)(2\pi) \int_{\varphi=0}^{\pi} \sin\varphi\, (1 - \cos^2\varphi)\, d\varphi = \frac{\pi k a^6}{3} \int_{\varphi=0}^{\pi} \sin\varphi\, d\varphi - \frac{\pi k a^6}{3} \int_{\varphi=0}^{\pi} \sin\varphi \cos^2\varphi\, d\varphi$$

Let $u = \cos\varphi$ such that $du = -\sin\varphi\, d\varphi$. When $\varphi = 0$, $u = 1$. When $\varphi = \pi$, $u = -1$.

$$I = \frac{\pi k a^6}{3} [-\cos\varphi]_{\varphi=0}^{\pi} - \frac{\pi k a^6}{3} \int_{u=1}^{-1} u^2\, (-du) = \frac{\pi k a^6}{3}(-\cos\pi + 1) + \frac{\pi k a^6}{3}\left[\frac{u^3}{3}\right]_{u=1}^{-1}$$

Note: The two minus signs made a plus sign for the second term.

$$I = \frac{\pi k a^6}{3}(1+1) + \frac{\pi k a^6}{3}\left[\frac{(-1)^3}{3} - \frac{1^3}{3}\right] = \frac{\pi k a^6}{3}(2) + \frac{\pi k a^6}{3}\left(-\frac{1}{3} - \frac{1}{3}\right)$$

$$I = \frac{\pi k a^6}{3}(2) + \frac{\pi k a^6}{3}\left(-\frac{2}{3}\right) = \frac{\pi k a^6}{3}\left(2 - \frac{2}{3}\right) = \frac{\pi k a^6}{3}\left(\frac{6}{3} - \frac{2}{3}\right) = \frac{\pi k a^6}{3}\left(\frac{4}{3}\right) = \frac{4\pi k a^6}{9}$$

$$m = \int dm = \int \rho\, dV = \int_{r=0}^{a} \int_{\theta=0}^{2\pi} \int_{\varphi=0}^{\pi} (kr)\, r^2 \sin\varphi\, dr d\theta d\varphi$$

$$m = k \int_{r=0}^{a} \int_{\theta=0}^{2\pi} \int_{\varphi=0}^{\pi} r^3 \sin\varphi\, dr\, d\theta\, d\varphi = k \left[\frac{r^4}{4}\right]_{r=0}^{a} [\theta]_{\theta=0}^{2\pi} [-\cos\varphi]_{\theta=0}^{\pi}$$

$$m = k\left(\frac{a^4}{4}\right)(2\pi)(-\cos\pi + \cos 0) = \frac{\pi k a^4}{2}[-(-1) + 1] = \frac{\pi k a^4}{2}(1+1) = \frac{\pi k a^4}{2}(2) = \pi k a^4$$

$$I = \frac{4\pi k a^6}{9} = \frac{4\pi k a^4 a^2}{9} = \frac{4(\pi k a^4) a^2}{9} = \boxed{\frac{4ma^2}{9}}$$

⓰ See the notes at the beginning of the solution to Problem 8 regarding the choice of coordinate system and the limits of integration. Note that $r_\perp = r_c$ for the cone.

$$I = \int r_\perp^2 \, dm = \int_{r_c=0}^{a} \int_{\theta=0}^{2\pi} \int_{z=0}^{h-hr_c/a} r_c^2 \left(\frac{m}{V}\right) (r_c dr_c d\theta dz)$$

$$I = \frac{m}{V} \int_{r_c=0}^{a} \int_{\theta=0}^{2\pi} [z]_{z=0}^{h-\frac{hr_c}{a}} r_c^3 dr_c \, d\theta = \frac{m}{\pi a^2 h/3} \int_{r_c=0}^{a} \int_{\theta=0}^{2\pi} \left(h - \frac{hr_c}{a}\right) r_c^3 dr_c \, d\theta$$

$$I = \frac{3m}{\pi a^2 h} \int_{r_c=0}^{a} \int_{\theta=0}^{2\pi} \left(hr_c^3 - \frac{hr_c^4}{a}\right) dr_c \, d\theta = \frac{3m}{\pi a^2 h} \left[\frac{hr_c^4}{4} - \frac{hr_c^5}{5a}\right]_{r_c=0}^{a} [\theta]_{\theta=0}^{2\pi}$$

$$I = \frac{3m}{\pi a^2 h} \left(\frac{ha^4}{4} - \frac{ha^5}{5a}\right)(2\pi) = \frac{6m}{a^2 h} \left(\frac{ha^4}{4} - \frac{ha^4}{5}\right) = \frac{6m}{a^2 h} (ha^4) \left(\frac{1}{4} - \frac{1}{5}\right) = 6ma^2 \left(\frac{5}{20} - \frac{4}{20}\right)$$

$$I = 6ma^2 \left(\frac{1}{20}\right) = \boxed{\frac{3ma^2}{10}}$$

Note: The volume of a right-circular cone is $V = \frac{Bh}{3} = \frac{\pi a^2 h}{3}$.

WAS THIS BOOK HELPFUL?

Much effort and thought were put into this book, such as:

- Including a variety of useful skills from multivariable calculus and from vector calculus.
- Introducing the main ideas at the beginning of each chapter.
- Providing examples to serve as a helpful guide.
- Working out the solutions to all of the problems at the back of the book.

If you appreciate the effort that went into making this book possible, there is a simple way that you could show it:

<u>Please take a moment to post an honest review.</u>

For example, you can review this book at Amazon.com or Goodreads.com.

Even a short review can be helpful and will be much appreciated. If you are not sure what to write, following are a few ideas, though it is best to describe what is important to you.

- Was it helpful to have the full solution to every problem at the back of the book?
- Were the examples useful?
- Were you able to understand the ideas at the beginning of the chapter?
- Did this book offer good practice for you?
- Would you recommend this book to others? If so, why?

Do you believe that you found a mistake? Please email the author, Chris McMullen, at greekphysics@yahoo.com to ask about it. One of two things will happen:

- You might discover that it wasn't a mistake after all and learn why.
- You might be right, in which case the author will be grateful and future readers will benefit from the correction. Everyone is human.

ABOUT THE AUTHOR

Dr. Chris McMullen has over 20 years of experience teaching university physics in California, Oklahoma, Pennsylvania, and Louisiana. Dr. McMullen is also an author of math and science workbooks. Whether in the classroom or as a writer, Dr. McMullen loves sharing knowledge and the art of motivating and engaging students.

The author earned his Ph.D. in phenomenological high-energy physics (particle physics) from Oklahoma State University in 2002. Originally from California, Chris McMullen earned his Master's degree from California State University, Northridge, where his thesis was in the field of electron spin resonance.

As a physics teacher, Dr. McMullen observed that many students lack fluency in fundamental math skills. In an effort to help students of all ages and levels master basic math skills, he published a series of math workbooks on arithmetic, fractions, long division, word problems, algebra, geometry, trigonometry, logarithms, and calculus entitled *Improve Your Math Fluency*. Dr. McMullen has also published a variety of science books, including astronomy, chemistry, and physics workbooks.

Author, Chris McMullen, Ph.D.

Essential
CALCULUS
Skills Practice Workbook
with Full Solutions
$\frac{d}{dx}\tan(5x)$
$\int \sqrt{1-x^2}\,dx$
Chris McMullen, Ph.D.

50 CHALLENGING
CALCULUS
PROBLEMS
$A = \int_{x=-2}^{2} (4-x^2)\,dx$
y
y = 4
y = x²
x
FULLY SOLVED
Chris McMullen, Ph.D.

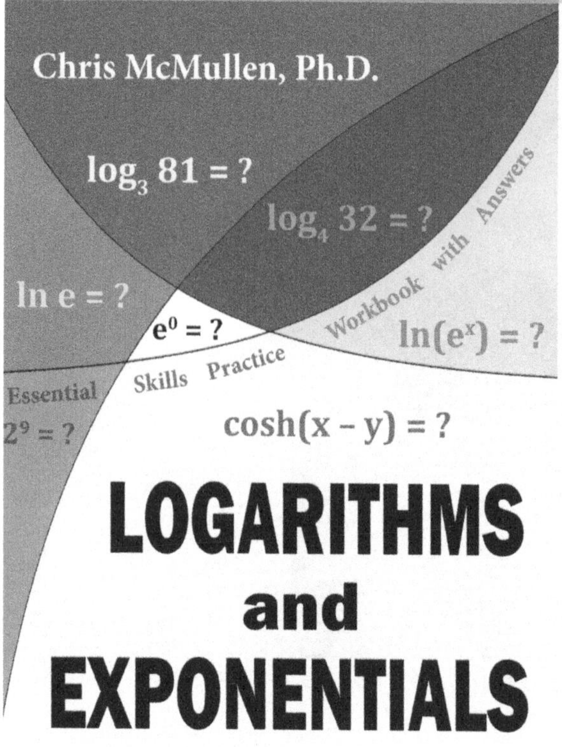
Chris McMullen, Ph.D.
log₃ 81 = ?
log₄ 32 = ?
ln e = ?
e⁰ = ?
ln(eˣ) = ?
Essential Skills Practice Workbook with Answers
2⁹ = ?
cosh(x − y) = ?
LOGARITHMS
and
EXPONENTIALS

The FOUR-COLOR
THEOREM
and Basic GRAPH
THEORY
M
J
E
D
A
F
K
C
B
I
G
H
L
Chris McMullen, Ph.D.

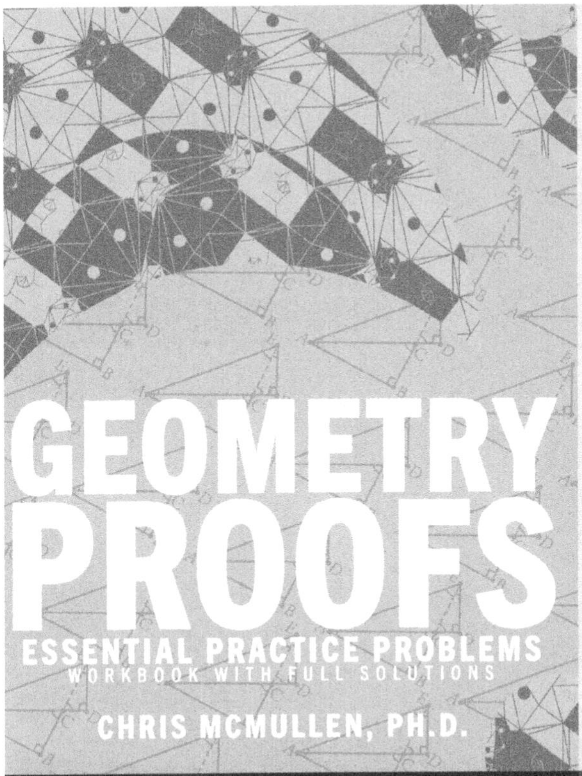
GEOMETRY
PROOFS
ESSENTIAL PRACTICE PROBLEMS
WORKBOOK WITH FULL SOLUTIONS
CHRIS MCMULLEN, PH.D.

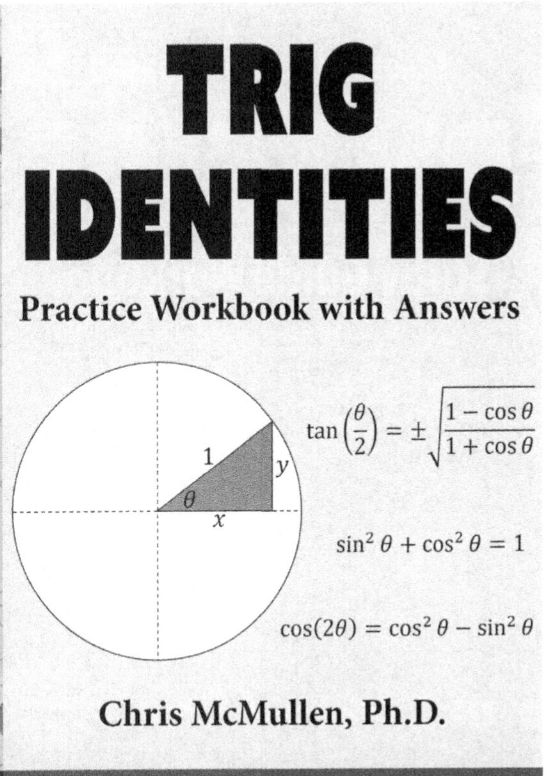
TRIG
IDENTITIES
Practice Workbook with Answers
$\tan\left(\frac{\theta}{2}\right) = \pm\sqrt{\frac{1-\cos\theta}{1+\cos\theta}}$
$\sin^2\theta + \cos^2\theta = 1$
$\cos(2\theta) = \cos^2\theta - \sin^2\theta$
Chris McMullen, Ph.D.

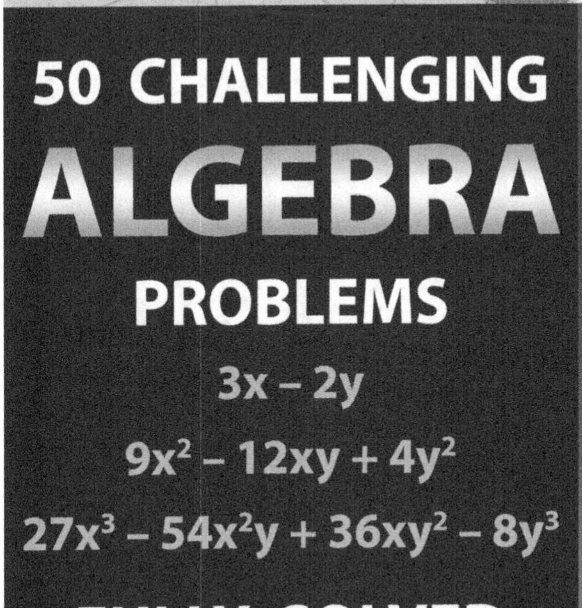
50 CHALLENGING
ALGEBRA
PROBLEMS
3x – 2y
$9x^2 - 12xy + 4y^2$
$27x^3 - 54x^2y + 36xy^2 - 8y^3$
FULLY SOLVED
Chris McMullen, Ph.D.

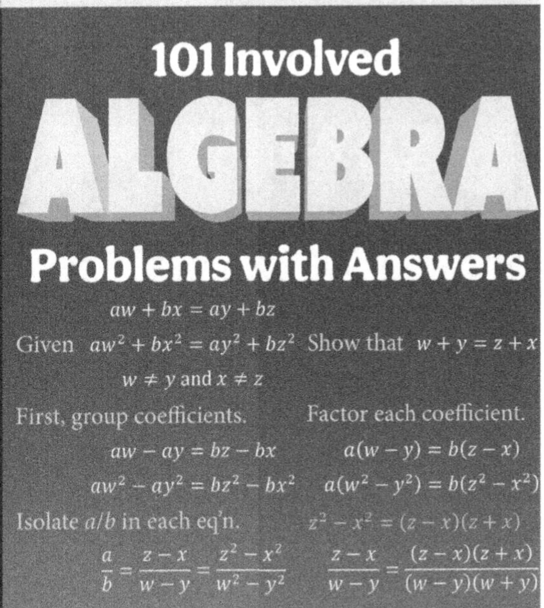
101 Involved
ALGEBRA
Problems with Answers
Given $aw + bx = ay + bz$, $aw^2 + bx^2 = ay^2 + bz^2$, $w \neq y$ and $x \neq z$. Show that $w + y = z + x$
First, group coefficients.
$aw - ay = bz - bx$
$aw^2 - ay^2 = bz^2 - bx^2$
Factor each coefficient.
$a(w - y) = b(z - x)$
$a(w^2 - y^2) = b(z^2 - x^2)$
Isolate a/b in each eq'n.
$\frac{a}{b} = \frac{z-x}{w-y} = \frac{z^2-x^2}{w^2-y^2}$
$z^2 - x^2 = (z - x)(z + x)$
$\frac{z-x}{w-y} = \frac{(z-x)(z+x)}{(w-y)(w+y)}$
Compare the two sides.
$1 = \frac{z+x}{w+y}$
Cross multiply.
$w + y = z + x$
Chris McMullen, Ph.D.

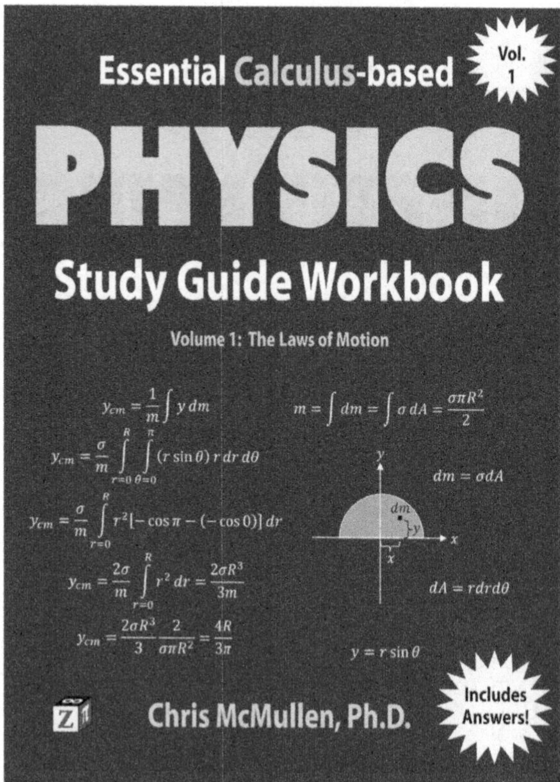

Essential Calculus-based — Vol. 1

PHYSICS

Study Guide Workbook

Volume 1: The Laws of Motion

Chris McMullen, Ph.D.

Includes Answers!

Essential Calculus-based — Vol. 2

PHYSICS

Study Guide Workbook

Volume 2: Electricity and Magnetism

$$\oint_C \vec{B} \cdot d\vec{s} = \mu_0 I_{enc}$$

Chris McMullen, Ph.D.

Includes Answers!

Essential Calculus-based — Vol. 3

PHYSICS

Study Guide Workbook

Volume 3: Waves, Fluids, Sound, Heat, and Light

$$W = \int P \, dV$$

Chris McMullen, Ph.D.

Includes Answers!

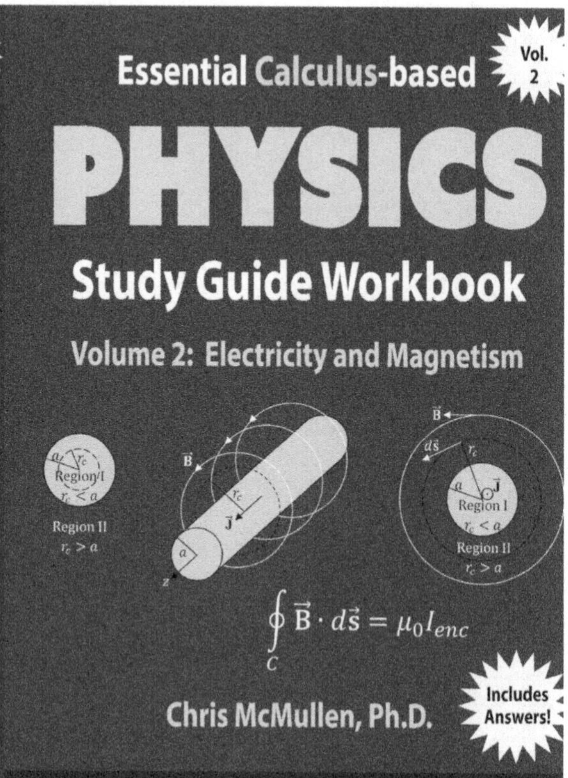

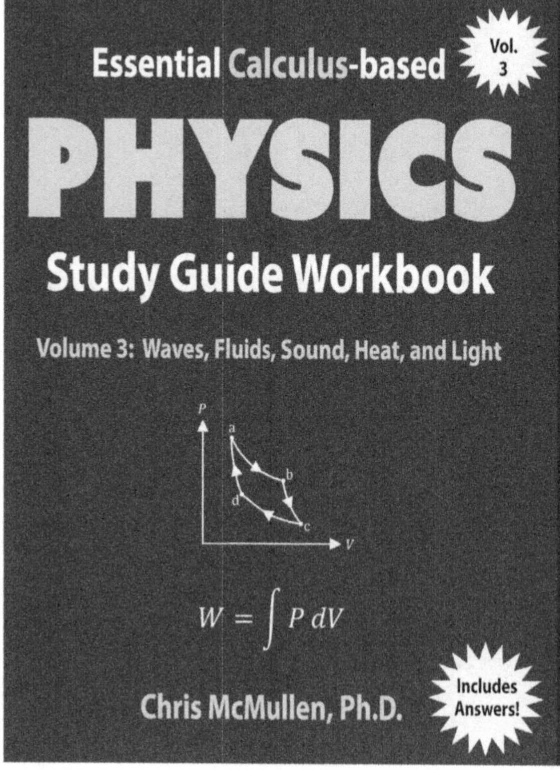

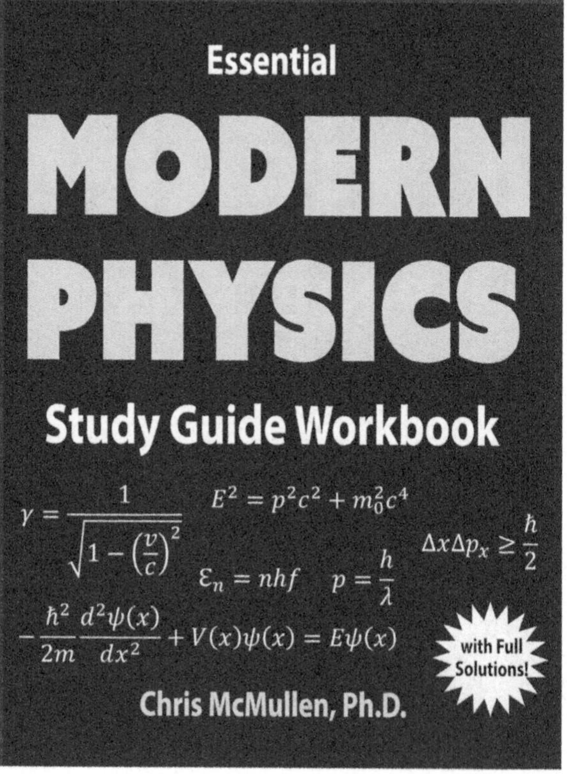

Essential

MODERN PHYSICS

Study Guide Workbook

$$\gamma = \frac{1}{\sqrt{1 - \left(\frac{v}{c}\right)^2}}$$

$$E^2 = p^2 c^2 + m_0^2 c^4$$

$$\varepsilon_n = nhf \qquad p = \frac{h}{\lambda}$$

$$\Delta x \Delta p_x \geq \frac{\hbar}{2}$$

$$-\frac{\hbar^2}{2m} \frac{d^2 \psi(x)}{dx^2} + V(x)\psi(x) = E\psi(x)$$

with Full Solutions!

Chris McMullen, Ph.D.

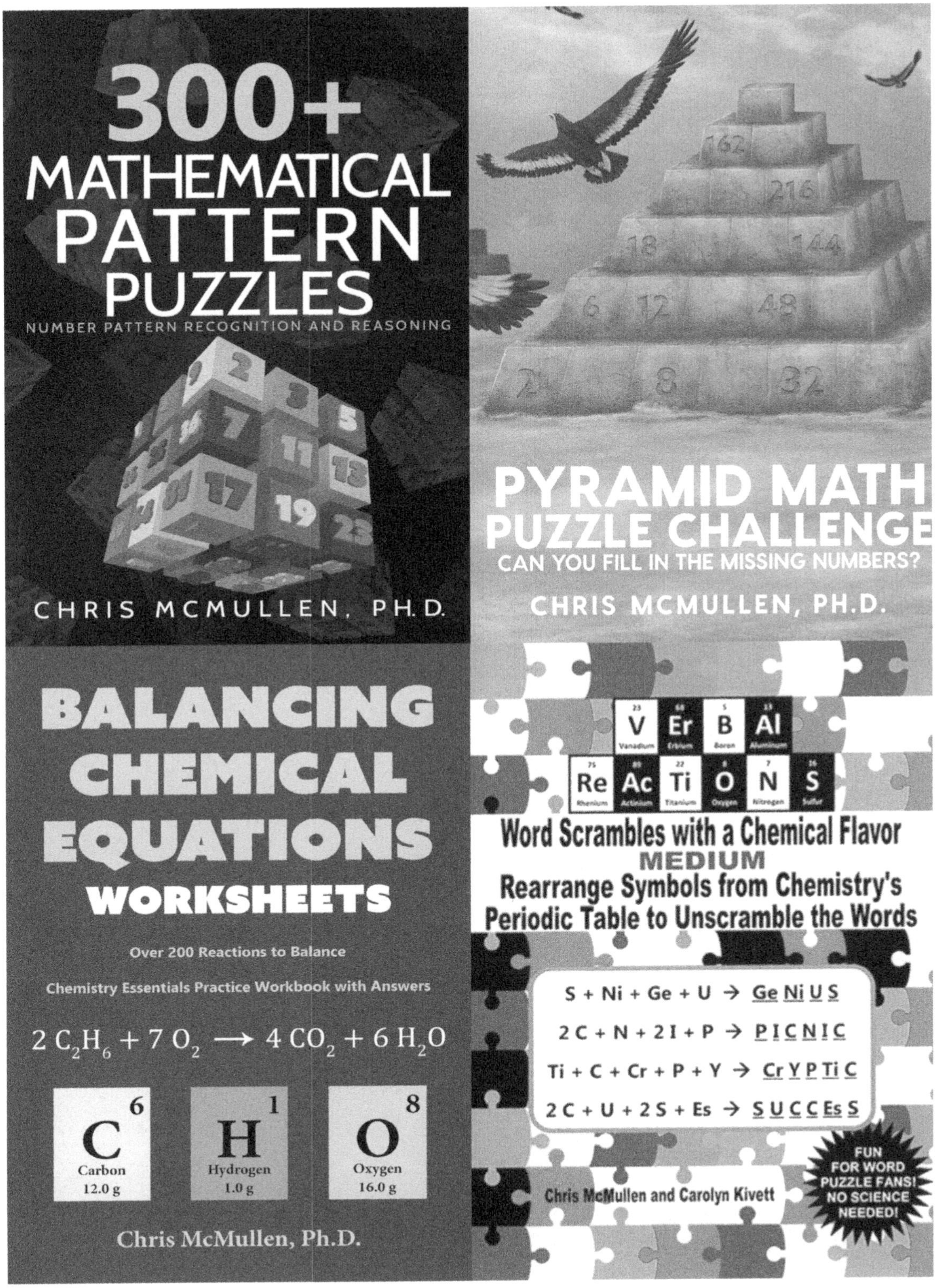
300+
MATHEMATICAL
PATTERN
PUZZLES
NUMBER PATTERN RECOGNITION AND REASONING
CHRIS MCMULLEN, PH.D.
PYRAMID MATH
PUZZLE CHALLENGE
CAN YOU FILL IN THE MISSING NUMBERS?
CHRIS MCMULLEN, PH.D.
BALANCING
CHEMICAL
EQUATIONS
WORKSHEETS
Over 200 Reactions to Balance
Chemistry Essentials Practice Workbook with Answers
2 C2H6 + 7 O2 → 4 CO2 + 6 H2O
Chris McMullen, Ph.D.
VErBAl ReAcTiONS
Word Scrambles with a Chemical Flavor
MEDIUM
Rearrange Symbols from Chemistry's
Periodic Table to Unscramble the Words
S + Ni + Ge + U → GeNiUS
2C + N + 2I + P → PICNIC
Ti + C + Cr + P + Y → CrYPTiC
2C + U + 2S + Es → SUCCEsS
Chris McMullen and Carolyn Kivett
FUN FOR WORD PUZZLE FANS! NO SCIENCE NEEDED!

Made in the USA
Las Vegas, NV
14 May 2023

72045544R00096